D1410878

A Time to Heal

PARTICIPANT'S WORKBOOK
ALL CANCERS GROUP

Stephanie Koraleski, PhD
Psychologist

Kay Ryan, PhD, RN
Cancer Survivor

Foreword by Lawrence LeShan, PhD, and Ruth Bolletino, PhD
Blessing by Joan Borysenko, PhD

www.MyTimetoHeal.org

Thank you

With grateful acknowledgment of the **Nebraska Affiliate of the Susan G. Komen for the Cure** (www.KomenNebraska.org) for a generous grant that helped in the development of *A Time to Heal*. The program has expanded its scope thanks to a grant from the **LIVESTRONG Foundation** (www.livestrong.org).

For information on bringing this program to your community, please contact the authors:

Stephanie Koraleski, PhD
Chief Executive Officer
A Time to Heal
(402) 401-6083 office
(402) 319-3124 cell
steph@atth.org

Kay Ryan, PhD, RN
President
A Time to Heal
(402) 401-6083 office
(402) 490-7614 cell
kay@atth.org

A Time to Heal, www.MyTimetoHeal.org, is a nonprofit 501(c)(3) organization.

Production Team

Cover design: Lou Anne Baker, www.ladesignco.com
Print production and marketing: Concierge Marketing, Inc.
Editor: Sandra Wendel, Write On, Inc., coauthor of *How Not to Be My Patient* (with Edward T. Creagan, MD, Mayo Clinic) and writer, *Chicken Soup for the Soul, Healthy Living with Breast Cancer*, www.SandraWendel.com

10 9 8 7 6 5 4 3 2 1

Contents

About Saint Peregrine—
the Patron Saint of Cancer Patients

Peregrine was born in Forli, Italy, around 1265. At that time, Forli was governed by the Pope as part of the Papal States, and Peregrine grew up in a family that was actively involved in the opposition, or anti-papal party. Because of anti-papal activity, the city was under the church penalty of interdict, meaning that Mass and the Sacraments could not be celebrated there. St. Philip Benizi, Prior General of the Servants of Mary, went to Forli to preach reconciliation. Young Peregrine, very intense in his political fervor, not only heckled Philip during his preaching, but, in fact, struck him.

The moment of striking Philip is said to have dramatically changed Peregrine. He began channeling his energy into good works and eventually joined the Servants of Mary in Siena, Italy. He returned to Forli, where he spent the rest of his life, dedicating himself to the sick, the poor, and those on the fringes of society. He also imposed on himself the penance of standing whenever it was not necessary to sit. This led to varicose veins, which later deteriorated into an open sore on his leg, eventually diagnosed as cancer.

Peregrine's leg wound became so serious that the local surgeon decided to amputate the leg. The night before the surgery, Peregrine prayed before the image of the crucified Christ, and when he awoke, the wound was healed and his leg saved. He lived another 20 years, dying on May 1, 1345, at the age of about 80. Peregrine was canonized on December 27, 1726, and has been named the Patron Saint of cancer patients.

ST. PEREGRINE

Foreword

by Lawrence LeShan, PhD, and Ruth Bolletino, PhD

The transition from cancer patient to cancer survivor can be as disturbing as the earlier crisis. Whatever medical treatment the person undergoes, and whatever reactions the person has to it, treatment is a structured event, a ritual that brings comfort. When it ends, patients often experience their own kind of post-traumatic syndrome.

Besides relief and gratitude, many also have the feeling of a sudden letdown. Reactions also often include a profound sense of loss, grief, uncertainty, confusion and fear.

Although they know that the end of treatment signifies progress, for patients, having treatment meant doing something against the cancer. Doing something is far easier than waiting and wondering, What happens next?

A Time to Heal is designed to ease this trauma. Because cancer affects the whole person, the program addresses the whole person—each section dealing with a different human facet. The program design is based on the recognition that everyone is different, that there is no "one size fits all." Information is presented in ways that provide alternatives and options, so that in each section, participants are involved in an adventure of self-exploration and discovery. They are led to experience a number of different ways in which they can learn about themselves and encouraged to choose those strategies they feel are the most appropriate.

The work takes place in a supportive setting involving a warm and caring group led by skilled and caring facilitators. The program ends with each participant making a specific plan for future actions, and a commitment to themselves to follow it.

The aim is that each person uses the cancer experience to grow and develop as a full, unique individual.

A Time to Heal has been shown to help participants to reclaim their strengths, their selves and their lives. It is also very likely to make their lives richer and more fulfilling.

Lawrence LeShan, PhD, and Ruth Bolletino, PhD

Dr. LeShan is the author of the highly acclaimed book *Cancer as a Turning Point.* Dr. Bolletino is the author of *How to Talk with Family Caregivers about Cancer.* Together they provide training to cancer patients, family members and professionals through their program called *Cancer as a Turning Point* (www.cancerasaturningpoint.org).

Blessing

by Joan Borysenko, PhD

To all cancer survivors who participate in this program, to their family and friends, and to the professionals who care for them all, a blessing:

May your healing journey be a gateway
to wisdom,
compassion,
peace,
gratitude,
love,
and trust in the Mystery of Life.
And may the courageous work
you do to realize these qualities in yourself
be an inspiration and a blessing to others.

Joan Borysenko, PhD

Dr. Borysenko is the author of *The Power of the Mind to Heal; Pocketful of Miracles; Minding the Body, Mending the Mind; It's Not the End of the World: Developing Resilience in Times of Change; The PlantPlus Diet Solution,* and many other books (www.joanborysenko.com).

A Special Welcome
to Those Who Have Had Cancer

Congratulations on making it through your diagnosis and treatment to the point where you can join *A Time to Heal* today! While each person is different and each person's cancer journey is unique, we know that dealing with cancer is a challenge for everyone. No doubt your life has been significantly affected. Dr. Lawrence LeShan has written,

> *Having cancer is like waking up each morning to a nightmare—not a bad dream, but a nightmare, with a nightmare's special psychologically weakening and physically exhausting effects. A nightmare has three characteristics. First, terrible things are happening and worse are threatened. Second, we feel helpless, impotent while other people or outside forces are in control. Third, there is no time limit, no end in sight. Being trapped in the nightmare of cancer weakens the coherence of the person's sense of self. (LeShan, 1994)*

Cancer can be overwhelming. It terrorizes the bravest among us. It shakes our understanding of ourselves and who we are. It weakens our physical strength and rocks our spiritual foundations. It threatens our mental stability with terrifying thoughts of death or disability. It chips away at our independence. It steals our confidence in the future. We can lose our sense of self.

And you have survived all of this. Despite being battered physically and emotionally by cancer, you have had the courage and the hope to enroll in this course. You come here now looking for a place and a time to heal. While no one can offer a treatment to erase what you have been through, we have done our best to bring you much of the bounty that other cancer survivors have discovered in their own journeys of healing. The topics and the information in this program are gleaned from the research in medicine, psychology, nursing, physical therapy, and many other healing professions. The ideas suggested have been shown to make a positive difference in the lives of people recovering from cancer. We are grateful to the cancer patients and researchers on whose work this program has been built. And we are also grateful to you for participating in the current group, which, we hope, will help not only you but others who participate with you.

There are many ideas and suggestions contained in this program. No one could possibly implement them all, and we do not presume to know what is best for you.

Our suggestion is that you listen to all of the ideas, try many of them, and reserve your opinions until the end of the 12-week program. Think of this as a buffet where you can taste many different items. At the end of the program, you can choose what you think would be most helpful to you at this point in your life.

We know that for each of us human beings, life is a journey of learning and experience. The best life one can create is a life that uses our unique interests, skills, and personality in a way that is satisfying. We also believe, along with many wiser scientists than ourselves, that pursuing one's "best life" is the best recipe for both health and happiness. Our goal is to help you think deeply about what your own "best life" would look like and to help you take the next steps toward making your best life a reality!

A Special Welcome to the Family and Friends of Cancer Survivors

We are happy to have you here supporting your loved one in *A Time to Heal*, and we welcome you not only as the support person for your loved one, but also as a full participant in the program. Cancer is not the disease of an individual; it affects whole families, friends, and coworkers as well. When your loved one was diagnosed with cancer, your world was probably shaken too. It can be particularly difficult to stand by and feel helpless watching someone you love suffer. It is exhausting to juggle your own schedule while trying to support your loved one, take on tasks he or she is unable to do, keep the household running, maybe care for children, manage the finances, deal with medical bills, communicate with medical staff, and keep yourself minimally healthy and sane.

You've been through a grueling time. The physical burdens of caretaking are immense, but the emotional toll may be even higher. You have felt your own fears. You may have been frustrated or even enraged at cancer or at the medical system. You may have found yourself resenting all the intrusions that your loved one's illness caused in your life. You may have felt a need to be strong even when you felt terrified. You may have been jealous of people whose lives were normal. You may have felt overwhelmed with questions and calls from friends or even angry that those calls took up the few free minutes you might have had to yourself. You may have felt guilty for wanting some time to yourself or for enjoying a respite from cancer and caregiving when your loved one could not get away.

In short, you need *A Time to Heal* too. While you may have joined the program to help assist your loved one's recovery, we encourage you to listen to the information for yourself as well. Most of the sessions will apply both to your life and to the lives of your loved ones. As you and your loved one move on, it's important for both of you to heal. It's especially important for you to take good care of yourself, to learn to relax again, and to find your own "best life." So, as you participate in the program, we'll be asking you to give as much good care to yourself as you have to your loved one.

Over many years of clinical experience and research, Dr. Lawrence LeShan developed a type of psychological therapy for cancer patients based on focusing people on what was right with them. In this method, he encouraged people to discover and use their own unique ways of being, relating, and creating. When people with cancer began doing this, many of them began to get better. Since then we have learned that this way of being in life—the continual commitment to creating one's "best life"—is healing for almost everyone.

In *A Time to Heal*, we'll be encouraging both you and your loved one to work toward discovering the wonders of yourselves and creating your own unique best lives. While your loved one may need some support, your role is not to abandon your life and interests for him or her. Your own health and the quality of your life necessitate that you also focus on yourself. Our hope is that as you and your loved one learn this material together, you can share your discoveries with each other and help each other not only to survive but to thrive as you move forward. Welcome to *A Time to Heal*!

A *Time to Heal* Weekly Protocol

Minutes	Time	Activity
15		Social with Snacks
20		Gentle Exercise
10		Introduction to Featured Speakers and Activities
40		Presentation with Q&A
45		Discussion
15		Relaxation or Meditation
10		Journaling of Personal Goals and Affirmations for the Week
10		Questions, Comments

OVERVIEW: TOPICS

You will be invited to participate in all 12 sessions presented in *A Time to Heal*. You will be assisted in setting goals for yourself in one or more areas you select. These are the featured weekly topics and session descriptions:

1. Building Resilience—The Skills of Survivors
2. The Power of the Mind
3. Advocating for Me—Building My Survivorship Plan
4. Comforting Myself
5. Moving Forward in the Face of Fear
6. Refuel for Health and Energy
7. May the Circle Be Unbroken
8. Renewing My Body, Regaining My Strength
9. Rebuilding My Core
10. Adventures and Misadventures in the Supplement Jungle
11. Where Am I Going Now?
12. Happiness Is …

1 Building Resilience—The Skills of Survivors

Do I have the skills I need to survive? Resilience is an active process of finding your personal strength to work through pain, setbacks, and challenges. You will learn about resilience—what it is, how it works, and how to use it to bounce back in your own lives. You will be able to identify protective factors, see resilience in yourself, begin to notice it in others, and start to develop a sense of survivor pride.

2 The Power of the Mind

How does my mind help heal my body? This session focuses on the powerful healing relationship between the mind and the body. Emphasis will be given to debunking harmful myths such as "I caused my cancer because I didn't cope well with stress," and to teaching about helpful strategies such as increasing social support, learning meditation and relaxation, and use of positive imagery.

3 Advocating for Me—Building My Survivorship Plan

Ending treatment brings relief and celebration for many patients, but it also brings anxiety about what to expect and how to stay healthy. This session will help you understand the many different types of treatments and why your treatment may have been different from someone else's. You will learn about the "seasons" of survivorship and what to expect moving forward, the role of a Survivorship Care Plan and how to construct your own plan, and how to cope with some of the normal side effects you may experience after treatment.

4 Comforting Myself

How can I help myself to feel better? You will explore the ways you can help your body relax, release pain, and feel comfort. Emphasis is given to the intention of being healed, nurturing self-care, the role of nurturing touch in healing.

5 Moving Forward in the Face of Fear

Do you spend a lot of your energy living in fear? Cancer diagnosis, treatment, and its aftermath can leave cancer survivors and their caregivers feeling vulnerable and afraid. Living in fear takes an excessive amount of energy when it takes control of and robs you of your ability to focus, to be happy, and to be fully present to your life. You will learn about strategies to address fear and put yourself back in control.

6 Refuel for Health and Energy

How can I use nutrition to help me heal? During treatment you may have tried to eat whatever you were able to tolerate. You may want to begin using nutrition as a tool to rebuild your health and prevent future medical problems. You will learn about the role of nutrition in healing, good nutritional strategies for you in recovery from cancer, and resources for quick and easy meals with high nutritional content.

7 May the Circle Be Unbroken

Will they still love me? You may be discovering that some relationships are strengthened and others weakened during your illness. In this session, you assess the status of relationships with families, friends, and colleagues at work; mending those that need help, ending those that need to be pruned, and nurturing those that mean the most.

8 Renewing My Body, Regaining My Strength

How can I become me again? After cancer treatment, you slowly renew and regain your strength. This session helps you understand the process of gradually improving muscle strength and endurance, choosing an exercise program that is right for you, and about coping with fatigue.

9 Rebuilding My Core

What brings meaning to my life now? When serious illness strikes, the repercussions are felt deep within the spirit. You will find ways to tune in to the spirit, to find and nourish the things that give meaning to your life, and to strengthen personal spirituality in whatever form that takes.

10 Adventures and Misadventures in the Supplement Jungle

Are nutritional supplements safe for me? It's difficult navigating the ocean of information on vitamins, nutritional supplements, and herbal remedies being marketed to cancer patients. This session discusses how to choose supplements that are research based, compatible with other medications, and safe for cancer survivors. Special focus will be given to making informed decisions about using nutritional supplements to help with your special (and common) symptoms such as fatigue, low energy, hormonal imbalance symptoms, poor concentration, and poor sleep.

11 Where Am I Going Now?

Where am I going? While all cancer survivors live with uncertainty, the research of Dr. Lawrence LeShan and others shows that people who are living a life they choose and love may have improved life quality and lifespan after cancer treatment. In this session you will identify what brings joy and zest to your life and set goals to enhance your life.

12 Happiness Is …

Will I ever be happy again? While many cancer patients are just happy to be alive after treatment, others feel that they may never be happy again. Fear, uncertainty about the future, and impairments in health, memory, and relationships leave some cancer survivors feeling empty and unhappy. This session guides you through information about what happiness is and about building happiness at home and in your life work.

Special Topics

These are additional resources that are of interest to many cancer survivors:

- Body Image

- Cancer and Sexuality

- Chemobrain

- Cure, Healing, and Palliative Care

- The Lymphatic System and Lymphedema

- Spontaneous Remissions and Miracles

- Talking to Children about Cancer

References

References from each of the sessions and Special Topics are listed at the end of the book.

Resources

This is a listing of websites devoted to providing information and support for people affected by cancer.

Guidelines for Group Participation

We recognize that we are all unique individuals and each person is entitled to his or her own thoughts and opinions. We share information and ideas with others, but we don't give advice or pressure other people to do things or see things our way.

We recognize that we each have different personalities. Some like to share out loud; others process things more privately. Each can participate according to his or her own style respecting the rights of all.

We recognize the courage of each individual in this group in sharing personal experiences, and we respect your privacy. We agree to keep personal information confidential and not to share stories naming others in the group outside of this group.

We recognize that the agenda for each session is full and there is some need to keep things running on time. We also recognize that the needs of people are more important than a schedule. We agree to help the group leaders meet the needs of all by keeping a flexible balance of discussion and activities.

We recognize that none of us is perfect and that people can say and do things that don't always feel right to us. We agree that we will not purposely hurt or disrespect each other and that if we do feel hurt or disrespected, we will either address the issue with the individual or in the group or decide to forgive it and let it go. We agree that we will not let any personal injury become an impediment to our participation in the group.

In order to maintain a feeling of safety and respect for all participants, we agree not to impose our questions or views on other members. Specifically, we agree not to talk about medical personnel by name. Each participant is entitled to his or her own opinion about people and institutions and may tell his or her story without being interrupted or interrogated. Similarly, we agree not to solicit any other group members. That means that we do not ask other group members to purchase products or affiliate with other organizations. Each individual is entitled to choose how to spend his or her own energy and resources.

As we come to know each other, we come to care about each other. Unexplained departures from the group hurt each group member. If for some reason, someone needs to resign from the group, we agree that that person will come at least one more time and say goodbye to the group members. As we proceed in the group, if other issues arise, we agree to bring them up in the group so that we can decide what kind of group guidelines we can all agree on for this group.

Exercise Protocol: Target Heart Rate

The purpose of the exercise protocol in *A Time to Heal* is to enhance pain-free movement of the extremities and increase flexibility. Therefore, the target heart rate is not an aerobic heart rate.

Check these ways to know if you are working harder than recommended (50% of your Heart Rate Max for *A Time to Heal* exercise protocol):

1. Measure your working heart rate and compare it to the target on the chart here.

2. Measure your Rate of Perceived Exertion (RPE) using the scale on the next page.

3. Take the talk test. Ask yourself if you can talk during exercise without becoming breathless. You don't want to be breathless.

Heart Rate Chart

AGE	Heart Rate Max	Target (50%) of Max
20-23	199	99
24-27	195	98
28-31	190	95
32-35	187	93
36-39	182	91
40-43	178	89
44-47	174	87
48-51	170	85
52-55	166	83
56-59	162	81
60-63	158	79
64-67	154	77
68-71	150	75

Please note: NEVER exercise beyond your comfort zone. STOP if you feel discomfort. DRINK when you feel thirsty. Tell the facilitator immediately if you are experiencing ANY symptoms of pain, lightheadedness, dizziness, or shortness of breath.

Borg CR10 Scale Rating of Perceived Exertion	
0	Nothing at all
0.5	Very, very weak
1	Very weak
2	Weak
3	**Moderate (recommended for *A Time to Heal* class)**
4	Somewhat strong
5	Strong
6	
7	Very strong
8	
9	
10	Very, very strong
Borg, G. (1998). Borg's Perceived Exertion Scales.	

SESSION 1
Building Resilience— The Skills of Survivors

Deborah Vonderharr Carlson, PhD

Key Points
- What resilience means
- How the cancer experience can result in growth
- How left side versus right side thinking affects us
- Identifying your personal resiliency builders
- Identifying and using alternative mirrors
- Overcoming barriers to resilience
- Developing survivor's pride

Not long ago I heard a story about an unusual accident. A man was out cutting his grass in his own front yard. A car driving down the street suddenly blew out two tires. The driver lost control and ran into the man. Luckily he was not killed, but he broke several bones and had to take several weeks off work to recuperate.

If this was your husband, your brother, or your good friend, what would you say to him?

Anyone who has been through a painful, frightening experience needs comfort, love, and support to heal. This 12-week program is designed to support your recovery from cancer. Think of treating yourself as compassionately as you would treat this man you love who had been hurt. That means several things:

1. You don't lecture him about what he did wrong or what to do better next time. It's clear that he was just in the normal process of living his life when this tragedy struck.

17

2. You don't push him to get out and mow his lawn again immediately. He's too beat up to do the work, and he might have some trepidation about being out in his front yard unprotected. It would be very normal for him to be fearful of cars and leery about being too close to the street.

3. You let him tell the story as often as he wants to. And if he expresses some anger or fear or his eyes fill with tears, you understand. Having and expressing our feelings is a way to release pain and fear and discharge the tension of the trauma from our bodies, minds and spirits.

4. You do focus a lot on how happy you are that he is here, alive, and a beloved part of your life.

5. You help him know that he will heal, but it will take some time.

6. And you remind him over and over that what happened was not his fault.

What he and you need is *A Time to Heal*. This is that time.

After cancer treatments are over, there is a phase of transition that researchers call "reentry." Challenges faced during reentry often revolve around the following "myths of treatment completion":

- I should be celebrating: Many find the work of processing emotions and finding meaning is just beginning.

- I should feel well: Effects such as fatigue linger, even though you or others perceive that you are cured. Being disease free doesn't mean being free of the disease's effects.

- I should be the precancer me: Physical and mental challenges altered your sense of who you are and where you are. Cancer touches all aspects of your health: physical, functional, psychological/ cognitive, social, economic, and spiritual.

- I should not need support: Active support— medical and personal—decreases sharply after treatment even though you may still need it (Stanton, 2005).

Cancer survivorship means understanding the four myths and that it's okay to give yourself the same love, comfort, and compassion you would give the man who had been injured. A powerful process to move you through the reentry phase and closer to creating your best life is resilience.

Resilience is an active process of finding your personal strength to work through pain, setbacks, and challenges. This session will focus on explaining the processes of resilience— what it is, how it works and how to use it in your own lives. By the end of the session, you will be able to identify protective factors, see resilience in yourself, and begin to notice it in others and start to develop a sense of survivor pride.

Introduction

This session will share with you something that you already have, something that no surgery or chemo can take away. In fact, in a strange way it is surgery, chemo, and other hardships that bring this out in people. Kind of like turning a piece of coal into a diamond, without the strong fires and pressure, there would be no shine. Or when an iron worker takes a piece of tin and, using intense heat and hard hammers, forges it into a harder piece of steel, something stronger and more beautiful.

We are talking about resilience, the ability to bounce back from and successfully overcome risks and adversity. You have all been through the "fire." Will you ever be the same? No. You will never be the same person you were, but resilience research has found that in many ways you will be a stronger, more self-assured, focused, and happier person because of these "fires."

Although the negative aspects of cancer and treatment have been well documented, there is new research that suggests there can be positive growth also (Molina et al., 2014). For example, a newly diagnosed adolescent showed her new awareness based on her cancer experience saying,

"After having cancer, just existing is the most important thing to me. I don't care if I do something slower than others do. It is okay. I can do it my own way." Interestingly, younger survivors showed more growth and older survivors reported better quality of life (Ishibashi et al., 2010).

So what is resilience? A look at a definition makes it clear.

- Resiliency "can be defined as the capacity to spring back, rebound, successfully adapt in the face of adversity, and develop social and academic competence despite exposure to severe stress…or simply the stress of today's world." (Henderson, 2000)

- Resiliency "is about bouncing back from problems and stuff with more power and more smarts." (Sean, a 15-year-old high school student)

- Resiliency "is an innate self-righting and transcending ability within all children, youth, adults, organizations, and communities." (Henderson, Sharp-Light, and Bernard, 2000)

Resiliency. Everyone needs it and the good news is that there is evidence that a focus on resiliency in cancer survivors may improve their quality of life (Ishibashi et al., 2010). Not only that, but everyone can develop it (Jacelon, 1997). Think about your own journey with cancer. A new theory of human development is arising from resiliency research, a belief in the "self-righting" tendencies within all. By taking the time and making the commitment to come to these sessions, you are looking for ways to bounce back. Your innate sense of self-righting is taking over so that you seek out ways to bring yourself back.

During this time you will review three points:

- How resiliency happens, according to the research

- The most important steps to take in fostering resiliency

- How to overcome the greatest barrier to fostering resiliency

A First Step

Just by doing this activity, you are taking the first, most important step in fostering resiliency.

Think of a concern that you have about yourself or your environment. What are the issues that you think are holding you back from full recovery? Now, complete this chart:

On the left side:

List all of the problems that hold you back from resolving the issues.

On the right side:

Identify all the strengths you have. Look for any "scrap" of strength (talent, potential talent, personality qualities, any support). Think of times you surprised yourself. What has helped you do as well as you have?

_____	_____
_____	_____
_____	_____
_____	_____
_____	_____
_____	_____
_____	_____
_____	_____

If you are like most people, the list on the left side is probably a lot longer than the list on the right. We're taught to see what's wrong with ourselves, others, and the world, and we sometimes have a difficult time seeing what's right.

To build resiliency, you must:

1. Look at the whole picture—problems and strengths.
2. Recognize that everyone, especially you, has strengths, and dig for those strengths, because research tells us those strengths are more powerful than the problems.

How the Shift Happens

When the shift to resiliency occurs, it happens because the strengths grow in power and influence and the problems diminish in power and influence.

If we want something to grow, what must we do? (Answer: nurture, reinforce). This is exactly what resiliency researchers say we must do. One important first step: Identify the qualities that make a difference so you can reinforce them.

The following characteristics are particularly helpful in building personal resiliency. Do you see some connections between your list of strengths that you identified earlier? Check the Personal Resiliency Builders that apply to you. These are more like a menu than a must-have list, so no one has everything, and we all have a few.

Personal Resiliency Builders

Individual Protective Factors that Build Resiliency

____ Relationships—sociability/ability to be a friend/ability to form positive relationships

____ Service—gives of self in service to others and/or a cause

____ Life Skills—uses life skills, including good decision making, assertiveness, and impulse control

____ Humor—has a good sense of humor

____ Inner Direction—bases choices/decisions on internal evaluation (internal locus of control)

____ Perceptiveness—insightful understanding of people and situations

____ Independence—"adaptive" distancing from unhealthy people and situations/autonomy

_____ Positive View of Personal Future— expects a positive future

_____ Flexibility—can adjust to change; can bend as necessary to positively cope with situations

_____ Love of Learning—capacity for and connection to learning

_____ Self-motivation—internal initiative and positive motivation from within

_____ Competence—is "good at something"/personal competence

_____ Self-worth—feelings of self-worth and self-confidence

_____ Spirituality—personal faith in something greater

_____ Perseverance—keeps on despite difficulty; doesn't give up

_____ Creativity—expresses self through artistic endeavor

(Richardson et al., 1990; Bernard, 1991;Werner & Smith, 1992; Hawkins et al., 1992; Wolin & Wolin, 1993)

All of us have **some** of these characteristics, but not **all of** them. Even one quality can be the life line a person needs to bounce back, and from which others can build.

Learn to Be Resilient

By learning about resilience, you can become resilient.
Some important lessons:

- We need to teach people about their strengths.

- To be more powerful, we need to specifically name the strengths.

- We then become "alternative mirrors."

"According to child development experts, we are born without an idea of who we are. We piece together a picture of ourselves by seeing our reflection in the faces of the people who take care of us.…In troubled families, the mirroring process goes awry, and children are (apt) to form an inner representation of themselves that says, 'I am ugly. I am unacceptable (or unlovable or unworthy).' …Resilient survivors rally courage, break free of the spell, and go in search of alternate mirrors in which they can see a more pleasing image.…These pleasing images collect over time and account for resiliency." (*The Resilient Self*, pp. 16-17, Wolin and Wolin, 1993)

Do you think that you hear either from others or yourself enough about your strengths?

About 90% of the messages we get, especially if we have adversity in our lives, focus on the left side of "our page." There is a tendency in all of us to focus on the negative. However, research shows that people who utilize a coping style that is able to redefine stressful events in order to make them more manageable are more resilient (Greef and Thiel, 2012). This is called reframing. An example is a woman who had cancer three times. Her family worried that she would give up when the doctor told her the cancer was back the third time. Instead, she was able to reframe it by saying, "I will be okay because my body knows how to fight cancer." This coping style may help families to live with cancer in a way that makes sense and gives them more power (Greef and Thiel, 2012).

Cancer patients and their caregivers often face statistical mirrors that show terrifying reflections. Just reading the package inserts on side effects on any medication can sap the courage of most strong adults.

Janet was 41 when she was first diagnosed with breast cancer, went through the standard treatment that was the norm for that time, and thought she was fine. A year later, the cancer returned. She underwent a year more of grueling treatment and heard many dire predictions about the likelihood that she would never live through chemo or that her prognosis could be measured in a few short years at best. Ten years later, cancer free, she would tell this story at the hospital's cancer support group when someone was newly diagnosed with recurrent cancer. She attributed her recovery both to good medical treatment and to her own refusal to see herself as hopeless. Her first grandchild was on the way when she recurred, and she preferred to see herself as someone who would be an active, loving grandparent and sought out people who encouraged that goal and provided helpful "alternative mirrors" and she often became the "alternative mirror" for other frightened patients.

Remember that statistics are only averages of the experiences of many, many people who often have very different health situations, personal strengths and weakness, resources, and support. If the statistical mirror is not a helpful reflection, take action to find other alternative mirrors that lift your spirit.

What does this mean for you?

- Know that you matter and believe in yourself. Know that what is right with you is more powerful than anything that is wrong with you. Nurture a positive view of yourself. Develop confidence in your ability to solve problems and trust your instincts in your own health care.

- Create a protective web. Resilience is first and foremost a person-to-person process. We tend to pull away from people when we are hurting. Resist that feeling and connect with other people because that is where true healing begins. Research has shown that the primary factor in resilience is having caring and supportive relationships within and outside the family. Work on cultivating and developing the relationships in your life. Accept help and support from those who care about you and find ways to help others in their time of need.

- Do something that you enjoy every day, even if it is just enjoying a piece of chocolate without guilt. Pay attention to your own needs and feelings and engage in activities that you enjoy and find relaxing. Taking care of yourself helps to keep your mind and body primed to deal with situations that require resilience.

- Accept that the cancer has happened and you can't change that fact, but try looking beyond the present to how future circumstances may be a little better. Note any subtle way in which you might already feel somewhat better as you deal with difficult situations. This will help you maintain a hopeful outlook. An optimistic outlook enables you to expect that good things will happen in your life. Try to visualize what you want, rather than worrying about what you fear.

- Remember, being resilient doesn't mean that you will not experience difficulty or distress. Emotional pain and sadness are common in people who have suffered major adversity or trauma in their lives. In fact, the road to resilience is likely to start with considerable emotional distress. But along the way resilient people learn to recognize the problems at hand and explore untapped resources within themselves (Harris, 2014).

- Make realistic goals. Do something regularly— even small steps help you feel a sense of accomplishment in moving toward your goals. Instead of focusing on what you can't do, ask yourself what is the one thing I can accomplish today that will help me move in the direction that I want to.

- Take time … persist: Don't give up!

"Mind these three: TTT; hear their chime: Things Take Time!" (Henderson)

Overcoming the Greatest Barrier to Resiliency

Some traits of resilience may be somewhat inborn, but many of them can be learned and thus promoted. However, the **greatest barrier to fostering resiliency is our cultural and institutional obsession with the negative:** risk, deficits, and problems. This negative focus destroys our hope so that people don't believe in resiliency.

We have a hard time looking at what is right with us because the world is focused on what is wrong. For example, when a child brings a report card home with all *A*s and one *F*, what do the parents talk about first? When you think of yourself and what you have been through, do you focus on the progress you are making and how well you are handling your cancer and how strong you've been during treatment and recovery, or do you focus on the few times that you had a "pity party" for yourself?

One woman remembers when her mother was recovering from cancer 15 years ago, she found her crying one day and she told her daughter that she was not handling this very well and felt like giving up. When asked how often she cried, she said every day and started crying harder. Then the daughter asked how long she cried every day. She said only a few minutes and then she told herself to "straighten up and face the day."

So the daughter said, "You cry sometimes 15-20 minutes a day and the rest of the 960 minutes that you are awake each day you're coping fairly well. That means that 98% of the time you are trying your hardest to survive. I think that is proof that you are an incredibly persistent, hopeful, and optimistic person."

Remember, it is okay to have a "pity party." Let yourself have one from time to time. We need to let our emotions out. The key is to only stay there 2% of the time. Don't let the cancer or the feelings define who you are.

Survivor Pride

One way to overcome the barrier of not believing in our own resiliency is to talk the resiliency talk, notice, comment upon, discuss and learn about the power of resiliency, about the capacity we are all born with to overcome problems and adversity. When people who have adversity or great stress in their lives learn to "name" the strengths that they use to survive, they develop a sense of "survivor pride."

Survivors say things like, *"I'm glad I got this and not my brother because I'm the strong one." "After going through this, I realized that I can handle things well." "I was able to reach out to help others because I understand what they are going through."* Does this mean you should never focus on the pain and suffering that you are going through? No, what happened to you is very real and hopefully you are learning in these sessions "tools" to help you move forward. But just like the mother who cried, remember that 98% of the time you should then focus on what is right in your life. You are more than a person with cancer, you are a survivor.

"It is not about talking people out of painful realities. But there is reframing to be done....To help develop an attitude, a vocabulary, a story about prospects and expectations, and a picture of a genuine individual lurking beneath the diagnostic label" (Dennis Saleeby, *The Strengths Perspective in Social Work Practice,* 1997).

Summary

Learn your strengths, your protective factors, and develop a sense of survivor pride. Remember that what is right with you is a thousand times more powerful than what is wrong with you.

"If we think we are fragile and broken, we will live a fragile, broken life. If we believe we are strong and wise, we will live with enthusiasm and courage. The way we name ourselves colors the way we live. Who we are is in our eyes. We must be careful how we name ourselves" (Wayne Muller, *How, Then Shall We Live?* 1996).

You are wonderful, strong, smart caring people. Remind yourself every day of your strengths and know that you are already resilient.

Questions for discussion and journaling:

1. Which of the personal resilience builders do you see in yourself?

2. As you were going through treatment, did you see other cancer patients showing signs of resilience? Which resiliency builders did you see in them?

3. Think about alternative mirrors. Was there ever a time when someone reflected encouragement to you when all you could see was negativity? Have you ever done that for someone else?

4. Collect some examples of helpful "alternative mirroring." Write them down so you can see them again on days when you might feel discouraged.

5. Which people, groups, books, or other support would you include in your "protective web"? Why do you include each of them?

Power Tool: Affirmations

The Power of Affirmation is all about the "mental pattern" we are creating and the one that is already there. If you have ever driven to someplace really familiar without even thinking about it—and wondered "how the heck did I get here?"—then you understand about mental patterns.

Feelings that we have about ourselves and our abilities to do or change something are all tied up in these mental patterns. For instance, you may have a lifelong mental pattern that is centered on what you do when you get into an unfamiliar situation. Do you feel scared or threatened or "not good enough"? If so, then you fight that "familiar neural pathway" (your roadmap) every time you face up to a challenge and meet it head on.

So, think about your current roadmap for healing: whenever I think about my cancer, I_____

_____

_____

_____

_____

Whenever I think about doing something healing for myself, I_____

_____

_____

_____

In short, when I tell my body to heal, I_____

_____

_____

_____

Now, let's create a new map TODAY—one pathway at a time! We can use affirmations to do this:

Step 1—Affirmations have to be important!

Step 2—Affirmations are POSITIVE!

Step 3—We have to be CLEAR—no wiggle room in them!

Step 4—Affirmations have to be REPEATED a LOT!

30

Repetition builds belief. That's how we came to believe what we believe now. That's how we learn everything from tying our shoes to driving a car. Put the affirmation on sticky notes on your mirror, computer, and other places where you will see it and repeat it many times a day.

Step 5—Affirmations convince you over time. Whether or not you believe them at first, stay with the practice. Your beliefs will change over time.

Every day I am HEALING more and more

Power Tool: Energy Pickup

1. **The 3 Thumps:** Find each of these spots on your body and tap or gently rub each.
   a. Both collar bone notches 15 seconds
   b. Thymus 15 seconds
   c. Under both breasts 15 seconds

2. **The Cross Crawl:** This alternating movement can be done sitting down in a chair or standing up and "marching." The cross-over movement is good for both your body and your brain.
   a. Left elbow toward right knee
   b. Right elbow toward left knee
   c. Alternately touch your elbow to the opposite knee. Repeat the set 20-25 times.

3. **Wayne Cook Posture** (90 seconds)
   a. Left hand on right knee
   b. Right hand on left knee
   c. Left ankle over right ankle
   d. Tongue on roof of mouth behind front teeth
   e. Breathe in through nose
   f. Breathe out through mouth

   Just sit and breathe in this posture. It's good for stress management and for reconnecting your right and left brain and increasing concentration.

4. **Neurolymphatic Flush**
   a. Rub the back of the neck, deeply into the grooves
   b. Move down and rub shoulders
   c. On the front of body, go down 4 inches from the base of the throat and 3 inches across and rub the sore spots in a circular motion

(Adapted from Donna Eden's Daily 5 Minute Energy Routine; see Donna Eden's *Energy Medicine*, New York: Tarcher or www.innersource.net for more information)

SESSION 2
The Power of the Mind

Stephanie Koraleski, PhD

Key Points
- Identifying what you believe about your life's purpose
- How cancer has affected your intentions about how to live your life
- Keeping your intention on track
  - Imagery
  - Music
  - Art
  - Affirmations
  - Acting with Love
- Taking time to set your intention and identifying ways to keep yourself on track

---

When cancer comes into your life, you're in shock and you immediately seek the best physicians and medical care you can find. But when treatment is over, you wonder what YOU should be doing to keep yourself well.

There are so many approaches you can take. You've learned about several of them so far in *A Time to Heal*. This week we'll be talking about the power of your mind: the internal, personal resources that you can tap into to boost your healing. Although you are unlikely to "think yourself well" without taking the practical steps to care for yourself, your mindset can make a big difference in the quality of your life.

Live with Intention

There are so many things that could be considered under the umbrella of mind power, but there is one that is the foundation of all. That is the *power of intention*. In our world, life is so rushed. We often get pushed and pulled from one thing to another, "putting out fires," reacting rather than choosing. When we are in such a rushed environment, we are likely to just do whatever is in front of us.

Living in an intentional way means that you consciously think about who you want to be, how you want to live, the way you want to act, the kinds of people you want in your life, the type of work you want to do and what is really important to you. You may not always get what you want, at least not immediately, but if you don't think about it, life will just happen around you. It's not fun being the pawn in someone else's chess game. **This is your life. Don't you want to play your game out yourself?**

So how do we begin? One way to begin living with intention is to spend some time reflecting on the purpose of life. This may sound grandiose, but there is no better time for thinking grand thoughts than when your life has been interrupted by illness. Most of us were taught something about the purpose of life. What were you told?

Are you here to be of service? To be successful? To serve God? To be happy? What were you told that a good person is supposed to do? A good spouse? A good parent? A good employee? Whether directly or indirectly, we learn who we are supposed to be from our parents, our schools, our religious teachers, our friends, our countries, and the culture that surrounds us as we are growing up.

What were you taught as a child? Do you still believe that? What have you come to believe at this point in your life? What have your own wisdom and experience taught you? It can be very helpful to write down what you were taught and what you currently believe and compare the two. What is similar? What has changed?

Having a creed of some kind that makes sense to you is essential in helping you know whether or not you are on track. Whether you learned that creed from your family, your religion, or your ethical practice or you developed a creed based on your own beliefs, it's important to know what your creed is. At a time of health crisis, **it can be empowering to write down what you believe as a way to make the subconscious**

Bishop

fully conscious. It may surprise you to really see what you think is most important. Did you list family, love, money, health, perfect attendance at work, a manicured lawn?

When you take time to think and write down the things that are most important, you gain clarity about how to spend your time. This is helpful both for cancer survivors and for caregivers. Having your beliefs written down in front of you acts as a roadmap to guide your thoughts and behaviors. With a roadmap, it's possible to take a wrong turn, but you're never truly lost.

Next, decide what you want now. You might think that anyone with cancer would want to be cured. That's not always true. Some people do want to be cured. Some are more concerned with enjoying life, meeting a specific goal such as seeing a new baby born, or finishing some task. A few want to die because they feel they have lived long enough or because their lives are full of problems they don't know how to solve or don't feel strong enough to handle. It's important to know what you really want, because your intention is powerful.

If part of you wants to live and part of you doesn't, you are sending a very mixed signal to your body. Be as specific as you can in your intention. Research on successful intention work generally shows that the more specific the intention, the better the results (McTaggart, 2007; Bengston, 2010; Schwartz, 2007).

As you try to figure this out, set aside some regular time to just be quiet, take walks by yourself, or just take some time alone to pay attention to your feelings. Dr. Kelly Turner's (2014) study of 1,000 people who achieved "radical remission" revealed that many of these people said that paying attention to their intuition was what helped them know what to do to heal and stay well. Intuition speaks in a quiet voice, and you often can't hear it when you are surrounded by noise and busyness. But, when you take the time to listen, you may hear that voice of wisdom inside telling you exactly what you need or what is lacking. Do you hear yourself saying things like this:

- "This job is killing me."

- "I'm happiest when I'm outside. Why don't I get out to nature more?"

- "I am really craving good, nutritious food; I need to make time to prepare good meals."

- "My heart is broken; I really need to grieve and heal."

Your intuition may help you identify what's lacking in your life or what would fill your life with more joy, help your body heal, or reignite your passion for life. Let it point you in the direction of healing. (For more information see Spontaneous Remissions and Miracles under Special Topics at the back of this book.)

Once you've identified what is truly important to you now (and this is an ongoing process—so don't get derailed if you can't define it completely at this point—just start with what you DO know and let the rest unfold over time), the next step is finding a way to keep your purpose at the forefront of your mind. It's like following a recipe. If you have the recipe in front of you, you know what the next step is. You may choose to make modifications along the way, but if you start out to make banana bread, you won't end up with vegetable soup.

There are many ways to keep intention on track. The wisdom of ages in nearly every religion and philosophy prescribes at least morning and evening prayer or meditation. The meaning of prayer is different to different people, but in terms of setting intention, it means taking some time each morning to say to yourself, or to God, how you would like to be during this day, and asking for assistance to do that. It means every evening taking a few moments to look back over the day and assess how close you came to fulfilling your intention, where you fell short of your vision, what made you happy, what got in your way, and giving thanks for your blessings and what you've learned. Each spiritual tradition has its own prescription for how to pray and set intent. Most of them say all prayer is good, but the highest form of prayer is just asking for the Highest Good to be done.

Some people like to set their intention by taking time each day to read a short meditation. The Daily Word (www.dailyword.com), *Pocketful of Miracles* (Borysenko, 1994), or other meditation books can be helpful. Other people keep a journal of their progress or write down things for which they are grateful.

If you are not religious, you might be saying, "I'm not into this spirituality stuff. This doesn't apply to me." That's okay. You can do it differently. If doing this through prayer or meditation doesn't make sense to you, research on self-help and management may.

Thousands of people have spent millions of dollars learning Stephen Covey's time management system. What does Covey say? Write it down. Put your intention on paper. Every day. Prioritize. Take stock each day to see what you've accomplished and what didn't get done. And how do you decide what to do? You base it on your values. Whether your value is to earn enough money to support your family or to add some love to your world or to help other people or to do your job the very best way you can, knowing what you are trying to accomplish and keeping that vision in your mind every day is the key to success.

The point is that it is crucial to set your own intention because as human beings we do have free will—in psychology this is called the power to choose. We can decide to do good or to commit crime. If we make no decision about how to think or act, we tend to get pulled into other people's ways of thinking or acting. We all do this from time to time, especially when we are young, but wouldn't you really rather steer your own ship?

Viktor Frankl, the famous psychiatrist who wrote *Man's Search for Meaning* about his experiences in Nazi concentration camps, talked about this by saying that even in the worst of circumstances, we always have some power. **The power we always retain is the power to choose our thoughts.** He sustained himself with images of his wife, choosing to remember love rather than to succumb to the barbarity and horror all around him.

So how do you stay on track? There are many ways. The goal is to keep your values and intentions in front of you daily, throughout the day. Our world is full of sounds and images that pull your attention in thousands of directions—ads to buy this, eat that, look like this. TV shows and movies are full of action and violence and crime. Newspapers and magazines detail the latest sexual escapades and drug involvements of movie stars and sports icons.

Your brain takes all of this in. If you want to stay on your own values, you need to give them a chance to compete with the stimulation from the outside. And you have to consciously choose to do this, because the world won't do it for you.

If the mind is powerful enough to make executives ultraefficient and successful or to keep someone alive and hopeful in a concentration camp, your mind is powerful enough to help you in your current situation. Much research has been conducted on the power of intention, and the good news is that you don't have to be a gifted psychic to get results. As with other skills, there are techniques that make intention more powerful, and people who spend time practicing get better over time.

What are the techniques of successful mind power?

First, much of the research seems to show that having a clear intention works best. Whether people were trying to change the pH (chemical balance) of water, make cells in a lab dish grow faster, improve athletic performance, or help others heal, the people who had the clearest intention seemed to get the best results. That means that these people spent time stating and visualizing exactly what they wanted to happen.

Second, making intention work for you takes time and attention. In most of the studies of mind power, the person using intention spends regular time every day or several days a week focusing his or her attention on the desired outcome. Visualize exactly how you would feel to celebrate success. Elite athletes often practice mental rehearsal every day by actually feeling what every movement of successful performance would be like in their bodies.

Buddhist monks spend years of daily meditation to increase their compassion, and their focus is so strong that they can sit in 40-degree temperatures and generate enough heat to dry cold wet sheets placed over them (Cromie, 2002).

So what happens when you focus this way? Does it make a difference? Body scans of athletes during actual skiing and during mental rehearsal of skiing showed that the brain sent the *identical* electrical impulses to the body in both real and visualized rehearsal (Siunn, 1985). Research at the Cleveland Clinic showed that people who lift weights regularly at the gym increased muscle mass by 30%, but those who sat in an armchair and mentally rehearsed without actually working out increased their muscle power by nearly half that much.

Researcher Sara Lazar at Mass General used MRI scans to compare the brains of regular meditators with nonmeditators and found that meditators had increased activity in the areas of the brain that control attention and autonomic functions such as blood pressure and metabolism (Lazar, 2000). The bottom line is this: you can actually achieve physical change in your body by using your mind.

Third, emotion seems to be a factor. Research has indicated that the most successful users of intention are people who maintain a neutral or compassionate but detached emotional state while practicing intention (Bengston, 2010). It can be difficult to move fear and time pressures and lists of to-dos from our thoughts, so most successful mind power practitioners practice some sort of regular meditation to help them detach from feelings and increase their ability to focus. In other words, they clear a spot in their minds first and then fill it with intention.

If you are interested in mind power, what are some ways to get started?

Imagery

Imagery refers to the pictures or beliefs or stories that run through our heads. We all have a constantly running stream of self-talk or pictures telling us about ourselves, others, and the situation.

Tuning into that and then turning it into what you want is very powerful.

Back in the 1960s Maxwell Maltz, a plastic surgeon, wrote a book called *Psycho Cybernetics*. In his clinical practice, he had noticed that nearly insignificant cosmetic surgeries could result in dramatic differences in his patients' personalities. He didn't think their appearance was that much different, so he thought something else must have changed. He began to study the correlation between beliefs and behavior and found many research studies showing that changing a belief about oneself could translate into a dramatic difference in behavior. For example, students who routinely flunked spelling tests began getting 100% papers, just by canceling out the belief that they couldn't spell and repeating the idea that they were able to spell well. Maltz's patients believed that a minor flaw made them ugly; when they had that minor flaw corrected, their belief about their own appearance changed—their IMAGE of themselves changed.

Since then, hundreds of case studies in hypnosis have confirmed this same principle. A few years after Maltz, the Lamaze childbirth system became popular in the United States, and millions of women experienced natural childbirth by setting the intent to relax, canceling out the idea of birth as a trauma, and substituting the image of birth as a beautiful natural process. The women were encouraged to use a picture that had meaning to them as a focus point. The success of this system—imagining birth as a natural, joyful process—has been instrumental in changing the entire labor and delivery paradigm in the US. At this point in time, even if they choose some anesthesia, almost every mom is awake to greet the birth of her baby. Almost every dad who wants to be a part of his child's birth is present when his baby is born. Contrast that with the "fathers in the waiting room, mothers under anesthesia" paradigm that was dominant in this country 60 years ago, and you see the impact of a strong intention being held by a large group of people.

Experiments have even shown that skills can increase just by imagining successful performance. One study showed that for high school students shooting baskets, there was nearly as much improvement in the group who imagined themselves sinking each shot as for the group that actually practiced their basketball skills every day. This research led to a demand for sports psychologists. Now it's almost a given that you'll see Olympic athletes mentally rehearsing their moves in the dressing area just prior to their competition.

Likewise, imagining failure often results in failure. Author Stephanie Koraleski tells this story. "Years ago right after graduating from college, I was an English teacher. During that time I also coached the high school speech team. We were a small school with no prior competition history, so I was delighted when one of my students qualified for the state tournament. She was very scared and I was nervous too. I really didn't know what to expect or how to prepare her because I was young and inexperienced. All the way to the tournament she kept saying, 'I just know I'll get up there and drop all of my notes and make a fool of myself.' And sure enough, the first round she got up and dropped all of her notes. To her credit, after experiencing her worst fear, she relaxed, picked up her notes in a dignified way, and went on to do well in the rest of the competition." When you catch yourself rehearsing some negative intentions, stop like this student did, collect yourself, and refocus on the intention you really want.

Imagery can be used to help you relax, to overcome fears, to motivate change. Imagery has been shown to decrease stress for breast cancer patients (Carlson et al., 2014). Imagery can support psychological coping and increase comfort for cancer patients (Roffe, Schmidt, and Einet, 2005; Leon-Pizarra et al., 2007) and has been shown to increase depressed white blood cell counts (Donaldson, 2000). Some of you may have used guided imagery tapes during chemo or radiation. In a recent study, 86% of patients receiving radiation reported that guided imagery was helpful, and biological monitoring showed that it helped those patients to relax, lower their blood pressure, and decrease their heart rates (Serra et al., 2012). Some people use imagery tapes to prepare for surgery. Research shows powerful effects of using imagery tapes in these ways. People have fewer side effects, feel more positive, change behaviors, and even heal more quickly. Guided imagery even helps people decrease the frequency and intensity of hot flashes! (Elkins, et al, 2013).

The power of purposefully setting a positive intention can't be overstated. Take the time to decide what you really want and who you really want to be. Develop a mental picture of that. Write yourself a slogan, draw yourself a coat of arms, or find a quotation or verse that reinforces your values. Keep referring back to those touch points to keep yourself on course. Just like a heat-seeking missile seeks its objective, having a programmed goal will help you self-correct when you are off course until you finally reach your target.

The most important thing is to know your intention. **Even if you never thought about it before, your behavior is being motivated by some belief.** Think deeply and carefully about the messages you are sending to your body. Be completely honest with yourself. What is it that you are trying to accomplish? Is your behavior projecting to others the you that you want them to see? Is it time to change your intention? It's perfectly fine and normal to change priorities when the situation changes.

Music

Another way to keep your intention in front of you is by using music. Go through your collection and put away anything that is not uplifting. For example, you may be a big Linda Ronstadt fan, but this may not be a good time to have "you're no good, you're no good, baby" playing through your head. Instead, locate everything that reinforces the values that you hold dear.

- Listen to the words. Do they inspire you? Do they evoke the feelings you need to feel?

- Listen to the music. Does it make you feel stronger, wiser, more powerful? Does it swell your soul with awe for life?

Thumb through old hymnals and find the songs that inspire you: *How Great Thou Art, Be Not Afraid.* Go to a music store and flip through sheet music collections looking for songs that build your spirit: *Imagine* by John Lennon; *You'll Never Walk Alone* from the musical *Carousel.* Check out the children's songs. Listen to the lullabies. Which ones comfort you, relax you, help you feel safe?

Look for new music. Ask friends. Ask people at the music stores. Many people have found strength and comfort in Jana Stanfield's "heavy mental" music titles like *Brave Faith* and *Even a Small Star Shines in the Darkness* or Karen Drucker's encouraging *I Will Be Gentle with Myself* or *Life Goes On.* Music like this can set the intention melodically; you'll find it playing through your head during stressful times, reminding you of your strength and courage; reminding you that you can cope.

Art

If music doesn't do the trick, how about art or photography? Find a picture that captures the feeling of who you want to be or what you want to happen. Maybe it's a print of a beautiful painting. Maybe it's a photo of your grandfather whose dignity and courage were always your ideal of strength. Maybe it's a picture of yourself when you were happy, healthy, and strong. Maybe it's a picture of healthy blood cells or of cancer cells disintegrating. It might be a favorite photo of you and your family when you were all happy and healthy.

Once you locate it, frame it, tape it on your bathroom mirror, or carry it in your purse. Just make sure you see it every day. Imagine yourself in that setting, being that person. Feel what it is like to be there; use as many of your senses as you can. Your mind will capture the picture and your intention to be like that image.

Affirmations

Affirmations are short, positive statements that express our intentions, goals, or images. They are always worded in the present tense, "*I am*" rather than "*I will be.*"

Whether you believe the statement or not doesn't matter. What matters is that you say it over and over. "*I am becoming stronger everyday.*" "*I act with loving kindness in all I say and do.*" "*I have satisfying work and I make a meaningful contribution.*"

45

Whatever you want to express. Just write it in a short, positive, present tense statement and repeat it several times a day. It can help to write the statement down and put it where you'll see it often, like on your bathroom mirror, refrigerator, or computer.

Another way to do affirmations is just to go to the mirror and look yourself in the eye and tell yourself what is right with you. *You have beautiful eyes. You are a compassionate friend. I'm so proud of you. Your strength has been inspiring. I love you.* This can be hard at first. Some people find themselves crying when they try it. Perhaps that's because we are so hungry to hear those words. Try it. Talk as lovingly to yourself as you would to your friends or to a precious child or grandchild. Remember, we become the image we hold in our minds. The more often we hear the good, the more like the good we become.

And does it work? Researchers at Carnegie Mellon showed that self-affirmation boosted problem-solving in stressful conditions (Creswell et al, 2013). Affirmations in a different study helped people be more receptive to positive health messages AND to actually change their behavior in the short run, which shows that you need to make affirmations a habit (Falk, 2015). Last, affirmations can both improve our performance and make us more aware of our errors so that we can self correct. (Legault, 2013).

The Intention to Act with Love

When you've been sick and you're tired and you feel like you're so behind on everything you'll never get caught up, it can seem overwhelming to try to do anything else. Some of you might be saying, I would love to exercise more, improve my nutrition, rake my neighbor's leaves, babysit for my daughter, or volunteer at church. But I'm so tired I can't even keep up with my own life. I can't help myself much less anyone else.

Not so. A counseling student told this story. Her beloved grandmother had had a serious stroke and was paralyzed and bedridden in a nursing home. Grandma had always been an active person, working hard well into her 80s taking care of the family and the farm. She was sad and depressed lying in bed and told her granddaughter, "I'm no good to anyone. I can't do anything anymore."

Her granddaughter looked incredulous. "But Grandma, you can still pray, can't you?"

"Why yes, I can do that."

So at each visit her granddaughter told her stories of people who needed help: family members, clients in her counseling practice, neighbors, people she read of in the newspaper. She and Grandma would pray together, and Grandma would promise to pray as she laid in the nursing home alone. And at each visit, her granddaughter would tell her what she knew of the outcomes of these stories. Some were unknown, but many of the prayed-for people did get well, settle their problems, or have a positive turnaround. Did Grandma's prayers help?

In his book *Healing Words*, Larry Dossey documents dozens of well-designed scientific studies on the power of prayer. Prayer made a difference in everything from the growth rate of seeds to the recovery of cardiac surgery patients. **Prayer is loving intention.** There are many documented cases of the positive effects of sending a positive intention or prayer for the wellness of another person (McTaggart, 2007; Bengston, 2010; Sicher,1998). Even if you can't physically do anything to help anyone, you have the power of prayer and intention.

Different cultures and religions may use different words for this loving intention, but many cultures recognize its power.

- Japanese Reiki masters set the intent before each healing session to "be a bamboo flute," in other words, a clear and open conduit for healing energy to flow through.

- Native American shamans ask for the Great Spirit to work through them.

- The Catholic saint, Francis of Assisi asked God to "make me a channel of Your peace...love...hope."

- Gandhi's intention to be nonviolent in India and Martin Luther King Jr.'s intention to be nonviolent in the United States instigated major changes in the social and political structures of those countries.

Think of your intention as being a path that energy can flow through. Decide on the type of energy you want to add to the world—love, education, encouragement, compassion—set the intention, and let it flow. There is an old saying, "The rising tide lifts all boats." Let your intention lift you, your family, and your world to a higher level.

Quantum physicists are more and more aware of the power of intention, saying that even the presence of an observer changes what is observed. Research in healing touch has demonstrated that loving intention, even without direct touch, has a positive effect on burn victims, premature babies, and people with cancer who are experiencing depression and anxiety (Peters, 1999; Jackson, 2008). Astronomers locate new planets and stars, not by seeing them directly, but by observing the influence of the unseen body on the bodies they can see. Life is much more than what we can see. If planets billions of light years away can influence the orbit of another body, it surely seems possible that your loving intention can influence someone on this earth.

Never underestimate the impact of kindness. The research on resilient children, children who came from difficult situations and managed to survive and thrive, shows that many of them had developed "protective factors" from experiences with someone who cared for them, and they held that caring image inside for years to comfort and encourage them through painful times. For some, it was a teacher. For others, it was a neighbor or a scout leader. For a few there was no loving, kind person in their lives, but they read about a loving person in a book and enfolded that image into their hearts. These children used the strengths they possessed to develop an image of a better life and then worked to create that life (Zolkoski, 2012). The change began with developing an intention, a picture of what could be.

Barring major mental illness, we tend to become who we choose to become. Your intention to be your highest self can change you at any time and can influence people for years to come. Can you choose to love today? **Might you be an image of love that sustains someone else in years to come?**

So, you have time. You have the power to choose. What will you pick?

- Do you want to find the joy and create some good each day?

- Do you decide to live every day to learn one new thing?

- Do you decide to live your days to bring a smile to one person?

- Do you live your days to teach the children in your life?

- Do you have a book to write, a song to compose, a legacy to document?

- Do you want to do something important?

- Do you want the world to be one drop kinder, smarter, or more peaceful because you were here today?

What is your intention?

Questions for discussion and journaling

1. What did you learn about the purpose of life from watching the important people around you?

2. As an adolescent, did you adopt the beliefs of your family or experiment with other ideas?

3. If someone who knew you were asked what your purpose in life has been up until now, what would they say?

4. How much of your mental thought is about how life affects you? How much is about how you affect others?

5. Have your ideas about the purpose of life changed over time?

6. At this point in your life, what do you believe the purpose of life is?

7. Are there people you want to connect with more deeply? How could you do that at this point in your life?

8. Are there people or situations you feel need your support?

9. Are there people who have supported you? Do they know how much their kindness, instruction, or mentoring meant to you?

10. Complete the following:
    I'll feel like my life was well lived if_____
    I'll be satisfied with myself today if I_____

11. If you were to die soon, what or who would have been better off because you were here? Has your existence made the world a better place in some way?

12. Write down your intention for how you would like to live life this week.

Power Tool: Breath Counting

Breath counting is one of many kinds of mindfulness training techniques. Many times when we're worried or ill, our minds take on a life of their own. Even though we may be really tired, our minds race along bringing up thought after thought and tiring us even more.

Breath counting is a very simple technique for helping your mind to calm down. Many of the participants in *A Time to Heal* have told us that this technique helped them learn to sleep again after a year or two of sleep problems after cancer treatment.

To begin, just breathe normally. Inhale. On the exhalation, say "one" to yourself mentally. Inhale again. As you exhale, say "two." Inhale. As you exhale, say "three." Inhale again. As you exhale, say "four." Inhale. As you exhale, start over with "one." Continue this breath counting for 5-10 minutes.

As you count your breaths, you'll notice that many thoughts enter your mind. Each time you notice a thought, very gently bring your mind back to the counting. Be gentle and loving with yourself: "Come back, honey. One." If you lose track of what number you are on, just go back and start again with "one."

It's impossible for most normal people to actually keep the focus on the counting for very long. It's normal for your mind to wander. But what you are doing is training your mind to come back to one focus, and you are learning to treat yourself with gentleness and compassion.

Other similar kinds of meditation you might have heard about are transcendental meditation (TM) and centering prayer. In TM, the meditator just keeps repeating a mantra, which is a special word you choose or which is given to you by a teacher.

In centering prayer, you select a holy word such as "peace," "shalom," or the name you call God when you pray. You imagine yourself sitting with God, just like two friends who care deeply about each other can sit together in silence. You say your word anytime your mind wanders, and then you sit in quiet when your mind calms down. If the mind wanders, you begin repeating your word again.

Any of these forms of mindfulness training can be helpful in learning to relax and stay in the present. You can find a variety of different types of breathing exercises online. Any of them can help you relax, calm your mind, and even sleep better. It helps if you can practice whichever technique you try for 5 to 20 minutes once or twice a day. The more regularly you practice, the better the effects seem to be.

SESSION 3

Advocating for Me—
Building My Survivorship Plan

Rhonda Wise, RN, MSN, OCN

Key Points

- Different treatment options are availabile because each cancer is unique
- Understanding the "seasons" of survivorship and how to keep moving through the transitions
- Understanding the role of a Survivor's Care Plan as a roadmap for your future health and a communication tool to use with your health care team
- Becoming aware of potential long-term effects and late effects of cancer treatment and how you can help to manage them

---

It is the last day of treatment, something you have been marking the days off on your calendar toward...there are smiles all around you, family may have come to bring you balloons, there may be cookies or cake to celebrate, you see so many familiar faces you have grown to trust, love, and look forward to seeing. You may ring a bell. YES you are happy that treatment is over. YES you are thankful to be alive, but then why do you feel so sad, scared, exhausted, guilty, and worried too? You may find yourself thinking, "Now what am I supposed to do?" or "What is wrong with me?"

When treatment ends, cancer survivors often are left with feelings of fear, confusion, anxiety, abandonment, and even anger. This is a far cry from the expected outcomes of joy, celebration, laughter, and renewed health. If this scenario resonates with you, you are not alone in feeling this way; in fact, these feelings are quite common.

In this chapter we will discuss the following topics regarding your cancer treatment. Better understanding of these areas may alleviate some of those difficult feelings

53

and empower you to advocate for yourself as you move forward in survivorship.

- Explore different treatment options available and why *one size does **not** fit all.*

- Describe the concept of "seasons" of survivorship and what you can do moving forward into the transitional phase of survivorship.

- Explain the role of a Cancer Survivor's Care Plan as a roadmap for your future and to improve communication between you and your health care team.

- Clarify potential long-term side and late effects of treatment and what you can do to help manage them.

- Identify credible resources when you are ready to seek information regarding your cancer, treatment, and survivorship.

The Many Faces of Cancer Treatment

There have been many advances in cancer detection and treatment in the past few decades, which is very encouraging. The basic treatment options appear to be the same such as surgery, chemotherapy, and radiation. However, when you look deeper, you will realize cancer treatment has become highly individualized. Here are some examples of personalized cancer care:

- **Surgery** may occur before or after chemotherapy. For example, neoadjuvant (before surgery) chemotherapy may be used to shrink the tumor making it easier to surgically remove. This is common in certain cancers if the tumor is large. (National Cancer Institute [NCI], 2009).

- **Chemotherapy** may be chosen depending upon your tumor's biological makeup. The pathologist will test a sample of the cancer tissue to determine the number of certain receptors and proteins on the cancer cell's surface. This information can determine if your cancer is hormone receptor positive and/or human epidermal growth factor receptor 2 (HER2) positive. This information helps your doctor choose the best treatment options for your individual cancer needs.

- **Radiation therapy** uses high-energy radiation to shrink and kill cancer cells. There are different types of radiation. External-beam radiation uses a machine to direct the radiation inside your body while brachytherapy involves placing radioactive material inside your body close to the tumor (NCI, 2010). Your radiation oncologist determines which method is best for you based upon your specific diagnosis.

- **Targeted Therapies** are drugs that treat cancer by interfering with specific molecules that promote growth (NCI, 2014). Information about your cancer's molecular makeup allows your doctor to choose the treatment that targets your individual cancer.

- **Immunotherapy** works in two ways to treat cancer. Immunotherapy can stimulate specific areas of your immune system to attack cancer cells or block the signal from the cancer cells that interfere with immune responses (NCI, 2015). This is a fast-advancing area of cancer research.

In addition to the expanding treatments available, each person's cancer journey is unique. People respond to their treatment differently. One person may experience severe side effects of treatment while the next person may breeze through treatment with few complaints. Another important thing to remember is that people may start treatment with different health backgrounds. For example, someone with diabetes, high blood pressure, and chronic back pain may have a more difficult time coping with treatment than someone who has no other health problems.

When it comes to cancer survivorship, it is important to address your individual needs. For the purposes of this chapter, topics will be discussed in general because it is difficult to give specific information on such a broad range of possibilities. Specific information related to your cancer may be accessed using the resource list at the back of this book. It is important to know that this chapter is for informational purposes only and is not meant as medical advice. You are encouraged to discuss any concerns or questions with your doctor.

So far we have been focusing on how different each cancer experience can be and the importance of focusing on individual needs. Let's look at some ways that survivors can feel united in their shared experiences.

Cancer's "Seasons of Survivorship"

What does it mean to be a cancer survivor? Some people wear the badge proudly and really identify with this terminology. These people often participate in cancer walks and wear survivor T-shirts or medals. Still some may chafe at being labeled a cancer survivor, and visibly wince when called a survivor. Finally, there are people who are confused as to what constitutes being a "cancer survivor." Whatever your feelings on being a cancer survivor, let's explore a deeper meaning of survivorship.

DeSantis and colleagues (2014) defines a cancer survivor as any person who has been diagnosed with cancer. This is significant because it encompasses all survivors at all points in life from diagnosis until end of life. Wow, that is huge! How can you know where you fit in this vast amount of time and space? Kenneth Miller, MD, codirector of the Perini Family Survivors' Center at Dana-Farber Cancer Institute, draws special meaning by thinking of survivorship in phases. Miller believes that being able to anticipate each phase of survivorship has the potential to improve your quality of life (Dana-Farber Cancer Institute [DFCI], 2010).

Here are the four phases and a brief explanation of the meaning of each:

- **Acute survivorship**: The time of diagnosis and treatment.

- **Transitional survivorship:** When treatment ends and "watchful waiting" begins.

- **Extended survivorship**: Comes in three forms: treatment-free remission; staying cancer-free with treatment; living with cancer as a chronic disease.

- **Permanent survivorship**: Comes in four forms: cancer-free symptom-free; cancer-free with side effects of treatment; developing a second cancer unrelated to treatment; developing a second cancer related to treatment.

(From "Cancer's 'Seasons of Survivorship,'" Dana-Farber Cancer Institute, 2010, *Paths of Progress*.)

You may notice there are no time frames associated with these seasons of survivorship. The focus is on what is going on in each individual person's life. There are positive and negative aspects of each phase or season, and not everyone will experience every phase of these seasons.

Being able to visualize yourself in one season may help prepare you for the possibilities of seasons to come. For instance, during the transitional survivorship phase when treatment ends, you may be feeling anxious about the future; it may help you to realize that you will be heading into a new phase in which your cancer may be in remission or stable with treatment.

Another way to make sense of survivorship is this analogy: assign calendar seasons and nature to the different phases of survivorship. Here are the calendar seasons and a brief explanation of the meaning of each:

- **Acute survivorship = Winter**: Harsh, blizzards, isolation, and cold. Plants are dormant waiting under all the cold snow for spring, because diagnosis and treatment can be hard to get through.

- **Transitional survivorship = Spring**: Cold at first but gradually warming, rainstorms, sunshine, new growth, plants are tender and need to be protected from too much sunshine, rain, or bunnies passing by, because treatment can leave you feeling vulnerable.

- **Extended survivorship = Summer**: Warmth, sunshine, thunderstorms here and there but learning to look for the rainbow, plants are growing strong maybe even blooming, because it takes time and patience to rebuild after cancer treatment.

- **Permanent Survivorship = Fall**: Warmth, sunshine, changing, stronger, sturdier, there are still storms but you are better able to cope and you know what to expect, because your spirit is strong and resilient.

Being able to understand what survivorship means for you is important. Take some time to read over these concepts and create a picture in your mind of where you are today. Be proud of what you have accomplished and who you have become as a result of it.

Most people reading this chapter will be in the transitional or spring season of survivorship. Take time to realize that this is a time of new tender growth that needs to be protected and nurtured. This is especially important to remember when your day may not be going the way you planned; picture yourself as a tender flower in the springtime and be kind, gentle, and nurturing to yourself.

Survivorship Care Plans—A Roadmap to the Future

People are living longer following cancer diagnosis and treatment. Nearly 14.5 million Americans with a history of cancer were alive on January 1, 2014. Of those, 64% were diagnosed 5 or more years previously and 15% were diagnosed 20 or more years ago (DeSantis et al., 2014). With these encouraging statistics comes a responsibility to ensure that the needs of 14.5 million Americans are being met. Let's begin by looking back at how the issue of survivorship began.

In 2005 the Institute of Medicine (IOM) issued a report titled, "From Cancer Patient to Cancer Survivor: Lost in Transition." This report was a call to action for the cancer care community to rethink how the complex needs of cancer survivors were or were not being met when treatment ended. As cancer patients moved forward into survivorship, they often did not know what to do or whom to call when they needed to see their doctor; and which doctor to go to for their health concerns. Cancer survivors were feeling lost.

The IOM report recommended the following: (a) use of a survivorship care plan (SCP); (b) a personalized treatment summary; (c) information on potential long-term and late effects of treatment and signs of recurrence; (d) recommended follow-up and wellness recommendations; (e) information on legal, employment, and insurance rights; and (f) resources for emotional wellness in the community (Jackson, Scheid, and Rolnick, 2013; Mayer, Birken, Check, and Chen, 2014). The overriding focus for all these recommendations was to ensure coordination of communication and care among the survivor, oncology team, and primary care physician (National Academy of Sciences, 2005).

Since that time, there has been much debate on the best ways to meet these recommendations. The Livestrong Foundation has created an online SCP and conducted multiple surveys to better understand the needs of survivors, caregivers, and their loved ones. One survey looked at whether that SCP improved the quality of life and health outcomes of survivors. The results showed that 90% were satisfied with their SCP and 75% found it useful (Livestrong, 2015).

To receive or continue to have accreditation, the American College of Surgeons' Commission on Cancer (COC) mandates that all cancer-care facilities provide eligible patients with an SCP at the end of their treatment (LaTour, 2014). This mandate was to go into effect on January 1, 2015, but due to the extensive resources needed to implement this plan, the COC has allowed more time for completion. The final date for 100% participation has been changed to January 1, 2019 (American College of Surgeons, 2014).

This mandate is exciting news for future cancer survivors, but this is not a likely benefit for you if you have already finished treatment. The good news is Journey Forward (www.journeyforward.org) promotes the use of cancer SCPs with free tools to build your own SCP for patients and health care professionals. Journey Forward has a free resource library that provides information on topics of symptom management and follow-up guidelines from the Oncology Nursing Society, American Cancer Society, American Society of Clinical Oncology, and the National Cancer Institute.

The template can be found later in this chapter. You are encouraged to share it with your oncologist and your primary care physician. **Make sure to keep a copy for yourself.** Although your primary care physician might not be familiar with SCPs, most oncology practices are and will be able to help answer questions you may have.

As you look through "My Care Plan," you will notice the different sections. The first section is a good place to start filling in all the contact information for your health care providers. The Self-Assessment section, is meant to be a communication tool between you and your oncology doctor to discuss any long-term side effects you may be experiencing. It is a good idea to fill this out before each appointment.

The Treatment Summary section provides the history of your diagnosis and treatment. You are not expected to know all this information, and your oncology provider can help you fill in the sections you don't understand. It is important to know exactly what treatments you received and discuss any potential late effects you might experience; this includes what signs to look for.

Last, the Follow-up Care section lets you better understand what your next steps are in survivorship. This is the section that answers those who, what, when, and where questions that can be so confusing. This section is also meant to give you guidance regarding wellness; this information can be found in the Journey Forward Survivorship Library as well as by asking your health care team.

As you can see, this SCP is a communication tool. Working through it with your oncology doctor and sharing it with your primary care physician should open communication about any physical, emotional, and practical needs you may have.

You will also find a list of potential long-term side effects and late effects of cancer and their treatment at the end of this chapter. This list includes common side effects. You may experience some of these or other symptoms. Be sure to discuss all concerns and questions you have with your doctor. There is a list of credible resources at the end of this book where you can access valuable information regarding survivorship.

Empowerment is defined as "to give power." During your acute phase of cancer diagnosis and treatment, you may have felt powerless both physically and emotionally. Now, as you move forward into the transitional phase of survivorship, remember you are tender and need to be nurtured; however, having access to reliable information may help you begin to advocate for your health care needs. You are getting your power back. You are empowered!

Common Side Effects of Cancer and its Treatment

Fatigue

Cancer-related fatigue is a persistent feeling of physical, emotional, and/or mental exhaustion related to cancer and/or its treatment. This type of fatigue does not improve with rest, does not reflect your level of activity and may interfere with your everyday functioning. Fatigue affects most people receiving cancer treatment (surgery, chemotherapy, and radiation) and can last for months and sometimes years after treatment ends.

Causes: Fatigue can be related not only to your cancer and treatment but also to anemia, sleep disturbances, pain, depression, anxiety, menopausal symptoms, and use of prescription or over-the-counter medications. There may be previous or new medical conditions such as heart disease, lowered lung and kidney function, hormone problems, and arthritis that may contribute to cancer-related fatigue.

Managing Fatigue: The first step in managing your fatigue is to talk to your doctor. Treating any medical causes for fatigue begins by openly discussing your pain, any sleep disturbances, how you're feeling about your cancer, and medications you are taking that may be making you drowsy. A simple blood test can determine if you are anemic or malnourished. These are all conditions your doctor can treat with medication or refer you to a licensed counselor or dietitian.

Lifestyle Strategies: Research suggests staying physically active or slowly increasing your physical activity helps relieve cancer-related fatigue and improves quality of life (Broderick et al., 2013). The recommendation is to slowly and gradually increase your activity (walking, cycling, or swimming) until you reach a level and type of activity you and your doctor agree are best for you (ASCO, 2015).

You can try managing your fatigue with these simple ways:

- Establish a sleep routine. This involves the following: avoid electronics and stimulating activities for two hours before bedtime, engage in calming activities (try a warm bath, reading, listening to music), go to bed and wake up at the same time each day (even on the weekends), sleep in a dark, cool, and quiet room (no television, computers, or electronics).
- Learn to balance activity with rest, plan your activities during the time of day when you have the most energy, and take short naps if possible (no more than 20 to 30 minutes) (Lee and Decker, 2012).
- Mindfulness-based approaches such as yoga, acupuncture, touch therapy, massage, music therapy, relaxation, and meditation may all be helpful for reducing fatigue, but more research is needed (ASCO, 2015).
- Other strategies for dealing with fatigue are discussed in session 8.

Pain

Most people experience some pain during their cancer treatment. Pain that is not relieved can worsen your ability to cope and seriously compromise your quality of life. Unrelieved pain can affect your sleep and mental clarity and increase anxiety, depression, nausea, shortness of breath, and fatigue. It is easy to understand why pain is considered the most feared of all symptoms associated with cancer (ASCO, 2015; Lee and Decker, 2012).

Causes: Pain can be caused by the tumor (pressing on organs or nerves), the result of cancer treatment (surgery, chemotherapy, radiation), and prior or current painful conditions (arthritis, migraine headaches, and chronic back pain). Pain can be related to a procedure and be expected to last for a short time (acute) or be related to cancer and its treatment and last for longer than three months (chronic) (ASCO, 2015).

Managing Pain: It is important to talk to your doctor about your pain. Some people hesitate to do this because they think it is something they have to learn to live with, while others fear becoming addicted to pain medication and fear the side effects (constipation, drowsiness, confusion). Open discussion with your health care team will enable your doctor to create a pain-relief strategy that will be effective for you.

According to ASCO (2015), keeping a pain journal can be an effective tool to communicate with your doctor about your pain (type, intensity, and location). Start with the following suggestions:

- Write down the date, time, and duration when you have pain.

- Note what you were doing when the pain started.

- Note where in your body the pain started and if it spread to other parts of your body.

- Give your pain a number (0= no pain and 10=horrible pain).

- Use words to describe your pain, for example, dull, sharp, stabbing, burning, or throbbing.

- Keep track of what you did to control your pain. Write down what worked and what didn't and how long did you get relief.

Keeping this pain journal may give you insight into your pain and will be helpful to share with your doctor.

Lifestyle Strategies: While your doctor may prescribe medications designed to relieve your pain (non-opioid, opioids, antidepressants, or antiseizure), it is important that you take the medications as prescribed. If you have side effects, let your doctor know immediately. Sometimes changing the timing, dose, or medication will relieve your symptoms.

Try these simple things to help manage your pain:

- Distraction: warm bath, read a book, watch television, take a short walk, sit in nature, engage in a hobby. All can distract your mind from pain.

- Guided imagery: use the Power Tools included in this book to practice. Be patient with yourself because this technique takes practice.

- Breathing exercises/meditation: Relaxation and stress reduction can reduce pain. These techniques are included in the Power Tool portion of this book.

- Physical therapies: massage, hot and cold compresses, acupuncture, biofeedback, physical therapy and occupational therapy have a positive impact on pain management (ASCO, 2015; Lee & Decker, 2012).

Lymphedema

The abnormal buildup of fluid in your tissues due to a blockage in the lymphatic system is called lymphedema (ASCO, 2015). Lymphedema occurs most often when the lymph vessels have been damaged due to cancer treatment (surgery, biopsy, radiation, or infection). This condition is discussed fully under Special Topics at the end of this book.

Peripheral Neuropathy

Peripheral nerves carry messages back and forth between your brain and spinal cord to the rest of your body. Peripheral neuropathy most often occurs in the hands and feet generally starting in the fingers and toes. It is often described as a change in sensation such as numbness, tingling, electrical zing, or burning (sensory nerves). Muscle weakness may also result, which can lead to problems with balance; your legs and arms may feel heavy (motor nerves).

Involuntary body functions such as blood pressure, bowel and bladder control can be affected; this can lead to diarrhea, constipation, dizziness, trouble swallowing, and sexual dysfunction (autonomic nerves). Peripheral neuropathy may improve over time or be permanent.

Causes: May be caused by a tumor pressing on a peripheral nerve, chemotherapy, radiation therapy, surgery, malnutrition or other conditions unrelated to cancer (diabetes, alcohol abuse, shingles, and kidney disease).

Managing Peripheral Neuropathy: Your doctor may prescribe medication to relieve the symptoms of neuropathic pain, but currently there is no medication available to reverse it. Over-the-counter pain medications may be used for mild pain. The most common medications used for neuropathic pain are antidepressants and anticonvulsants. If your pain needs are not met, your doctor may prescribe analgesics, topical creams, or lidocaine patches.

Lifestyle Strategies: Eating foods high in B vitamins (B1 and B12), folic acid, and antioxidants may help. Avoid drinking too much alcohol. Complementary medicine (massage, acupuncture, and relaxation techniques) may help reduce your pain. Physical or occupational therapy may improve your strength, balance, and coordination as well as offer assistive devices if needed (cane or walker).

Safety is a priority. Keep your home (especially stairways) uncluttered and well lit. To decrease fall risk, remove all area rugs; install grab bars in bathrooms and if needed a second handrail in stairways. When in the kitchen use potholders and wear rubber gloves to avoid burning your skin. Use a thermometer to test the water temperature before getting in the bath. Use caution when using scissors or a knife to avoid cutting yourself. Be aware of your ability to operate a car safely. If you cannot fully feel the steering wheel or quickly move your feet from the gas pedal to the brake, it is unsafe for you to drive.

Sleep Problems

Sleep problems come in many forms; cancer and its treatment may cause the following sleep problems:

Insomnia: Having trouble falling asleep or staying asleep at night, which may cause you to be tired, irritable, and confused during the day. The risk of insomnia increases with age and serious illness. Insomnia can cause pain, fatigue, depression, or anxiety to worsen.

Causes: To determine the cause of your insomnia, your doctor may take a sleep history (sleeping habits, snoring, sleep environment, breathing pattern, physical symptoms, emotional or financial concerns, and any medications/ supplements you are taking).

Managing Insomnia: The first step to managing insomnia is to determine the cause. Your doctor may recommend medications for relief for short-term use. A sleep study may be ordered to measure your quality of sleep. There is some evidence that exercise and Mindfulness-Based Stress Reduction (Power Tool) may improve the quality of sleep.

Hypersomnia: Feeling very sleepy during the day or wanting to sleep for longer than 10 hours at night. Being unable to stay awake during the day even if you take a nap.

Causes: Brain or central nervous system tumors; anemia; prescription and over-the-counter medications (pain medications, antinausea medications, antidepressants); anemia; depression; hormone level changes.

Managing Hypersomnia: The first step to managing hypersomnia is to determine the cause. Treating the cause should relieve the symptoms. Behavioral changes may help such as exercising in the morning or early afternoon, going to sleep and waking at the same time, avoiding heavy meals during the day, and avoiding alcohol and caffeine.

Nightmares: Having vivid or frequent frightening nightmares that cause you to wake up and remember at least part of the dream.

Causes: Increased emotional stress may cause nightmares as well as some medications such as antibiotics, iron supplements, pain medication, and heart medications. Withdrawal from alcohol, pain medications, and some antianxiety medications can increase nightmares. Uncontrolled pain may also lead to nightmares.

Managing Nightmares: It is normal to experience some nightmares, but if they increase in frequency, cause anxiety, or keep you from sleeping, discuss them with your doctor. It is important to honestly discuss your fears and feelings with trusted family or friends. It is better to discuss nightmares earlier in the day than close to bedtime.

Menopausal Symptoms in Women

Menopause is a natural process of aging and usually occurs during a woman's mid-40s to mid-50s. During this time hormone levels decrease gradually and menstrual cycles become irregular until menstrual periods stop. Some cancer treatments can cause abrupt menopause such as surgery to remove the ovaries, chemotherapy, hormone therapy, and radiation therapy involving the pelvis. This may be temporary or permanent, which impacts fertility.

Symptoms: Irregular periods, hot flashes, night sweats, vaginal dryness, lack of interest in sex, fatigue, sleep problems, memory problems, thinning of the bones (osteoporosis), bladder control problems, depression, mood swings, and weight change are all possible symptoms of menopause.

Managing Menopausal Symptoms

Osteoporosis: Your doctor may prescribe medications such as Fosamax, Evista, or calcitonin, which are used to prevent or treat osteoporosis in postmenopausal women. To lower the risk of developing osteoporosis, the following is recommended: weight-bearing exercise (walking) 20-30 minutes daily, maintaining ideal body weight, and taking calcium and vitamin D as recommended by your doctor.

Sexual Changes: See Special Topics.

Hot Flashes: Your doctor may prescribe medications such as Neurontin (anticonvulsant) and Effexor (antidepressant) to relieve your hot flashes. Other tips include quit smoking, drink plenty of water, maintain ideal weight, exercise (weight-bearing and muscle-strengthening) at least 5 days a week, eat a healthy diet, sleep in a cool room, dress in layers, use cotton sheets and clothing, and limit alcohol, caffeine, and spicy foods.

Heart Disease: Studies have suggested that estrogen has a protective factor for the heart. After menopause, your cholesterol levels may increase, which can lead to diseases that affect your heart and blood vessels. It is important to talk to your doctor about your risk factors and recommendations for heart health.

Osteoporosis

Osteoporosis begins when bone tissue is lost faster than the body can replace it. Bones become fragile making them easier to fracture (break). At first there may be no symptoms, but as the bones become more weak you may experience the following symptoms: back pain, gradual loss of height, stooped posture, a broken bone from a minor injury.

Causes: Increased age, cancer that has spread to the bone (metastasis), some chemotherapy, radiation therapy (pelvic radiation increases risk of hip fracture), being a woman, hormone therapy for breast or prostate cancer, heavy smoking or drinking alcohol, family history of osteoporosis, steroid therapy, heartburn medications, inactivity, poor nutrition, being white or of Asian descent.

Managing Osteoporosis: Your doctor may order a test to measure your bone mass called a dual energy x-ray absorptiometry (DEXA) scan. This test will allow your doctor to know how strong your bones are. If you are diagnosed with osteoporosis, your doctor may prescribe a medication called a bisphosphonate, which slows bone thinning, reduces new bone damage, and may help heal the bone. Before starting this medication, it is important to schedule a dental visit and notify your dentist that you are taking a bisphosphonate before any procedure. Talk with your doctor about the recommended dose of calcium and vitamin D.

Lifestyle Strategies: Weight-bearing activities (walking, dancing, stair climbing, jumping rope, hiking, tennis) send a signal to your body to make more bone cells. Regular weight-bearing exercise also helps improve muscle strength and helps with balance. It is important to talk to your doctor before starting any exercise program. Maintaining a healthy weight and eating a well-balanced diet are also important factors in bone health. Being underweight or malnourished can lead to bone loss and fractures. Safety is a big concern with osteoporosis. Prevent falls by wearing proper fitting shoes, keep living space uncluttered (especially stairways), remove throw rugs, and be aware of drowsiness or confusion related to medications.

Weight Changes

Weight Gain: Increase in weight during treatment.

Causes: Some chemotherapy can cause your body to hold onto fluids (edema), decrease your metabolism, increase hunger and food cravings, and cause menopause in women. Steroid medications, which are often used to treat swelling, pain, or nausea, may increase belly fat and fullness in the face and neck. Hormonal therapy used to treat breast, uterine, prostate, and testicular cancer decrease estrogen/progesterone in women and testosterone in men, which leads to increased fat, decreased muscle, and a lowered metabolism.

Managing Weight Gain: It is important to talk to your doctor about your concerns; the doctor may refer you to a registered dietitian who can help you begin a healthy eating plan. Discuss with your doctor physical activities you enjoy such as walking, biking, and strength-building exercises that will be safe and healthy for you to begin. Be patient with yourself, begin slowly, and remember your health and safety are the priority.

Weight Loss: Weight loss is common in people with cancer. When weight loss is combined with muscle wasting, it is called cachexia, which comes with extreme fatigue, weakness, and inability to do everyday things.

Causes: Weight loss usually begins with appetite loss, which may be from the side effects of cancer and its treatment. These are some of the common causes: increased metabolism, nausea and vomiting, constipation, taste changes, mouth sores, difficulty swallowing, depression, and unrelieved pain.

Managing Weight Loss: Your doctor may prescribe medications to increase your appetite or help your body absorb nutrients. Your doctor may refer you to a registered dietitian who can help you develop a healthy eating plan.

Lifestyle Strategies: Start with five small meals a day; try eating the foods that were your favorites before treatment; experiment with different temperatures (sometimes hot, warm, cold, or icy foods will taste better); taking a short walk before meals may stimulate your appetite. Be patient with yourself, don't force yourself to eat, try to stay positive and think of your food as the nutrients that will continue to heal your body.

Late Effects of Cancer Treatment

A late effect is a side effect that appears months or even years after treatment ends. Being aware of the potential for these side effects and seeking immediate medical advice is an important part of cancer survivorship.

Heart Problems

Chemotherapy and radiation therapy to the chest may cause heart problems. Common heart conditions and their symptoms are listed here:

Congestive Heart Failure is a weakening of the heart muscle, which can lead to shortness of breath, dizziness, and swollen hands or feet.

Coronary Artery Disease is a condition more common to people who had high doses of radiation to the chest. Symptoms include chest pain and shortness of breath.

Irregular Heartbeat is characterized by lightheadedness, chest pain, and shortness of breath.

High Blood Pressure is common in people whether they have gone through cancer treatment or not. It is important to continue to monitor your blood pressure regularly because sudden or prolonged rises in your blood pressure can lead to heart damage.

Managing Heart Problems: Safety is the priority when it comes to heart problems. You are encouraged to talk to your doctor and discuss whether your individual treatment may put you at increased risk for developing heart problems. If you develop any of the symptoms, take it very seriously and seek medical help immediately.

Lung Problems

Chemotherapy and radiation therapy to the chest may damage the lungs. This may change the way the lungs work, cause thickening of the lining of the lungs, inflammation of the lungs, and difficulty breathing. People with a history of lung damage may be at greater risk for developing these problems.

Managing Lung Problems: Safety is the priority when it comes to lung problems. You are encouraged to talk to your doctor and discuss whether your individual treatment may put you at increased risk for developing lung problems. If you develop any of the symptoms, take it very seriously and seek medical help immediately.

Post-Traumatic Stress Disorder

This is an anxiety disorder that may be experienced by cancer survivors, caregivers, family, and close friends. It can develop after experiencing a life-threatening event such as a cancer diagnosis and treatment. Each person will react to his or her experience differently, and it is important to be aware that there is help if you are struggling:

Managing Post-Traumatic Stress Disorder: It is important to talk to your doctor if you are struggling with the negative emotions surrounding cancer and its treatment. Your doctor can refer you to a licensed mental health professional who can help you sort through your emotions. Talking about your feelings is the first step toward healing.

Secondary Cancers

A secondary cancer is new cancer that is different from your original cancer. It may develop due to previous cancer treatment such as chemotherapy and radiation therapy.

Managing Secondary Cancers: Talk to your doctor about the potential for developing a secondary cancer related to your individual treatment. It is important to understand how to monitor for early detection, lifestyle changes you can make to reduce your risk, and signs and symptoms to report to your doctor.

From American Society of Clinical Oncology (ASCO) http://www.cancer.net;

Journey Forward http://www.journeyforward.org/library

Sample Care Plan

Thanks to Journey Forward (www.journeyforward.org) for their permission to reprint their example of a Survivorship Care Plan on the next page.

 **My Care Plan**

This Survivorship Care Plan will help you manage your health care after treatment for cancer. Fill in the *General Information* and *Self-Assessment* to the best of your abilities. Then, work with your oncology provider to fill in the *Treatment Summary* and *Follow-up Care* sections. Be sure to visit the Journey Forward Survivorship Library (JourneyForward.org/Library) to view and print factsheets related to your cancer, symptoms and ongoing needs, and keep these with your Care Plan. When your Plan is complete, make an appointment to review it with your primary care provider. Keep your Plan handy when talking with healthcare providers over time.

Reviewed with my oncologist	☐	Reviewed with my primary care provider	☐

General Information

Last updated

Your name

Your date of birth

YOUR CARE TEAM	NAME & CONTACT INFORMATION
Support contact	
Primary care provider	
Hematologist/oncologist	
Surgeon	
Radiation oncologist	
OB-GYN ♀	
Nurse/nurse practitioner	
Mental health/social worker	

Self-Assessment

Check any symptoms you are experiencing. **Discuss symptom management and treatments with a healthcare professional.**

☐ Abdominal pain	☐ Pain or problems with eating
☐ Changes in appetite	☐ Pain with urination
☐ Chest pain	☐ Painful eyes
☐ Chronic constipation	☐ Pins and needles or numbness
☐ Chronic diarrhea	☐ Recurrent colds/coughs/infections
☐ Cough or wheezing	☐ Relationship problems
☐ Decreased exercise ability	☐ Sexual dysfunction/lack of desire
☐ Dental problems	☐ Shortness of breath
☐ Difficulty breathing	☐ Skin changes, rashes, lumps or bumps
☐ Dizziness	☐ Sleep-wake disturbances
☐ Dry mouth	☐ Slurred speech
☐ Easy bruising or bleeding	☐ Swelling of arm or leg
☐ Fatigue	☐ Swollen lymph nodes
☐ Fertility concerns	☐ Urinary incontinence
☐ Fever and sweats	☐ Vision problems
☐ General weakness	☐ Weight gain or overweight
☐ Hair loss	☐ Weight loss or loss of appetite
☐ Hearing loss	
☐ Heartburn/indigestion	♀ **WOMEN ONLY**
☐ Hot flashes/night sweats	☐ Abnormal vaginal bleeding
☐ Irregular heartbeat/palpitations	☐ Irregular menses (periods)
☐ Jaundice (yellowing of skin or eyes)	☐ Vaginal discharge
☐ Joint pain or muscle aches	☐ Vaginal dryness
☐ Leg pain with exertion	☐ Painful intercourse
☐ Memory/concentration issues	☐ Premature menopause
☐ Negative body image	
☐ New/changed moles or freckles	♂ **MEN ONLY**
☐ Numbness/weakness on one side	☐ Erectile dysfunction

	NOT PRESENT . . . . WORST IMAGINABLE									
SYMPTOM	0	1	2	3	4	5	6	7	8	9	10
Pain	○	○	○	○	○	○	○	○	○	○	○
Anxiety/worry	○	○	○	○	○	○	○	○	○	○	○
Fear of recurrence	○	○	○	○	○	○	○	○	○	○	○
Depression/sadness	○	○	○	○	○	○	○	○	○	○	○

Adapted from the UCLA Survivorship Center Medical History Intake Form.

Treatment Summary

This is a summary of your diagnosis and treatment. Most of this information can be found in your pathology report, operative report, and chemotherapy and radiation treatment summaries. **Please consult with your oncology provider.**

Diagnosis date

Type of cancer

Location of cancer

Pathologic stage

TNM staging   T   N   M

Histology

Surgery

Chemotherapy regimen

Clinical trial?

THERAPEUTIC AGENTS	DOSE	SCHEDULE/# CYCLES	DOSE REDUCTIONS/COMMENTS

Treatment goal

Response to treatment

Serious toxicities during treatment

Ongoing toxicities

Radiation therapy (type, dose, site)

Comments

Follow-up Care

Visit the Survivorship Library (JourneyForward.org/Library) to see guidelines for follow-up care. **BE SURE TO CONSULT WITH YOUR ONCOLOGY PROVIDER TO DETERMINE THE RIGHT SCHEDULE OF FOLLOW-UP TESTS AND VISITS FOR YOU.**

FOLLOW-UP TESTS & VISITS	WHEN/HOW OFTEN?	PROVIDER TO CONTACT
Medical oncology visit		
Physical exam		
Bone density scan (DEXA)		
Imaging (X-ray, CT, MRI, PET scan)		
Mammogram		
Pap smear & pelvic exam ♀		
PSA & rectal exam ♂		
Colonoscopy		

WELLNESS		COMMENTS
☐	Diet & nutrition	
☐	Exercise	
☐	Mental health	
☐	Bone health	
☐	Immunizations	
☐	Cholesterol management	
☐	Diabetic screening/management	
☐	Hypertension control	
☐	Smoking cessation	

OTHER COMMENTS

Questions for discussion and journaling:

1. What have you found that has helped any of your cancer-related symptoms?

2. Have you had any problems getting information or answers to your questions from medical personnel? How did you handle the situation? What have you learned?

3. How can people keep informed about their treatment and its side effects (for example, do they rely on their personal physicians for information, do they get information from friends, newspapers, websites)?

4. What is the role of second opinions?

5. Where can you get reliable information? How much do you trust salespersons, blogs, or purely anecdotal accounts? How does the scientific process work? How do researchers determine what does and doesn't have an effect?

Power Tool:

The Relaxation Response

This is the generic technique that Dr. Herbert Benson designed to teach patients to elicit the Relaxation Response:

- Pick a focus word, short phrase, or prayer that is firmly rooted in your belief system.

- Sit quietly in a comfortable position.

- Close your eyes.

- Relax your muscles, progressing from your feet to your calves, thighs, abdomen, shoulders, head, and neck.

- Breathe slowly and naturally, and as you do, say your focus words, sound, phrase, or prayer silently to yourself as you exhale.

- Assume a passive attitude. Don't worry about how well you're doing. When other thoughts come to mind, simply say to yourself, "Oh well," and gently return to your repetition.

- Continue for 10 to 20 minutes.

- Do not stand immediately. Continue sitting quietly for a minute or so, allowing other thoughts to return. Then open your eyes and sit for another minute before rising.

- Practice the technique once or twice daily. Good times to do so are before breakfast and before dinner.

You can also elicit the Relaxation Response while exercising by paying attention to the cadence of your feet on the ground, the tempo of swimming strokes, the beat of the music, or the rhythm of your breathing. When other thoughts come into your mind, say, "Oh well," and return to the rhythm of the exercise.

Power Tool: "Jane's Jar"

This power tool is the brainchild of one of our *A Time to Heal* graduates.

When Jane's children were young, she wrote down "fun things to do" on brightly colored pieces of paper to be held in reserve in case her children got bored. She kept all the ideas folded up in a jar. When an idea was needed, she let the children reach into the jar.

We sometimes need an idea for relaxing or having fun, and at the very time we need it, no ideas seem to be forthcoming.

We invite you to write down ideas for reserve—just like Jane did. Maybe your jar could be full of things to think of that relax you (like special memories, mellow music, a bubble bath, or a beach you've seen in a movie or on a vacation). It just takes a minute to write them down when you think of them. When you really need a boost, your jar full of relaxation will be waiting for you! Try it and see.

SESSION 4
Comforting Myself

Joyce Swanson, MS, LMPH, NCBTMB

Key Points
- The relaxation response is a simple tool for healing that anyone can learn.
- Identify techniques that help each person most effectively relax.
- Relaxation has many health benefits.
- Relaxation can help your body after even one session, but the more you practice, the more the benefits increase.

Introduction

Comfort: To console, strengthen, inspirit

If someone offered you a "magic pill" that could decrease your pain, help to build your immune system, bring a glow to your skin, and create a sense of overall well-being, would you be interested? If so, you are in luck. We are going to explore and experience some of the many benefits of nurturing touch. Some techniques will fit you like a glove. Others may need alterations. You are the expert on what feels good to you and what comforts and strengthens your body and spirit.

"How does it work?"

A diagnosis of cancer sets in motion a whirlwind of appointments, decisions, and medical treatments. Your body has been poked and prodded and overwhelmed with medical procedures. Your body's stress response—fight, flight, or freeze—immediately shifted into overdrive. This is an automatic response. It looks something like this:

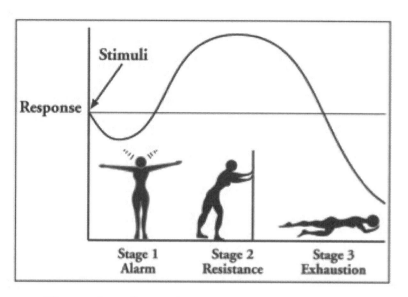

Illustration: Generalized stress response: Alarm, adaptation or resistance and, finally, if there is no intervention, exhaustion.

Being in this chronic state of stress is very hard on the body. Being in a state of exhaustion leaves little reserve available for the process of healing and regenerating.

Robert Sapolsky, author of *Why Zebras Don't Get Ulcers,* compares this process to balancing on a seesaw. When stress is low, the seesaw is easy to balance, as if a small child were on each side. The children can balance themselves with relative ease, and it doesn't take a lot of energy. However, when a major stressor arrives, the picture changes. Now, the process is as difficult as balancing two massive elephants on each side of the seesaw. Their enormous potential energy has to be put into the immediate short-term task of balancing, leaving very little for long-term building projects.

With cancer, the body is so busy trying to deal with the immediate threat that it does not have time to work on repair. Another problem is that the elephants cause damage just because they are so large and lumbering. In other words, it is hard to fix one major problem in the body without knocking other systems out of balance. The final issue with the elephants is that, once they get on the seesaw, it is hard to get them off without causing even more damage.

So what can you do? To help tame your elephants, you need to develop your body's ability to trigger a relaxation response.

The Relaxation Response

Herbert Benson, MD, author of *The Relaxation Response,* has been conducting research about the healing qualities of relaxation at the Mind/Body Medical Institute at Harvard for over 25 years. He lists four essential components to elicit the Relaxation Response:

- A quiet environment

- A mental device—a sound, word, phrase, or prayer repeated silently or aloud, or a fixed gaze at an object

- A passive attitude—not worrying about how well one is performing the technique and simply putting aside distracting thoughts to return to one's focus

- A comfortable position

Dr. Benson has documented the positive physiological changes associated with the relaxation response. Some of these changes include:

- Lower blood pressure

- Breaking the anxiety cycle and relieving anxiety-related symptoms

- Decrease pain levels

- Decrease nausea associated with chemotherapy

- Lower cholesterol levels

- Enhance immune function

- Increase healthful sleep

- Increase creativity

The basic message of Dr. Benson's research is that relaxation is good for your health. It stimulates the brain's production of endorphins, which are natural opiates (feel-good brain chemicals) that act to decrease your perception of pain and create a state of well-being. He describes this relaxation response as a mental and physical sigh of relief.

In recent years, tools have been developed to assess gene-based changes as a result of the relaxation response. The Benson-Henry Institute of Mind Body Medicine in Massachusetts has conducted research by assessing gene expression before, after 20 minutes, after eight weeks of practice, and after long-term meditation routines (Bhasin et al., 2013). Results demonstrated evidence of changes to gene expression—specifically antioxidant production, telomerase activity, and oxidative stress. These findings indicate that the relationship between gene expression optimization and relaxation response is dose-related, so that increasing amounts confer increasing benefit. However, after even one session, positive changes were noted.

Further research on stress and the tumor microenvironment sheds more light onto this subject. The authors (Cohen et al., 2014) say that while the health-damaging effects of chronic stress are well documented, there is little convincing evidence that chronic stress in and of itself causes cancer. However, there is extensive evidence that chronic stress can promote cancer growth and progression.

To heal, the body needs to remember how to slow down and relax. Unfortunately, this process is not automatic. The good news is that your body can learn to do this more effectively. The power tools in *A Time to Heal* can help you learn to relax. This chapter focuses on nurturing touch, a powerful and effective learning tool for relaxing.

The power of touch: Years ago, scientists were researching the effects of a high-fat diet on health and longevity using rabbits (Nerem, 1980). Simultaneous experiments were being conducted in the United States and Japan. The protocol was very strict to make sure that all of the rabbits receiving the equivalent of a junk food diet were getting the same food at the same time. The hypothesis was that the high-fat diet would have a negative effect on the subjects and that was true for all the groups except one from Japan.

Nothing seemed to explain why these particular bunnies were defying the odds and seemed to be healthy. They had the same genes as the rest of the rabbits whose arteries were clogged. Everything was checked and rechecked, but no breach in protocol was found.

The lead researcher finally flew to Japan to meet these hardy bunnies and to find the missing factor. He went over all of the numbers and still found nothing. In frustration, he finally walked down to the lab and found the tech doing the morning feeding. As the tech fed the bunnies, he spent several minutes with each of them. He called them each by name as he took them out of the cage. He petted them and talked to them while he put in the prescribed amounts of food.

That short, simple intervention had produced a significant healing response. It can do the same for you. Your body will respond to the message you send it. Nurturing touch sends a loving message to your body that you value it and will help give it what it needs to win this fight. It is a message of life.

Does this mean that you should find someone to pet you as they bring your food? It would be nice. There are many ways to incorporate nurturing touch and intention into your lives. You probably already have developed some practices that are important to you such as hugging family and friends or playing with a pet. Sometimes in the middle of treatment, it's hard to take the time to fill this need. We're going to take time to explore some easy ways to help your body relax and rejuvenate. Pay attention to your body's response and, when we finish each activity, rate your body's response. In the weeks to come, you will be adding more possibilities.

Activities

Daily Self Massage: Your skin is the largest sense organ in your body. Simply spending three or four minutes rubbing lotion all over your body does several things. Touching and rubbing taps into your own internal pharmacy by releasing wonderful, healing substances like endorphins and serotonin (brain chemicals). It also gives your body and spirit the message of life and love. You can start with your hands and arms or any part of your body. An added benefit is the scent of the lotion. Aromatherapy is powerful because smell goes directly into the emotional brain. If you find a scent that is pleasing to you, it reinforces the healing nature of this exercise.

Positive Points: These points are on the forehead right above the eyes. Holding them helps to move from survival processing (in the brain stem at the back of the head) to gentler thoughts (in the frontal area). Most of us have stroked a baby's forehead to help soothe them. It works for us too!

How do you rate this activity?

Boo! Hiss!   Hmmm   Eureka!
— — — — — — ◆ — — — — — —

Heavy Hand: (use of hand, weighted bag, etc.) The use of weighted objects is a simple technique that signals the body to let go and to relax. Most of us have placed a hand on someone's shoulder to calm or comfort them. You can try having a friend or family member stand behind you and place a hand on your head; experiment to see how much pressure feels comfortable to you. Or have your helper put his or her hands on your shoulders. Again, see how much pressure feels comforting.

When a person is not available, be creative. You can use a sack of rice from the pantry. Or make a weighted bag. Cotton workman's gloves or small stuffed animals can be filled with beans or sand and sewn shut. You can purchase beanbags or neck pillows filled with sand or seeds. You can make or buy these in different weights. And some of them can be heated or chilled, whatever is most comfortable for you. You place the weighted bag on the top of your head, on your shoulders, or lay it over your forehead as you lie down. Be creative and see what feels good to you. You may like different weights or different placements of the weighted bags at different times.

How do you rate this activity?

Boo! Hiss!   Hmmm   Eureka!
— — — — — — ◆ — — — — — —

Hand and/or Foot Massage: You may be used to applying hand lotion, especially during the dry, cold times of the year. But do you slap the lotion on in a hurried fashion or do you take the time to really massage your hands with love? Experiment with slow gentle massage of your hands or feet. Caress each finger or toe like you would massage a little baby you loved. Notice what type of touch feels good to you, firm or light, slow or faster. Does anything hurt? If so, don't do that. Remember, all of these activities are supposed to feel good and comforting. [The group will view a demonstration and may choose to try a portable foot massager.]

How do you rate this activity?

Boo! Hiss!   Hmmm   Eureka!

— — — — — — ◆ — — — — —

Use of Brain Tools: Have you ever noticed that the beat of music affects your mood? Something fast and intense may excite you or even make you anxious. Something slow and ponderous may make you sad or depressed. When we are stressed, the brain can be comforted and slowed down by many things. In addition to music, the brain is comforted by calming sights. Remember the fascination with lava lamps? Watching the thick, colorful globs of color float through liquid engages our brain in something that slows us and interests us in the changing shapes. Taking some time to enjoy kaleidoscopes, ooze tubes, and other visually interesting devices can help our brains take a "time out" to rest, relax, and reset our stress level. [The group will experiment with ooze tubes and other devices.] If you like these kinds of toys, you can generally find them at toy stores, the gift shops of museums and hospitals, or at websites like www.OfficePlayground.com.

How do you rate this activity?

Boo! Hiss!   Hmmm   Eureka!

— — — — — — ◆ — — — — —

Energetic Lymph Drainage: Lymphedema is a problem for some cancer survivors. This is an easy technique that can help to stimulate lymph drainage throughout the body.

Directions: Put your right hand under your left armpit. If you have sufficient range of motion, rest your left hand on the back of your neck. Simply hold this position for 3 to 10 minutes. Repeat as necessary. This is excellent for prevention of lymph buildup and blends well with the more specific techniques used by physical therapists and lymphedema specialists. Whether the lymphedema is on the right or left side, having your hand under your left armpit is the preferred method of lymph drainage due to the way most people's bodies drain lymph fluid.

These activities are just a sampling of the thousands of ways you can bring some physical comfort or pleasure to your body. Remember that your body has been poked, prodded, and made uncomfortable many times during your treatment. You may still be tensing up waiting for the next affront to your comfort. Pay attention now to anything that feels good or helps you relax. Use whatever is comforting to you to give your body some time to relax and feel good every day. It's not selfish. It's not a waste of time. Relaxation is one of the very best things you can do to promote your healing and recovery.

Questions for discussion and journaling

1. When you are really relaxed, how does your body feel? What is going through your mind? When is the last time you were really relaxed but not asleep?

2. Describe a time when you were really relaxed. What were you doing? Where were you? Were you alone or with others? What were you seeing? Hearing? Smelling? Feeling? Tasting? When you write a detailed description of a beautiful experience you have had, you are creating your own guided imagery. Try re-reading your journaling description sometime when you want to relax. Read this description, and then take a few minutes to replay the scene in your mind. How do you feel after doing this?

3. Which of the mind-body tools did you like the best in this demonstration? What attracted you to that particular thing? Do you find yourself drawn to color, texture, smell, touch? What around your house or office might have similar qualities?

4. What does "playing" mean to you? Do you see value in play?

5. Did you like the "heavy hand" feeling of touch on your head or your shoulder? Would you be comfortable asking someone to do this type of calming activity with you?

6. In your journal or in a separate notebook, you may want to begin compiling a list of "Tension Tamers." This could include pictures of people, animals, places you love; ideas for relaxing; poetry; sayings or quotations that give you peace of mind. Keep this book or box at home or in your office for times when you need a relaxation break. What would you like to include? If you like this idea, when could you start making your kit? Will you do that?

Power Tool: Journaling

Write to Wellness: Guidelines for Using Journaling as a Healing Tool, Jeanné Beavers, MSN, RN, CNS

Expressive writing promotes healing. There is no one right way to write. A variety of methods have been shown to produce profound benefits. Experiment to see what works best for you and trust the process. The following suggestions stem from decades of personal experience teaching and participating in individual and group journaling. They are based on multiple studies and represent practices commonly utilized by experts in the field. I am indebted to Dr. James Pennebaker* whose pioneering work influenced the development of many of these guidelines and demonstrated the value of writing as a healing tool.

1. Your journal is private. It is written for you alone. If you decide to share any of your writing, do so only in a nonjudgmental environment of complete trust and confidentiality.

2. Find a safe, comfortable place where you will not be interrupted.

3. Breathing exercises, meditation, yoga or other movement, candles and music are among some of the things that can help you relax and tap the inner self.

4. Date your entries.

5. Write for at least 20 minutes.

6. Write quickly and continuously. Do not stop to analyze.

7. Be nonjudgmental. Avoid criticizing your thoughts, feelings, writing ability or results. Do not be concerned with penmanship, spelling, punctuation or grammar.

8. Express emotion. Emotions are neither right nor wrong. Openly describe your thoughts and feelings—both positive and negative.

9. Be real. Write in your own true voice. Express your authentic self with complete honesty.

10. Write from the heart—whatever comes. Go with your first response. Trust your pen or keyboard to take you where you need to go.

11. No topic is off limits in the privacy of your journal, but deal only with what you can handle now. If you feel you will lose control by writing about a situation, just sit, take a few deep breaths, doodle, or write about something else.

12. Tell your story. It can be helpful to organize your thoughts from beginning to end. How has it changed your life? How has it influenced your ability to be who you want to be? What were the lessons? What good has come from your experience?

13. Change perspective. Include other points of view. How would the story sound if told by another person, a pet or even a piece of furniture?

14. Pay attention to your body from time to time as you journal. What do you notice? How does it feel in your face, your heart, your stomach, etc., as you write about certain persons, life situations, decisions or courses of action? What is your body telling you?

15. Reflect on what you have written.

16. If something has been especially disturbing, write about the same issue in different ways over time. Pennebaker (2004) demonstrated the effectiveness of a 4-day writing method.

17. Writing about stressful situations provides release and improves health. It is also beneficial to write about strengths, positive experiences, and positive emotions such as gratitude, love and joy. This can provide balance and help you feel better.

18. Write as often as you need to, preferably on a regular and frequent basis. The more you write, the better you will be at expressing and understanding your authentic self, and the more likely you will be to enhance your emotional, physical and spiritual health.

*Pennebaker, James W. 2004. *Writing to Heal: A Guided Journal for Recovering from Trauma and Emotional Upheaval.* Oakland, Calif.: New Harbinger Publications.

SESSION 5
Moving Forward in the Face of Fear

Kay Ryan, PhD, RN

Key Points
- Fear is a normal part of life.
- Fear is real and you came by it honestly. A cancer diagnosis can shake your feelings of safety and confidence.
- Fear isn't always bad. For instance, it can help you identify and follow up on important health factors.
- Fear CAN take control of your thoughts and your life. It can cost you too much energy.
- There are strategies to help you take back control and free up your energy to create your best life.

It Felt Love

How
Did the rose
Ever open its heart

And give to this world
All its
Beauty?

It felt the encouragement of light
Against its
Being,

Otherwise,
We all remain
Too

Frightened.

—Hafiz

93

Introduction

While most cancer survivors and their caregivers reclaim their former work and family responsibilities, and even some new ones, many describe an energy drain that compromises their ability to focus, to be happy, and to be fully present to their lives. It pops up without invitation—especially when a new symptom arises or it's time to go in for a checkup or more lab tests.

Those who find a name for this unwelcome companion might call it fear. For some survivors and their loved ones, fear becomes a constant specter in their lives.

Afraid of What?

So what are they afraid of? That's the million-dollar question. For some, these post-cancer fears are directly related to the cancer coming back or never leaving. Survivors sometimes report that anything from a stubbed toe to a sneeze leads them down a slippery slope of mental leaps to presuming that this issue was caused by cancer—that it is back or spreading.

Newsflash: caregivers are not immune. They have witnessed firsthand the unpredictable and scary nature of a disease that threw their lives out of balance, and they can also succumb to fear, not only about their loved one, but also about their own health, safety, and security.

For some, symptoms such as "chemobrain" or mental fuzziness evoke the fear that normalcy is forever gone. And some survivors suffer grave fears around how other people see them now: whether they are still intelligent, lovable, attractive, desirable, or capable of meaningful work or even intimacy.

Sometimes fear becomes the "usual" way of thinking and reacting for a survivor or caregiver, and he or she doesn't even recognize it as unusual anymore. It just accompanies them everywhere all the time. Fear becomes that "well-worn path" in the brain—the first place to go for every unknown.

Is Fear Real?

It seems healthy to point out that survivors and their caregivers often come by fear honestly, at least in the beginning of their journey. What happens to a survivor when that sense of security or invincibility is shattered by a diagnosis of cancer? Although cancer survivors are unique in their journeys, one reaction seems prevalent: fear.

Cancer shakes the confidence that many people felt in their health and internal wisdom, and it replaces that confidence with uncertainty for the present and the future. A cancer diagnosis may feel like a betrayal to some, a shock to others. And it sometimes opens the doors to self-doubt or even self-blame. Even after the cancer has been treated, and there is no evidence of disease, fear is highly prevalent (Koch, 2014).

With all the repercussions of a cancer diagnosis, it is not surprising that a survivor or a caregiver or both might experience less trust in their ability to "know" what is coming next. Max Lucado in *Fearless* says that fear is no more than uncertainty mixed with doubt, and he quotes scripture to demonstrate that fear happens to the very best of us!

Rachel Naomi Remen, a noted physician and author states that courage is not the opposite of fear—that the opposite of fear is joy. We have all likely been in situations where fear has kept us from being our best selves or doing what we want with our lives.

To compound the problem, some fears turn out to be true. It is tempting to become negative and look for the predictability in things going wrong. "I'll bet the phlebotomist can't find a vein," or "I'm sure I will get really sick with chemo" can turn out to be very accurate— especially if you've convinced yourself ahead of time.

The truth is you didn't ask for any of this. Treatment is not easy, surgery is never a picnic, and cancer is a very serious diagnosis. There is much to confirm a cancer survivor's or caregiver's sense of gloom if he or she is looking in those directions. And if this is how you've come to see the world, you may find fear controlling your life, stealing your joy, and making your decisions. *But you have a choice!*

Recognizing Fear

Cancer is one of many people's worst nightmares. You might know how it feels to be locked in a nightmare unable to wake up. It feels **real**. It feels **powerless**. Moreover, it feels **exhausting**. It reminds you of drowning because, as hard as you struggle, you feel as if you are losing to the nightmare. The nightmare sometimes seems stronger than your ability to end it.

Fear is like that. It feels like your worst nightmares are closing in on you. It can make you feel weak, sick, hopeless, or even powerless. It can evoke symptoms such as nausea, headache, tight muscles, pounding heart, or sadness. Sometimes people react with anger, tears, or a sense of defeat. Survivors and their caregivers may become "paralyzed" by their life's upheaval—unable to know what to do next: as if standing still would be the only safe place to be. And sometimes they describe feeling overwhelmed, incompetent, or just plain scared.

Fear has physiological effects on our body. Fear can lead to the stress response, and if it is long term, the body adopts this stress reaction as its constant, chronic state. It can affect blood pressure, heart rate, and our immune system's ability to protect us. Scientists have identified that food preferences, hormone production, and body metabolism change over time when a person is chronically stressed like this. It seems that fear can even be fattening!

Fearful people cannot be happy, according to Rabbi Harold Kushner. They cannot be generous, charitable, or forgiving either. We cannot find our best life, much less live it, in fear.

Judge Jim Tamm, coauthor of *Radical Collaboration*, once started a lecture with this statement:

"When you live in fear, you spend almost all of your energy defending yourself, leaving little of your energy for being your best self."

That's where some survivors/caregivers find themselves: spending most of their energy defending themselves from their fear. Sometimes they don't even recognize that is where their energy is going. Judge Tamm is quick to point out that sometimes there really are lions and tigers and bears out there, but that living in fear does not give us our most effective tools or most effective self for dealing with them. You can spend your energy defending yourself from your fear or you can choose/plan another way.

The Facts

We all need the facts. Survivors and caregivers need to know the truth. They need to know the likelihood of recurrence for the type and stage of cancer they have been diagnosed with. They need to know the strategies that are available to help them boost their body's defenses including nutrition, exercise, and relaxation. They need the most up-to-date information in order to make informed decisions and choices. According to Dr. Lawrence LeShan, author of *Cancer as a Turning Point,* they need to create their best lives—starting now.

The facts are that some choices we make may give our immune system a healthy boost. A wellness lifestyle does not have a lot of bad side effects, so it's a plus no matter how you look at it. Regular exercise, for example, has been shown to decrease the likelihood of recurrence in cancer survivors, as well as improve their mood and sense of well-being. It seems to give some people an edge!

However, we can't control everything. Lack of perceived control can feed fear in some individuals. Interestingly, worry can feed itself. In a 2015 study conducted with cancer survivors, those with the strongest beliefs about the uncontrollability and danger of worry actually reported more worries and fears about cancer recurrence.

Fear feeds exhaustion. It takes up energy that could be used for healthier pursuits. It sometimes causes tension, anxiety, and sleep disturbances. Most importantly, it does not boost the immune system or make a person less likely to manifest the fears. It costs energy.

Toolbox

There are many tools to deal with fear: in the moment and long term.

- Breathing techniques can be used to calm yourself down in the moment.

- Practicing meditation, imagery, or yoga regularly can produce a permanent calming effect on the mind and body.

- Journaling is a well-researched tool for dealing with feelings and fears.

- Expression, in many forms such as art or music, has been shown to decrease anxiety and improve well-being.

- Cognitive reframing (seeing the situation in a different way) can be very helpful, as well.

- Questioning the basis for fears (*Is this fear arising from something that is realistic or am I catastrophizing?*) is a technique that can point the brain in a different direction.

- Sometimes it is healthy and helpful to imagine what you would do if you were not afraid.

Addressing Fear

Perhaps you can already identify some of your fears or even some of the ways you react to fear.

- Do you hold your breath or walk around with tight shoulders, a pounding heart, or a stiff neck?

- Do you cry?

- Do you become irritable and short with people around you?

- Do you clam up or talk incessantly?

- Do you sleep a lot or not at all?

- Do you imagine all the bad things that could possibly happen and do they cycle over and over again in your mind?

- Do you awful-ize to the max?

- Do you completely deny what is going on?

We all have a mental pathway for the way we automatically react to fear. What is yours? How do you react to fear? And what could you do differently? While we cannot control everything, we can control what we do to cope with the circumstances and the fear.

If you are aware that you spend a lot of your energy defending yourself from fear and you don't want to, you could create a different mental pathway. Knowing that fear isn't always bad is a good thing! We have it on good authority (Judge James Tamm, author of *Radical Collaboration*): sometimes there *are* lions and tigers and bears out there. However, the most effective mental state for dealing with worries and threats is grounded in reality and reasoning—not fear.

The Plan

You can choose to counteract the helplessness that comes from fear.

Create your plan now:

Step 1: **Know your personal "fear signal."**

What behavior or behaviors of yours would tip you off that you are now spending a lot of energy being afraid. Write it/them down.

*When I start to feel or do*_____,
I know that I am spending my energy in fear.

Step 2: Decide and declare what **your next step** will be once you recognize your fear signal.

You can choose to stop (some people actually visualize a stop sign or raise their hand in a "stop" gesture here). Then step back, deep breathe, and start again from a place of calm. What is your best approach? Write it down:

*When I recognize my fear signal(s), I will*_____

_____

_____

_____(adapted with permission from *Radical Collaboration*).

Some additional examples of how to get to a place of calm include these:

- Dispute the fear with contrary evidence (find the opposite truth).

- Shift attention to a pleasant memory or holding the image of someone or something you love.

- Visualize an army coming to your rescue (or an army of angels).

- Use distraction to your advantage (a good time to write out the Declaration of Independence or a verse or song you once knew).

- Practice mindfulness or relaxation.

- Stand up and physically relocate to a different place.

- Get your thoughts to focus on the smallest moment of "now" where there is nothing but this tiny present moment to pay attention to—no past and no future.

Step 3: **Practice.**

Once you have decided on your specific plan, practice it! It takes repetition to create a new roadmap for your brain and behavior. At first it takes effort to do things differently than you have always done them in the past. After you have repeated your new process several times, it becomes automatic.

For some people, having one method of dealing with fear is not enough. You might be one of those who needs to have several different methods to deal with different types of fears or different types of situations.

For example, if frightening thoughts arise during the day, recognizing your fear signal is still the first step. At work or at home, it might work to use distraction as an immediate strategy. Get busy doing something that takes a little thought: balance the checkbook, type an email, feed your pet. But distraction may not work for those fears that keep you awake at 2 a.m. when you're really trying to calm your mind and your body and get some sleep.

At that point, breath counting or prayer or singing a song over and over in your head might be enough to pull your mind away from turning scary thoughts over and over. Some people think that putting on headphones and listening to a guided imagery CD or some positive-message music helps; it seems harder to worry over sounds coming directly into your brain through headphones.

If you are feeling the fear arise in situations where you're getting too much information too fast, for example, when a doctor is trying to explain test results or new treatment or when some new procedure is being implemented at work, it might work to excuse yourself for a bathroom break so you can take a few deep breaths and re-center yourself before you go back in to hear the rest.

But leaving the situation might not work in all situations; sometimes if you leave, you lose the opportunity to ask a question or the other person might not be there when you come back. It might be helpful to switch to the "student" side of your brain, ask for paper, and start writing things down as if you're taking notes in school. Letting your cognitive brain do the work might give your emotional brain a rest. Then, later, you can process your feelings with the information in front of you.

Remember that fear is natural response, but it can be like a fire. If you keep adding logs, the fire burns longer. Thinking about something scary once and trying to figure out what you would do if the various outcomes actually happened is good planning; doing that over and over is called rumination and can be exhausting.

Rumination comes from the word *ruminant*—it means chew the cud like a cow—and that's what we do sometimes. We play a scene over and over in our minds, chewing it like a cow. This works for cows, but for cancer survivors, the research shows that ruminating over negative things is associated with depression for both cancer survivors and for their caregivers (Steiner et al., 2014). When you dwell on what can go wrong, you make yourself feel powerless, and feeling powerless and helpless is a strong path to depression.

It can help to take a few minutes to journal.

1. Write down the types of situations that evoke fear for you. It can be fear about cancer, about work, about money, about a relationship—anything that arouses fear.

2. Is there a time of day when each of those fears tends to arise? Or a situation that starts the fear up (for example, seeing a certain person, reading an article about cancer, feeling a different sensation in your body).

3. Write down at least two possible ways to cope with each of these fears. Try to think of something that might work during the day or if other people were around and something that could work when you are alone or in the middle of the night. If you can think of more than one, that's great. You can always add to the list.

4. Are there coping techniques that seem like they might work in more than one situation? If so, start practicing them first. Try them out and keep practicing. As you get better at the first one or two, keep working down the list.

5. Your goal is to build yourself a tool kit of several ways to cope with fear.

CAN YOU REALLY CHANGE YOUR THINKING ABOUT FEAR?

While you may always have some fear around lab tests or doctor visits, the evidence shows that you *can* get some relief from fear. Many different techniques can work. Current research about helpful strategies includes the following:

- Mindfulness techniques: Try the breath counting or other meditative techniques in the power tools.

Focusing on one thing at a time, even just breathing, can help (Lengacher, 2014).

- Cognitive existential learning groups: Cancer survivors in a 6-week program where patients met and talked about the reality of living with uncertainty, ways to control worry, and managing things by thinking clearly significantly reduced their levels of fear of recurrence. Keep talking about your feelings with other survivors and share how you cope, even after *A Time to Heal* is over (Lebel, 2014).

- Music: Music you choose yourself has been shown to be the best at taming depression, anxiety, pain, and fatigue (Tsai, 2014).

- Exercise: Even people with advanced cancer decreased their anxiety and increased their emotional well-being with exercise (Quist, 2015).

- Prayer: If you believe in a loving God, prayer can help. If religion is a positive thing for you, you're likely to get some anxiety reduction from a religious intervention (Koenig, 2012).

- Reframing your thoughts: Mindfulness helps here, again. When you notice that negative thoughts are flowing through your mind, notice them. Then make an effort to talk to yourself in a rational, constructive way. Get help if you need it. This kind of counseling is called cognitive behavioral therapy and has strong research support.

Choosing love

In "Beyond Fear," Don Miguel Ruiz describes fear as the opposite of love and proposes a way to understand this theory. He says: "Love has no expectations while fear is filled with expectations."

This statement seems so true for cancer survivors and those who love them. The fears they express are often of expectations that things may go badly. Ruiz guides the fearful to focus on love's healing virtues of respect, patience, and kindness to combat the fears.

Being Brave

Occasionally survivors or caregivers seem embarrassed to admit that they've been riddled with fear/feelings of helplessness over their diagnosis, prognosis, or even the way they are coping. They often feel that others who have it "much worse than they" are obviously braver and stronger, and they put themselves down for their "weakness."

We've heard so many stories about cancer and none of them were easy. Life is hard. Life with cancer is really hard, no matter how "well" you handle it. Courage is not about being fearless, according to Lisa Rankin, author of *The Fear Cure*. Courage, she believes, is about adjusting to the uncertainty of life. Dr. Rankin advises all of us to seek out the support of other people and offer our support to others as one strategy for cultivating courage.

The way each of us deals with our fears is unique, but we are all doing the best we can, one step at a time. It takes a lot of courage to make this journey!

Encouragement

We know from the research on resilience that having someone who believes in us goes a long way in making us more resilient, more able to rise up from life's most painful setbacks. It gives us courage to keep going when we see ourselves through the eyes of someone who loves us and thinks not only that we can make it, but also triumph. Often survivors report that they were surprised how loved they were while they were going through cancer treatment and that they didn't realize how much people thought of them before their diagnosis.

Caregivers can fall through the cracks in this respect if everyone is so focused on the cancer survivor that they forget about the struggles of the loved ones who are supporting them. Encouragement comes in many forms. For some, it is having someone see strength and hope in them—something they can't see in themselves because of their fears. For others, it might be someone who can listen with compassion and not give advice or judge.

We began with Hafiz's poem "It Felt Love": How did the rose ever open its heart and give to this world all its beauty? It felt the encouragement of light against its being. Otherwise, we all remain too frightened.

In many ways and many instances, love takes the form of encouragement, and love can certainly help us to open our hearts and share our beauty.

Faith

Rabbi Kushner in his book *Conquering Fear: Living Boldly in an Uncertain World* takes on the question of "where is God?" in the face of terrible events. The wisdom that he shares is that God is not in the terrible event, but in your response to it. You find God in the tiny voice that helps you to bravely put your life back together amidst all the difficulties and the fears.

In his book *The Courage to Teach*, Parker Palmer wrote:

Fear is so fundamental to the human condition that all the great spiritual traditions originate in an effort to overcome its effects on our lives. With different words, they all proclaim the same core message: "Be not afraid." ... It is important to note with care what that core teaching does and does not say. "Be not afraid" does not say that we should not have fears—and if it did, we could dismiss it as an impossible counsel of perfection. Instead it says that we do not need to BE our fears, quite a different proposition.

The Goal

You have been through a great deal of worry and stress, in addition to the physical challenges and life changes of cancer and treatment. Now a different journey lies before you: the journey for survivors and caregivers, family, and loved ones of putting life back together and moving forward; this is the journey of survivorship. The goal for cancer survivorship is to embrace life fully and create your best life.

Fear is a normal part of life, and it has its place. There are many choices to make along the way. Choosing from a place of calm (not fear), now that you are back in control, gives you an edge. Fear is real for survivors and for caregivers, but it can take control if we let it. When you are in control, you can decide what is best for you.

NOTE:
Anxiety is strongly supported by diet for some people. Caffeine in all its forms can rev up your mind so that it doesn't settle down well. This can lead to a lot of sleepless nights full of worry. Likewise, alcohol may seem to relax you and help you sleep, but it has the nasty habit of making you wake up a few hours later, just in time for the worries to set in.

On the other hand, limiting caffeine and alcohol and adding foods and herbal teas that help you relax can help both your body and your mind relax. Eating turkey or other foods with tryptophan can help make you sleepy; teas with chamomile can help you unwind. See other sections in this book for more suggestions on dealing with insomnia and tension.

Questions for discussion and journaling

1. Do you think fear is very influential in your life?
2. What steps can you take for recognizing fear?
3. What is your plan for dealing with fear?
4. Do you feel as if you need different plans for different situations? Write down the best options you have now.
5. Are there other anxiety-management strategies you would like to learn?

Power Tool: Safe Harbor

A harbor is a place where ships refit and refuel before they go out to sea again. We all carry our own "safe harbors" inside ourselves. These safe places are the memories of times and places where we have felt safe and fulfilled. As you learned with other guided imagery and relaxation tools, your mind can't tell the difference between what is happening now and what you are vividly imagining. You can revisit these safe harbors anytime you need to refuel yourself.

- To experience the Safe Harbor, get comfortable. Get yourself quiet and calm. Many people find that it helps to start with a few minutes of breath counting or another meditation that helps you get into a quiet space. Set your intention to remember a special time—a time when, for the moment, everything was perfect. Then wait for a memory to come.

- If other less-than-wonderful memories come, let them pass on by. It's like waiting for a bus. If a bus comes that is not going where you want to go, you don't get on. You wait for the right bus. Just wait for the special memory; invite your mind to produce it.

- When the memory comes, recall and re-experience it as fully as you can. Use all five senses if possible. Stay with it until it is fully experienced. If your meditation time is over, bring yourself back gently. If not, wait again for another special memory.

- When you are finished, take a few extra moments to reflect on that time. How did you feel about yourself then? How did you feel about others? How did you feel about the universe?

This is a particularly good technique to use during bad times or illness. During times like that, we don't feel good and we don't feel like there are any good times left. Using Safe Harbor can remind us that life is not just fear or suffering or discouragement. It's a time to use the storehouse of good memories we've accumulated.

One word of advice: When the good memory comes, stay in the moment. One woman had a wonderful memory of receiving a kitten for her birthday when she was a little girl. She was ecstatic and could remember the feel and the smell of the kitten and the excitement of the moment. But then her face fell and she looked heartbroken. When we asked what had happened, she said, "Ten years later the kitten died." Don't fast forward the memories. Stay in the good part where everything is wonderful and just relish the sights, senses, and feelings of that wonderful time. Let your wonderful memories renew your soul.

[Special thanks to Dr. Lawrence LeShan, author of *Cancer as a Turning Point*, for sharing this meditation technique with us.]

SESSION 5

SESSION 6
Refuel for Health and Energy

Chandy Lockman Hoke, MS, RD, CSO, LMNT;
Marilyn Wadum, RD, LMNT; James Reilly Jr., MD

Key Points
- The foods we eat can be a very important part of our healing.
- The WCRF/AICR report is the most complete analysis done so far about the effect of nutrition on health.
- The 10 guidelines from this report are the best recommendations both for preventing cancer and for cancer survivors to maintain their best health after cancer.
- Food is more than just something to eat; it is a way to feel loved, connected, and share fellowship with our families and friends. It nourishes our souls as well as our bodies.
- Several Frequently Asked Questions are answered at the end of this chapter.

"Let thy food be thy medicine and medicine be thy food.."

Hippocrates

Food: Friend or Foe?

It's difficult trying to keep up with all the emerging research on nutrition, surfing the Internet for answers, reading conflicting reports: Will eating certain foods harm you? What should a person eat to be healthy? What about all the different supplements and potions being advertised to prevent cancer? Are they safe? What should I do? What can I do?

After experiencing the trauma of a cancer diagnosis and treatment, it takes time to come to terms with what has happened to you, and an even longer time to feel you are safe. In regard to foods, you may experience emotions you didn't even know you had.

- You may have felt *guilty* that you did something wrong to cause the cancer—"Did I cause my own cancer with what I ate?"

- Or *angry*—"I ate healthy, exercised and never smoked: why did I still get cancer?"

- Perhaps *anxious*—"Will my cancer return because of what I eat now?"

- *Hopeless*—"What difference does it make what I eat because I have genetic factors?"

Caregivers may feel the same emotions. Or, they may be angry at the patient—"I told him/her that was not good, but he/she ate/drank it anyway!"—or at themselves "I should have cooked better or insisted that he/she ate a healthier diet."—or scared—"Now what will I do? It will be up to me to make sure that he/she eats well."

To add to the emotional roller coaster, food may not have been a friend during recovery. The taste changes and nausea, weight gain or loss, constipation, vomiting, loss of appetite, and other effects of treatment further weaken a once-strong body. Food had been something you once enjoyed. Now you may wonder what you should eat, how much to eat, and what to avoid. Those and other food worries only add to your concerns.

In this session, we'll address these issues and answer your questions.

Eating to Nourish Your Body

The good news is this: the foods you choose every day are some of the most powerful factors in protecting your health.

While all the studies contribute to our knowledge about the health effects of different aspects of our diets, they also show that **no single food or diet is a magic bullet for preventing cancer or its recurrence. While the research shows that most Americans eat a diet too high in meat and calories, what may be more important is what the average**

diet lacks: a variety of vegetables, fruits, beans, and other plant-based foods.

These plant-based foods give your body not only the nutrients it needs for good health, but an arsenal of compounds (phytochemicals) that help protect against naturally occurring cancer risks you face every day, according to the American Institute for Cancer Research (www.dietandcancerreport.org) and the American Cancer Society (www.cancer.org).

There are no bad foods. Rather, it's the balance of a variety of healthy foods combined with regular physical activity that lowers our cancer risk and contributes to overall good health. How exciting to learn that there is something we can actually do to strengthen and help protect our bodies!

Specific Recommendations for Cancer Survivors and for Cancer Prevention

In 2007, the World Cancer Research Fund and the American Institute for Cancer Research (WCRF/AICR) published the most comprehensive report on food, nutrition, physical activity and cancer. This report was an analysis of thousands of studies—over 7,000 to be exact. It included high-quality, well-conducted studies on specific cancer types as well as individual dietary factors on a global scale.

The following 10 guidelines in this chapter are from this report: WCRF/AICR *Second Expert Report: Food, Nutrition, Physical Activity and the Prevention of Cancer: A Global Perspective,* November 2007 (Reprinted here with special permission from the American Institute for Cancer Research, www.AICR.org).

This base report is now part of a Continuous Update Project (CUP). This means as more research is published, it continues to be rigorously evaluated on its merits. Well-conducted, high-quality studies are added to this ongoing report making it the world's largest resource of scientific studies on food, nutrition, physical activity and cancer.

Of note is the compelling fact that these guidelines have not radically changed from year to year. The details may get more specific, but the basic recommendations have stayed the same. The 10 guidelines are ranked and discussed in order of the amount and quality of the research support for them. This means that guideline number 1 has the most research support and therefore is discussed first.

As a survivor, take comfort in knowing that these guidelines will continue to be the golden standards for information on credible, evidence-based advice on how to eat, and they are just as relevant for YOU as they are for your friends or family members who have not had cancer.

1. **Be as lean as possible without becoming underweight. Scientists have discovered that fat, or adipose tissue, is actually a metabolically active tissue. It is not just a place to store excess calories to help humans survive in times of famine, but a tissue that affects systems or processes of the body.**

   Fat affects processes such as how our bodies handle inflammation and control our hormone levels. Carrying excessive fat around our waists can be particularly harmful. It can act like a "hormone pump" releasing estrogen into the bloodstream as well as raising levels of other hormones in the body. There are certain cancers that thrive in a hormone-saturated environment. These associations have been linked to colon cancer, breast cancer in postmenopausal women, and possibly in cancer of the pancreas and the endometrium.

   We do not know all the reasons why excess weight can increase the risk of cancer; however, we do know that maintaining a healthy body weight is one of the most important things you can do to reduce your risk of cancer. Despite the accuracy and importance of that statement, it can be a difficult message for a survivor to think about.

   It might be helpful to have a personal talk with your health care provider about a healthy weight goal for you. Dr. James Reilly Jr., Medical Director of the Nebraska Methodist Hospital Breast Care Center, offers some reasons to continue this conversation with your health care provider.

According to Dr. Reilly, "Discussing our weight is a sensitive issue for many of us. More than 60% of Americans are overweight or obese. The extra weight we carry puts us at higher risk for heart disease, stroke, diabetes, and many other health care problems. Did you know that being overweight puts you at an increased risk of cancer? The American Cancer Society estimates that about a third of our cancers could be prevented by diet and lifestyle modification."

He explained: "Men and women who are overweight are at higher risk of thyroid, esophageal, gall bladder, renal, and colorectal cancers. Women with excess body weight are also at higher risk of uterine and breast cancers. For breast cancer, the risk seems higher for weight gained in the postmenopausal years. In addition, women who have already been diagnosed with breast cancer and are obese have both greater likelihood of reoccurrence and higher risk of second breast cancers."

The good news, according to Dr. Reilly is this: "There appears to be some good news with breast cancer in that this increased risk may be lowered with weight loss. Weight management through diet modification and increased physical activity will reduce cancer risk, reduce the risks of dying from other causes, and will help you feel better."

Many people think it is too late to change—too late to quit smoking, to exercise, to lose weight. But even minor changes will help improve your health. You will start to feel better. Gradual change may be better sustained than using extreme diets or drastic exercise regimens. People who are overweight and exercise have lower cardiac risk than people who are the same weight but sedentary.

"Diet and exercise are cheaper than chronic medications, surgery, and radiation. You have to start from wherever you are right now. Even if you have a bad day, don't give up. Start again. You don't have to be perfect, but you can be better," Dr. Reilly said.

If you would like to learn more about this guideline, check out the American Institute for Cancer Research's tool for managing healthy weight goals. This can be found at http://www.aicr.org/reduce-your-cancer-risk/weight/tools_bmi_calculator.html. AICR provides an excellent interactive and teaching tool to help assess your healthy weight goals. Also located at the end of this chapter is additional information about stress, physical activity, and cancer risk. And, keep reading, because following guidelines 2 and 3 can have a profound impact on your weight goals as well.

2. **Be physically active for at least 30 minutes every day. Physical activity in any form helps to lower cancer risk.**

Aim to build more activity, such as brisk walking, into your daily routine.

As well as helping you avoid weight gain, research shows that activity itself can help to lower your risk of developing certain cancers. Regular physical activity continues to provide preventive qualities **regardless of weight status or Body Mass Index (BMI)**. This is exciting information! It tells us that even if our BMI is greater than the healthy range, and we weigh more than what is recommended, being physically active has wonderful protective qualities. Studies show that regular activity can help to keep your hormone levels healthy, which is important because having high levels of some hormones can increase your cancer risk. Physical activity may also

116

strengthen your immune system, help keep your digestive system healthy, and eventually allow you to consume more food—and more cancer-protective nutrients—without gaining weight.

Best of all, a brand new study of almost 4 million people showed that those who were the most active had a 17% lower risk of dying from cancer compared to the least active. For cancer survivors, the association was even higher! Survivors who were the most active had a 22% reduced risk of dying from cancer (Tingting, 2015). This supports the overall AICR recommendation that we all should be physically active at least 30 minutes every day.

In a later session, you'll read more about the value of physical activity for cancer survivors.

3. **Avoid sugary drinks. Limit consumption of energy-dense foods (particularly processed foods high in added sugar, or low in fiber, or high in fat).**

Choosing healthy foods and drinks instead of those that are high in refined carbohydrates and often in added sugar and fat (energy-dense foods) can help you avoid becoming overweight and obese and thereby reduce your cancer risk.

What are energy-dense foods? Most foods provide you with energy (calories), but some foods contain more energy ounce-for-ounce than others. Energy-dense foods tend to be processed foods with sugar and fat added to improve the taste. Examples are desserts, sweets, candy, chips, and fried foods. The result is more calories per ounce.

For example, 3.5 ounces of chocolate contains 10 times more calories than the same amount of apple:

3.5 oz. of milk chocolate = 520 calories

3.5 oz. of apple = 52 calories

You can easily consume too many calories if you eat a lot of energy-dense foods. *It's okay to eat energy-dense foods occasionally, or in small quantities, but try not to make them the basis of your diet.* By choosing a diet based on low-energy-dense foods, you can actually eat more food but consume fewer calories.

Foods that are low in energy density, like the apple, are high in fiber and water. Most vegetables, fruits, and beans fall into the low-energy-dense category. It is yet another reason to plan your diet around plant-based foods.

Sugary drinks and weight gain. The expert report found that regularly consuming sugary drinks contributes to weight gain. These drinks are easy to drink in large quantities but don't make you feel full, even though they are quite high in calories. Eating a meal along with a sugary drink can easily double the amount of calories consumed.

Sugary drinks include soft drinks like cola, juice-flavored drinks, and gourmet coffee-flavored drinks. You should try to avoid regular consumption of these drinks and save them for special occasions.

Water is the best alternative. Unsweetened tea and coffee are also healthy options, in moderation. Natural fruit juice counts as one of our recommended 7 or more daily portions of vegetables and fruits, but it does contain a lot of sugar. It's best not to drink more than one glass a day.

4. **Eat a variety of vegetables, fruits, whole grains and legumes such as beans.**

    Basing your diet on plant foods (like vegetables, fruits, whole grains, and legumes such as beans), which contain fiber and other nutrients, can reduce your risk of cancer.

    For good health, AICR recommends that we base all of our meals on plant foods. This does not mean you have to become a vegetarian, but it might involve a little shift in how you fill your plate. When preparing a meal, aim to fill at least two-thirds of your plate with vegetables, fruits, whole grains and beans.

The New American Plate

2/3 (or more) vegetables, fruits, whole grains and beans

1/3 (or less) animal protein

Research shows that vegetables and fruits probably protect against a range of cancers, including mouth, pharynx, larynx, esophagus, stomach, lung, pancreas, and prostate. There are many reasons why vegetables and fruits may protect against cancer. They contain vitamins and minerals that help keep the body healthy and strengthen your immune system, and they are also good sources of phytochemicals, which can help to protect cells in the body from damage that can lead to cancer.

Foods containing fiber are also linked to a reduced risk of cancer. These foods include whole-grain bread and pasta, oats, and vegetables and fruits. Fiber is thought to have many benefits, including helping to speed up "gut transit time"— how long it takes food to move through the digestive system.

Power foods that heal. Active substances in food that have been found to be extremely health protective are called antioxidants. Antioxidants are substances found in fruits and vegetables that have been shown to protect the body from cell damage resulting from free radicals. They help reduce the risk of diseases and also protect the person who has developed a disease process. Research shows us the amount of antioxidants we consume is important too. To date, the most beneficial amount exists in levels found naturally in fruits and vegetables, not in high amounts found in supplemented pill or powder forms. Plant foods can also help us to maintain a healthy weight because many of them are lower in energy density (calories).

Are there foods that fight cancer? Some of the plant-based foods studied for their potential cancer-fighting properties include apples, blueberries, broccoli and other cruciferous vegetables, cherries, cranberries, dark green leafy vegetables, dry beans and peas, flaxseed, garlic, grapefruit, grapes, soy, squash, tomatoes, walnuts, and whole grains.

To learn more about the research supporting these foods, including cooking and preparation tips and recipes, please visit the website for the American Institute for Cancer Research (www.aicr. org). (One note: be careful about using grapefruit if you are currently taking any medications. Grapefruit can interfere with the action of some medication, so check with your pharmacist to see if your current medication requires you to eliminate grapefruit or any other foods.)

5. **Limit consumption of red meats (such as beef, pork and lamb) and avoid processed meats.**

    To reduce your cancer risk, the expert panel advises *limiting* red meat and *avoiding* processed meat.

    - *Red meat* refers to beef, pork and lamb—foods like hamburgers, steak, pork chops, and roast lamb.

120

- The term *processed meat* refers to meats preserved by smoking, curing, or salting, or by the addition of preservatives.

- Carcinogens or cancer-causing substances, occur when meat is preserved by smoking, curing or salting, or by the addition of preservatives, specifically nitrites. These substances can damage cells in the body, leading to the development of cancer (examples include ham, bacon, pastrami, and salami, as well as hot dogs and sausages).

- Red meat and processed meat contain substances that are linked to colon cancer. For example, heme iron, the compound that gives red meat its color, has been shown to damage the lining of the colon. Studies also show that people who eat a lot of red meat tend to eat less plant-based foods, so they benefit less from their cancer-protective properties.

Studies show we can eat up to 18 ounces a week of cooked red meat without raising cancer risk. Research on processed meat shows cancer risk starts to increase with any portion.

6. **If consumed at all, limit alcoholic drinks to 2 for men and 1 for women a day.**

   For cancer prevention, AICR recommends not to drink alcohol. However, the expert report recognizes that modest amounts of alcohol may have a protective effect on coronary heart disease.

   - If you do drink alcohol, limit your consumption to no more than 2 drinks a day for men and 1 drink a day for women.

   The evidence that all types of alcoholic drinks increase the risk of a number of cancers is now stronger than it was in the mid-1990s. There is convincing evidence that alcohol increases the risk of cancer of the mouth, pharynx, larynx, esophagus, and breast, as well as colorectal cancer in men.

Alcoholic drinks also probably increase the risk of colorectal cancer in women as well as liver cancer.

Scientists are still researching how alcohol causes cancer. One theory is that alcohol, the actual ethanol content of the beverage, can directly damage our DNA, increasing our risk of cancer. All alcoholic drinks contain ethanol, so one alcoholic beverage is no "better" or "safer" from a cancer risk perspective. One serving of alcohol in the US is 12 ounces of beer, 5 ounces of wine, or 1.5 ounces of spirits. Research shows that alcohol is particularly harmful when combined with smoking.

7. **Limit consumption of salty foods and foods processed with salt (sodium).**

Consuming too much salt can be harmful to our health, increasing our risk of stomach cancer as well as high blood pressure. Studies have shown that high salt intakes can damage the lining of the stomach. This is one way in which it might increase the risk of stomach cancer.

Most of the salt in our diets comes from processed foods. We are not always aware that these foods are high in salt because they may not taste "salty," so make sure to read the sodium content on the Nutrition Facts label. As you read the labels on breakfast cereals, bread, frozen meals, pizza, chips, canned soups and sauces, check the sodium content.

Look for individual items that contain less than 600 mg per serving. Even sweet foods like cookies can contain high levels of salt.

- Our daily intake of salt should be less than 2,400 milligrams.

8. **Don't use dietary supplements to protect against cancer.**

To reduce your risk of cancer, choose a balanced diet with a variety of foods rather than taking dietary supplements, unless specifically prescribed by your doctor.

The expert report found strong evidence that high-dose supplements of some nutrients can affect the risk of different cancers. This means that while some high-dose supplements can be protective, some might even promote cancer. The problem with the current research is there is not a good way to predict who it will help and who it will harm in the general population.

The fact that high-dose or single supplements are available over-the-counter or are natural does not make them safe. For example, most people know that eating double cheeseburgers with onion rings everyday would not result in great health. The noticeable damage does not happen with the first cheeseburger, but happens after weeks to months to years of use. This situation is very similar with supplements. The damage may not be noticeable on day one, however, after repeated use may actually be causing long-term damage to your body and health.

People who decide to take supplements should discuss it with a health professional, such as a physician or registered dietitian. The panel judged that, in general, the best source of nourishment is food and drink, not dietary supplements.

Nutrient-rich whole foods contain substances that are necessary for good health—such as fiber, vitamins, minerals, and phytochemicals. Some studies have shown that supplements can upset the balance of nutrients in the body. More research needs to be done, but this is one way that they might affect our risk of cancer.

There are some situations when supplements are recommended. These are the most common situations when taking a supplement can be beneficial:

- All women of childbearing age intending to conceive a child should take a folic acid supplement before conception and up to the twelfth week of pregnancy.

- Pregnant women and nursing mothers should also take a vitamin D supplement and possibly an iron supplement if their iron levels are low.

- Children between 6 months and 5 years could benefit from taking drops containing vitamins A, C, and D, although children with a good appetite who eat a wide variety of foods may not need them.

- Frail older people who have low calorie needs may benefit from a low-dose, balanced multi-vitamin.

- Older people should consider taking a vitamin D supplement, as should people who rarely go outdoors, people who cover up all their skin when outdoors, and those who don't eat meat or oily fish.

If you want more advice on any of these situations, it's best to contact your doctor or a registered dietitian.

Special Population Recommendations

9. **It is best for mothers to breastfeed exclusively for up to 6 months and then add other liquids and foods.**

Evidence shows that breastfeeding can help protect mothers from breast cancer. It also protects babies from excess weight gain that can lead to their being overweight in adult life. And overweight adults have higher cancer risk.

According to the expert report, the evidence that breastfeeding protects mothers against breast cancer is convincing. Having been breastfed probably protects children against overweight and obesity. Overweight and obese children tend to remain overweight in adult life.

Breastfeeding lowers the levels of some cancer-related hormones in the mother's body, reducing the risk of breast cancer. At the end of breastfeeding, the body gets rid of any cells in the breast that may have DNA damage. This reduces the risk of breast cancer developing in the future.

Research shows that babies who are breastfed are less likely to consume too many calories and too much protein than babies who are fed infant formula. This means that they are less likely to become overweight or obese as they grow up.

If you're planning to breastfeed your baby, your doctor or certified lactation consultant will be able to provide more information and support.

10. **After treatment, cancer survivors should follow the recommendations for cancer prevention.**

Anyone who has received a diagnosis of cancer should receive specialized nutritional advice from an appropriately trained professional. Once treatment has been completed, if you are able to do so (and unless otherwise advised), aim to follow the cancer prevention recommendations for diet, physical activity, and healthy weight maintenance.

Cancer survivors are people who are living with a diagnosis of cancer, including those who have recovered from the disease. There is growing evidence that physical activity and other measures that help us to maintain a healthy weight, such as a balanced diet, may help to prevent cancer recurrence.

The AICR Report and CUP currently include specific lifestyle modification recommendations specific to diet, weight, and/or physical activity for 17 different cancer sites: breast, colorectal, endometrial, esophageal, gall bladder, kidney, liver, pancreatic, prostate, stomach, ovarian, cervical, bladder, skin and cancers of the mouth/pharynx, larynx and nasopharyngeal. You can check out these special recommendations at www.aicr.org. There are also additional resources on the website such as tips and recipes to help you put these guidelines into practice.

These recommendations from AICR can also reduce the risk of other chronic diseases such as heart disease and diabetes. **And always remember—do not smoke or chew tobacco.**

Many times when a family is in the throes of cancer treatment or recovery, eating patterns fall apart. Even if you had a healthy diet before, the chaos and fatigue of cancer treatment often lead to suppers of fast-food take-out or ordered pizza. Friends may bring over lots of casseroles and no fruits and vegetables. An alternative is to take the family to the store and let each family member pick a variety of healthy frozen dinners he or she would like. Store these in the freezer to be used on those "no time to cook" nights. You can supplement the dinners with "sack-o-salad" and a loaf of whole-grain bread (buy ahead and freeze it). Dessert can be a piece of fruit. Voila! You have a fast, healthy meal that everyone will eat. You can continue this practice long after treatment is finished.

Body Weight, Physical Activity and Cancer: What Is the Connection?

Maintaining a healthy weight is one of the most important things you can do to reduce your risk of cancer. Scientists have discovered that carrying excess fat, especially around our waists, can be particularly harmful. Why?

- Fat cells produce estrogen (which promotes cell growth).

- Fat at the waist is even more active in producing these growth stimulants.

- The fat acts like a hormone pump releasing estrogen into the bloodstream.

- Fat cells also produce a variety of proteins that cause inflammation and insulin resistance (which promote cell growth and cell reproduction).

- So overweight people—particularly if they are apple-shaped—have higher levels of certain substances circulating in their blood system.

- Abdominal obesity (which pushes up against the stomach) can also lead to acid reflux, which damages cells in the esophagus, which can lead to cancer cell growth.

- Inadequate physical activity (less than one hour per week) may result in weight gain.

Many people, especially women, struggle with their weight. Understand that many factors influence your weight:

- Age, gender, medications (steroids, antidepressants, for examples), hormones, physical activity, metabolic level.

- The important thing to remember is that *we can only change things that we have control over* (what we eat, when we exercise, not smoking), and to understand what we have no control over (our gender, our age).

127

This is a time we need to heal, reenergize, and begin to feel whole again. We need to avoid extreme dieting, restrictions of food and stresses that we put upon ourselves about our weight. Instead, we recommend taking a slow, healthy, and fulfilling route to weight loss when needed.

The Stress-Weight Connection

You may have recently read about the theory that chronic stress causes elevations in cortisol, a hormone produced by the adrenal glands that releases glucose and fat to give us fast energy. According to the theory, when we are under stress, we produce high levels of cortisol, which sends a message to our bodies to pack on weight. Cortisol helps when we are under stress because it helps metabolize carbohydrate and fat and give us fast energy. This works when we really can "fight or flee" in a stressful situation, but as Dr. Pamela Peeke, author of *Fight Fat after Forty*, pointed out, when was the last time you responded to stress by running or fighting?

In most of today's stress situations, you just have to stand there and cope with the stressor. When you are under chronic stress, cortisol levels may remain high and that makes your appetite increase too. Then, if you are also a stress eater, you can see how weight gain can happen. Not only that, but a constant state of cortisol production stimulates glucose production. The glucose gets converted to fat and deposited somewhere on your body, particularly around your waistline. Few controlled laboratory studies have been done to help us understand how cortisol status relates to weight gain. However, if you do accept that stress could be contributing to weight problems, it makes sense to take some steps to manage stress.

Several strategies can help:

- Regular exercise

- Regular practice of relaxation (techniques learned in this book)

Change the way you think. We all know that some people react to many situations with fear and worry and seem to obsess about the outcome while others seem to take things in stride. Learning to view situations as challenges rather than as threats could help. A counselor or therapist can help if you are not successful in doing this on your own.

Don't let your weight become another stressor. Even if you really want to lose weight, take it slow and refrain from blaming and shaming yourself. Making yourself feel bad only adds to your stress and this is not helpful. A slow and steady approach with lots of encouragement is more likely to succeed.

Tips to Obtaining a Healthy Weight (it's no secret)

- Become more active. Once we gain the excess weight, the only "tool" to remove it is burning the calories that are being stored. Activity helps control weight and control hormones (insulin, stress hormones which increase body fat deposits). Start where you are now: if you're walking 10 minutes, increase it to 15 minutes. Every week, increase your walk 5 more minutes until you reach 30 minutes, 5 days a week.

  Remember, your goal is to become moderately active at least 30 minutes, 5 days per week. Daily activity includes taking the stairs instead of the elevator, gardening, dancing and generally moving more.

- Consume more plant-based foods, which are naturally lower in fat and calories and higher in fiber and nutrients, such as whole grains, fruits, vegetables, seeds, and nuts.

- Select foods low in fat. Examples are low-fat and fat-free milk and dairy products, lean meats.

- Make just one change at a time. Purchase 1% milk instead of 2% and whole. Begin with taking the steps instead of the elevator.

If you continue to struggle, seek guidance and assistance from a health professional. A Registered Dietitian (RD) is trained to help and work with people struggling with dietary issues. Also helpful would be exercise coaches and family counselors.

Food Is More Than Just Something to Eat

There's more to food than just its nourishing and healing properties. There is the joy, fellowship, feeling of community, celebration and gratitude of sharing our food and meals with family and friends.

Research has shown that feeling connected, loved, accepted, and secure releases healthy hormones resulting in a stronger immune system. One of the biggest outcomes of sitting down and sharing a meal with our family, or celebrating special occasions with family and friends, is the sense of well-being and emotional support.

We need to feel safe. And loved. And whole. And grateful. And fulfilled. We can use our meal and celebration times as the bridge to our healing. We can give thanks for our daily bread and be grateful for those who share it with us.

We can center our thoughts on the food in front of us and be mindful of this special gift, which will nourish not only our souls, but also our bodies.

Body Mass Index Table

Height (inches)	Normal						Overweight					Obese										Extreme Obesity														
BMI	19	20	21	22	23	24	25	26	27	28	29	30	31	32	33	34	35	36	37	38	39	40	41	42	43	44	45	46	47	48	49	50	51	52	53	54
												Body Weight (pounds)																								
58	91	96	100	105	110	115	119	124	129	134	138	143	148	153	158	162	167	172	177	181	186	191	196	201	205	210	215	220	224	229	234	239	244	248	253	258
59	94	99	104	109	114	119	124	128	133	138	143	148	153	158	163	168	173	178	183	188	193	198	203	208	212	217	222	227	232	237	242	247	252	257	262	267
60	97	102	107	112	118	123	128	133	138	143	148	153	158	163	168	174	179	184	189	194	199	204	209	215	220	225	230	235	240	245	250	255	261	266	271	276
61	100	106	111	116	122	127	132	137	143	148	153	158	164	169	174	180	185	190	195	201	206	211	217	222	227	232	238	243	248	254	259	264	269	275	280	285
62	104	109	115	120	126	131	136	142	147	153	158	164	169	175	180	186	191	196	202	207	213	218	224	229	235	240	246	251	256	262	267	273	278	284	289	295
63	107	113	118	124	130	135	141	146	152	158	163	169	175	180	186	191	197	203	208	214	220	225	231	237	242	248	254	259	265	270	276	282	287	293	299	304
64	110	116	122	128	134	140	145	151	157	163	169	174	180	186	192	197	204	209	215	221	227	232	238	244	250	256	262	267	273	279	285	291	296	302	308	314
65	114	120	126	132	138	144	150	156	162	168	174	180	186	192	198	204	210	216	222	228	234	240	246	252	258	264	270	276	282	288	294	300	306	312	318	324
66	118	124	130	136	142	148	155	161	167	173	179	186	192	198	204	210	216	223	229	235	241	247	253	260	266	272	278	284	291	297	303	309	315	322	328	334
67	121	127	134	140	146	153	159	166	172	178	185	191	198	204	211	217	223	230	236	242	249	255	261	268	274	280	287	293	299	306	312	319	325	331	338	344
68	125	131	138	144	151	158	164	171	177	184	190	197	203	210	216	223	230	236	243	249	256	262	269	276	282	289	295	302	308	315	322	328	335	341	348	354
69	128	135	142	149	155	162	169	176	182	189	196	203	209	216	223	230	236	243	250	257	263	270	277	284	291	297	304	311	318	324	331	338	345	351	358	365
70	132	139	146	153	160	167	174	181	188	195	202	209	216	222	229	236	243	250	257	264	271	278	285	292	299	306	313	320	327	334	341	348	355	362	369	376
71	136	143	150	157	165	172	179	186	193	200	208	215	222	229	236	243	250	257	265	272	279	286	293	301	308	315	322	329	338	343	351	358	365	372	379	386
72	140	147	154	162	169	177	184	191	199	206	213	221	228	235	242	250	258	265	272	279	287	294	302	309	316	324	331	338	346	353	361	368	375	383	390	397
73	144	151	159	166	174	182	189	197	204	212	219	227	235	242	250	257	265	272	280	288	295	302	310	318	325	333	340	348	355	363	371	378	386	393	401	408
74	148	155	163	171	179	186	194	202	210	218	225	233	241	249	256	264	272	280	287	295	303	311	319	326	334	342	350	358	365	373	381	389	396	404	412	420
75	152	160	168	176	184	192	200	208	216	224	232	240	248	256	264	272	279	287	295	303	311	319	327	335	343	351	359	367	375	383	391	399	407	415	423	431
76	156	164	172	180	189	197	205	213	221	230	238	246	254	263	271	279	287	295	304	312	320	328	336	344	353	361	369	377	385	394	402	410	418	426	435	443

Source: Adapted from Clinical Guidelines on the Identification, Evaluation, and Treatment of Overweight and Obesity in Adults: The Evidence Report.

Questions Registered Dietitians Are Often Asked (and Their Answers)

Question: What do you do when you must not take supplements to avoid "feeding" the cancer?

The most recent published report from the American Institute for Cancer Research does not recommend supplements or supplementation as a way to protect against cancer. It recommends meeting your nutritional needs through diet alone. However, if you feel you are unable to eat a variety of nutrient-rich whole foods such as fruits, vegetables, and whole grains, you may benefit from a supplement. Good multi-vitamins come from reputable companies, only need to be taken once a day, and have 100 percent or less of each vitamin and mineral listed in the % DV column on the nutrition facts label. Please avoid all high-dose single vitamin or mineral supplements unless directed by your physician. As always, please discuss all vitamin, mineral, and herbal supplementation with your physician.

Question: Some people tell me that cancer grows on sugar and that I need to completely cut sugar out of my diet. Is that true?

Let's start with some basic background information on human digestion/metabolism and sources of "sugar" in our diet to help shed some light on the relationship with "sugar" and cancer. All digestible carbohydrates break down through digestion in our bodies to make "sugar" also as known as glucose. Carbohydrates are widespread throughout our food supply. They can be found in the Grain group, which includes foods like breads, cereal, rice, pasta, muffins, and tortillas; in the Fruit group in the whole fruit or fruit juices; the Dairy group including foods like milk, yogurt, and ice cream; and in the Vegetable group in foods like carrots, sweet potatoes, tomatoes, corn, and peas. The list could go on and on.

Fruit, vegetable, and grain sources of carbohydrates are known as complex carbohydrates, simply meaning they need to be broken down more. They make our bodies work a little harder to be able to use them for energy.

Also, let's not forget the added-sugars or simple sugars we can have in our diet from table sugar, brown sugar, honey, and corn syrup, for example. These are found mainly in candy, sweets, and other processed foods. These sugars do not need as much work to digest or break down to be available to use for energy. So both simple and complex carbohydrate sources will turn into glucose (sugar). Bottom line: all carbohydrates turn to "sugar" in our body.

The next key point is that every cell in our bodies needs glucose (or sugar) for energy. Every cell! This includes all organs and systems and also includes abnormal cells like cancer. However, we need carbohydrates to function properly. For example, glucose (sugar) is the sole energy source for our brain and nervous system. Our bodies are so smart that if you do not give them carbohydrates, they can make a form of them from protein and fat sources. Bottom line: our bodies need glucose (sugar) to work properly.

The bulk of the research done on cancer prevention and diet shows that diets high in plant foods (fruits, vegetables, and whole grains) can significantly reduce our cancer risk. So let's summarize what we now know. **Carbohydrates (sugar) are widespread in our food supply, in those plant-based foods. Our bodies require glucose (sugar) to work properly. Diets high in plant-based foods have been shown to reduce disease risk, especially cancer risk.**

So now you might be asking yourself, where did this question about cancer and sugar come from and is there any cause for concern? This question is made to instill fear. You need to put effort into your diet. Everyday food choices should include a variety of plant-based foods, lean sources of protein, and healthier fats. However, **your food choices should not instill fear**. There is no such thing as a magic bullet or a single food that is a cure-all—giving us instant good health. It does not exist. Likewise, there is no such thing as a single "bad" food that will give us instant bad health or cancer. There are many more factors involved, such as a lifetime of overall food choice, physical activity, lifestyle choices, and genetics in disease risk than just one single food choice.

Our bodies produce a hormone called insulin. On a very basic level, insulin allows our bodies to take glucose (sugar) and convert it to energy. Without insulin, glucose (sugar) is only potential energy. This means our bodies would not have a usable form of energy without both glucose (sugar) and insulin working together.

Insulin and other hormones have been studied in their relationship with cancer. Some cancers are hormone dependent—meaning high levels of certain hormones make it more favorable for cancers to grow. The amount of insulin circulating in our bodies is dependent on the amount of circulating glucose (sugar). This means if we eat a very large amount of food, high in simple sugars, our body responds by making an equally large amount of insulin available. A lifetime of eating like this, having a high or large amount of circulating insulin, does not promote good health.

We can change this by eating smaller, more frequent meals; think snack-type portions and not Thanksgiving- meal portions. This may help us to not overeat, but actually consume a moderate amount of energy. We also need to eat a diet higher in complex carbohydrates—those fruits, vegetables, and whole grains. Not only do complex carbohydrates take longer to break down, think small trickle of glucose in the body versus a tidal wave. They also have higher amounts of vitamins, minerals, phytochemicals, and fiber, which we know through research are needed for overall good health.

The bulk of your diet, therefore, should be from fruits, vegetables, and whole grains (and that occasional piece of cake). We also need lean sources of protein and healthy fats in our diet to be healthy.

Question: My neighbor brought me a supplement package of pills and says if I take two of these capsules every day, it's the equivalent of 11 fruits and vegetables. Is it worth the money and would it do me any good?

There are lots of different health properties in fruits and vegetables. Just to name a few would include vitamins, minerals, phytochemicals, and fiber. It is likely that these components have a synergistic effect—meaning, to work the best, they need to work together. Case in point would be thinking a fiber supplement has the same health properties as a whole apple. Fiber is just one component of many in an apple, but not the only one needed for good health.

There is also something to be said about processing fruits or vegetables into pill or powder form. Many components are lost or reduced when exposed to light and heat. Also, physically there is no way to get every health component of just one apple squeezed into a little tiny pill without losing something in the process.

Take the money you would have spent on supplements and buy or update your kitchen appliances. Get a food processor or blender. Then see the suggestions for the next questions.

Question: I know we're supposed to eat lots of fruit and vegetables, but I really don't like them (or with my kind of cancer, I'm told not to eat raw fruits and vegetables).

Just because you may not be able to or like to eat a crunchy salad or a whole apple does not mean you can't enjoy "eating" fruits and vegetables. For example, you may be able to shred or grate them and sneak them into baked items such as bread, muffins, or casseroles. You can blend them and add them to smoothies, soups, or sauces. You could squeeze or juice them and enjoy just drinking them.

These are just a few of the many ways you can get fresh fruits and vegetables into your diet. If you would like more tips on eating fruits and vegetables, please contact a registered dietitian in your area or for more information, go to www. fruitsandveggiesmatter.gov.

Question: What is the best recommended multi-vitamin?

Good multi-vitamins come from reputable companies, only need to be taken once a day, and have 100% or less of each vitamin and mineral listed in the %DV column on the nutrition facts label. See session 10 of this workbook for information on finding a reputable source for vitamins and other supplements.

Question: What about artificial sweeteners?

Question: My weight management class says that it's okay to use artificial sweeteners, but my health newsletter says there are all kinds of problems with them and they could make me sicker. How do I know what's true?

Artificial sweeteners and cancer risk have been studied for years. Some laboratory studies used doses of artificial sweeteners higher than any human could possibly get in the diet. On the other hand, the research in human studies is clear that the available evidence just doesn't support a connection between sweeteners and cancer risk. That being said, like in everything, moderation is the key. If you start to evaluate your diet and find that you have an excess of anything, you might want to reevaluate your food choices for a more balanced approach.

Question: What have the studies shown regarding grilling meats and cancer?

It is clear that grilling animal products (both red and white meat) causes potent carcinogens called heterocyclic amines (HCAs) and polycyclic aromatic hydrocarbons (PAHs) to arise within food.

These substances have been shown in laboratory experiments to trigger the cancer process. The AICR report concluded that there is limited but suggestive evidence that these substances factor in human cancer, providing one more reason to limit consumption of red and processed meat, however it is cooked.

Grilling vegetables and fruit produces no HCAs or PAHs, and thus poses no potential cancer risks. Diets high in plant foods are associated with reduced risk of several cancers.

If you do choose to cook any kind of meat on the grill, take these precautions:

- Select smaller cuts of meat, such as kabobs, and limit your portion size.

- Select leaner cuts, to prevent dripping fat from causing flare-ups, which deposit carcinogens on the meat.

- You can also reduce flare-ups by spreading aluminum foil on the grill. Make small holes in the foil to allow fat to drain.

- Try a marinade. Some research suggests that even briefly marinating meat significantly reduces the formation of HCAs.

- Partially precook meat in the microwave before grilling, to speed up grilling time.

- Flip meat frequently, which reduces the amount of carcinogens that arise.

- Avoid eating the charred "black" part of grilled meats.

Question: Are organic foods better?

As with many things in life, the question about organic foods being "better" than conventionally grown does not produce a simple yes or no answer. This topic is highly debatable so please consider your source of information when making a decision about whether organic food is right for you or your family.

First, "organically grown" is defined as grown without the use of conventional pesticides, artificial fertilizers, or food additives while "conventionally grown" is just the opposite, meaning they might use conventional pesticides, artificial fertilizers, or food additives.

There are pros and cons for both organic and conventionally grown foods. Current research supports that some organic fruits and vegetables might be higher in vitamins, minerals, and antioxidants, when compared with conventionally grown produce. Another possible benefit of choosing organic food is that it may be one way of reducing your overall exposure to pesticides. Some of the disadvantages of organically produced food are that they may spoil faster because they are not treated with preservatives. Also, they may cost more money and be harder to find when compared with conventionally grown produce.

Hundreds of research studies support the fact that populations that consume more fruits, vegetables, and whole grains have a lower risk of cancer and other diseases. These studies examined fruit, vegetable, and whole grain consumption in the general public (and they probably ate conventionally grown food).

To be safe, follow these guidelines:

- Select produce with no cuts, decay, insect holes.

- Scrub produce under running water.

- Peel off skin and discard outer leaves.

- Trim visible fat on meats (which can store pesticide or chemical residues).

- Eat a variety of foods to reduce your exposure to any one chemical.

Eating fruit, vegetables, and whole grains is important for reducing cancer and other disease risk despite how they are grown.

Question: I feel like my metabolism is all off after my cancer treatment. Is there any weight loss supplement that will really boost my weight loss?

Part of the natural aging process is that our metabolism decreases or slows down. We do not need as many calories at age 50 as we did at age 20. Most of the time if a 50-year-old eats like a 20-year-old, he or she will gain weight. Unfortunately, some cancer treatments can prematurely decrease your metabolism. You might be more aware of this change because it happened so quickly and not over the course of years.

The only way to increase your metabolism to produce a significant decrease in weight is by exercising. There are no magic bullets in the dietary or natural supplement industry. Save your money and "invest" in ways we know will produce weight loss, by changing your diet and physical activity levels.

There are some prescription medications available to assist you with your weight loss. Please discuss medication options with your physician to decide which one would be right for you, if any. For these medication options to work the best, you still need to make changes in your diet and physical activity to get the desired results: weight loss.

Summary

The importance of maintaining healthy eating and activity patterns extends throughout your lifetime—whether you have cancer or want to prevent cancer. You have control over the decisions you make for what you eat and do. You have today; you have the power; you pray for the strength and courage to do your best.

Questions for discussion and journaling

1. What feeling or feelings did you have after reading or hearing the information on nutrition? For example, some feel hopeful that they can do more to improve their health; some feel angry that they were eating well and cancer invaded their lives anyway; some feel guilty or ashamed that they aren't the perfect BMI and haven't eaten enough fruits and vegetables. What do you feel?

2. How do your feelings affect your thoughts about this chapter? For example, do you just get discouraged and head for the chips? Do you say, "I might as well eat what I like because I've had cancer anyway and I deserve to have what I want when I feel like it?" Do you immediately start thinking about running out to buy vegetables?

3. When you think of improving your nutrition, what one or two small steps would be possible now? Which would be the easiest to start?

4. Do you think better nutrition will be part of the "best life" you are creating? Is this something you want to start now or do you think something else will take priority first?

5. Remember that there are many ways to heal, and improvement in any area—mind, body, spirit, relationships, work, fun, humor, etc.—counts. Which area of your life would you most like to upgrade now? Which area of your life would be the easiest to work on now?

Power Tool: Guided Imagery

It's been said that our bodies cannot tell the difference between what is actually happening to us and what we are vividly imagining. This is especially true when we are alone and thinking.

You may remember a time when you were facing something scary—maybe something like giving a speech in front of a group. Though you only had to give the speech once, you may have had anxiety for days ahead of time as you imagined yourself at the podium. Your body reacts about the same to a real life situation or to imagining that situation. We can use this quality to help ourselves feel good. Remember daydreaming as a child? The classroom disappeared as you lost yourself in some wonderful daydream. The trick to getting a good effect in guided imagery is to try to bring in as much detail for each of your five senses as possible. Sometimes the daydream really doesn't involve all five senses, but try to bring in as many senses as possible. Here is an example:

- Start by taking a few deep relaxing breaths. Just be aware of how the air feels as it moves in through your nose, down your throat, and into your chest. Pay attention to the rise and fall of your chest. Just let go of other thoughts for right now, and focus on your breathing. As your body begins to relax, let your mind relax too.

- Remember for a moment a very beautiful place. This may be a place from your childhood, a place you visited once, a scene you saw in a movie, or even an imaginary place. Whatever you choose, let it be a place that is beautiful, comforting, and safe. Imagine this place right here in front of you now. And imagine yourself slowly walking into this place. It is right in front of you, beckoning you forward. You move toward it, feeling drawn to its comfort and beauty. And you enter into the space.

141

- Now that you are in this beautiful setting, take a moment to look around. Let your eyes feast on the beauty of this place. Look up above and notice what is overhead. Notice the colors. Look down at your feet and notice what the ground is made of. Notice the colors and textures of the material beneath your feet. Look from side to side, noticing the shapes and colors of the objects around you. Take time to notice and appreciate all of the small details that make this place so wonderful. Let your eyes be bathed in this beauty.

- As your eyes continue to soak up the beauty of this place, let your body begin to feel this place as well. Notice the temperature of the air against your skin, cool or warm, just right for this place. Notice the movement of the air against your body, whether it is very still or whether there is a breeze. Notice the feel of the ground beneath your feet, hard and firm like oak floors, soft and shifting like sand on a beach, or however this ground feels to you. Reach out and touch things here in this place. Feel whether they are cool or warm, moist or dry, smooth or bumpy, soft or hard. Let your skin absorb the comforting sensations of this place. Let it wrap you in comfort like a baby being swaddled in a soft fleecy blanket.

- As your eyes and your skin continue to absorb the comforts of this place, let your ears begin to hear the sounds of this place. Notice what you hear. It may be the gentle sound of water lapping against a shore, or the sound of a gentle breeze moving through the leaves of nearby trees. Maybe there is music in the distance or the lilting sound of happy voices. Or maybe just the deep soothing sound of silence. Whatever the sound, it falls gently on your ears, soothing and comforting.

- Now take a deep breath and breathe in the scent of this beautiful place. Feel the air in your nostrils and enjoy the pleasant smells of this comforting place. You may sense the fresh salty smell of ocean air, or the clean pine smell of a forest; maybe the warm toasted smell of summer sun in a meadow, or maybe the mouthwatering smell of fresh bread baking in the kitchen of someone you love. Whatever the smell, breathe in the comfort and let it fill your body.

- Here in this comforting place, let yourself relax. Bask in the safety and beauty. Breathe in the comfort and safety and let your body be filled. Take some time to soak up this feeling of comfort. Knowing that you carry this place with you at all times, promise yourself that you will return. And then, when you are ready, slowly and gently bring yourself back to the current place and time, carrying with you all of the peace and calm you experienced in your own special place.

SESSION 7

May the Circle Be Unbroken

Stephanie Koraleski, PhD

Key Points

- The experience of having cancer affects how you feel about yourself.
- Because you may feel differently about yourself, the people who are important to you may notice a change in their relationships with you.
- The relationship with your partner (spouse, closest friend, or caregiver) is often the most affected.
- Certain styles of communication can help.
- Partners have their own issues and may also need help coping.
- If relationships are not working as well as they did before, there are ways to address those issues.
- A strategy for assessing and addressing relationship issues is presented.

When you've come this far through your cancer treatment, you realize that you're not the only one who has been affected by cancer. Many people say they don't know how they could have survived cancer without their friends and family. Both you and your loved ones have been through a really stressful time.

While you were going through treatment, you may have had a lot of fears and doubts. Being tired and feeling sick and worn down can bring up every relationship fear we ever had. Will anyone care? Can I trust people to stay with me and love me if I can't do everything I did before? Will my friends and family get tired of me or disgusted with my illness or think I'm being a hypochondriac? Will my children or grandchildren or friends be afraid or repulsed by me when I have no hair? Will my partner still find me sexually attractive if my body is scarred? Having to face these and other fears can add to the stress of cancer treatment.

145

Meanwhile, your loved ones had stresses of their own. Many of them needed to take on extra work around the house, manage paying the bills, extra caring for children, facilitating transportation for you when you were too ill to drive yourself to treatments, and many more tasks. They worried about you, about whether your treatment would cure you, about whether they would be able to do what they needed to do. They wondered what life would look like in the future, whether or not you would be able to resume "life as usual," and whether you could pursue the dreams you had together. They worried that they might lose you and have to face life alone.

And into that stressful time and all of those fears, you had to factor in your personalities, your own backgrounds, and the history of your relationship. It's a lot.

The research seems to show that having positive social connections and support is really good for your health—that more socially connected people fare better (Umberson, 2010). This doesn't necessarily mean that you need a large number of friends, but the quality of contacts and reliable support felt from family and friends all seem to correlate with better health outcomes for cancer survivors (Kroenke, 2006). Some people come into the cancer world with strong relationships. Others come in with problems in their relationships. Some others find themselves mostly alone because their friends and family are not around.

This chapter focuses on what happens to your relationships when you have cancer and how to strengthen the relationships now.

Your Relationship with Yourself

All your relationships have one thing in common: YOU. The relationship with yourself is one of the most important relationships you have. It can't help but be affected by the experience of cancer and treatment. Think about what has happened. No matter how you felt about yourself prior to the cancer, cancer upset the balance in several ways.

- It made your life more unpredictable so that sometimes you barely knew yourself.

- Your body has changed. Surgery, radiation, medications, and chemotherapy (or some combination of these treatments) have changed your appearance and changed your internal chemistry balance.

- Your mind may feel different. The stress, fatigue, and treatment may have left you with some "chemobrain" (and yes, you can have these effects even if you did *not* have chemotherapy)

- Your values and priorities may have changed as you've had to focus on what was really most important to you.

Almost everyone is distressed by the changes in such basic facets of self. It's very normal to grieve or be angry about changes to yourself that you didn't want. But many people also begin to develop that "survivor pride" that was discussed in chapter one. (If you are interested in knowing more about possible changes in you, see the Special Topics sections on Chemobrain and Body Image.) The important thing is that this new, changed you is the one you are bringing into your relationships now, and that is part of why your relationships may feel different.

Cancer Changes Relationships with Others

Most people find that family, friendship, and work roles change when they have cancer. As adults, most of us are more accustomed to taking care of other people than we are to receiving care. Learning to ask for or even just to accept help from other people can be one of the big stresses of the cancer experience. Many people can listen to friends' problems and provide comfort and support all day long, but expressing their own sadness, anger, or fear feels overwhelming or even shameful.

And because your energy and mood vary with the phase of treatment, you may feel exhausted and need help one day and be full of energy the next day. It's hard to know how you feel yourself and hard for friends and family to predict. You need more love and support when you feel awful, but you don't want to be treated like an invalid when you are better.

Couples and Cancer

The relationship that is most integral to most people is the one with their spouse or significant other. This primary person might be a husband, wife, or significant other, but for some people the most significant caregiver might be a parent, adult child, or best friend. When we talk about this, we mean the person who was with you from the beginning until now. For the sake of keeping things short, we'll call this person your spouse, but know that it could be someone else who is the other part of your "couple."

There is a lot of research about the effect of cancer on both partners in a couple, and what we've learned is that the outcome depends on the individuals' personalities, the unique relationship the couple has, and the type of communication they use.

Personality and Relationships

We all have different personalities, and we all handle stress differently. Some of the things that seem to really help minimize stress for cancer survivors are optimism and an ability to manage personal stress fairly well. Caregivers have their own issues, but many times their moods seem to be related both to the cancer survivor's mood and health. It helps when both partners are trying hard to get through the cancer in the best possible way.

Research shows some styles that help and some things that hurt:

Styles That Help

- Open communication

- Empathetic listening

- Trying to appreciate your partner; empathize with the way he/she is stressed or suffering

- Talking about what you are thinking

- Sharing *both* positive and negative experiences

- Celebrating good news with your partner (even small things like a great sunset or a funny joke you heard)

- Facing cancer as a *team*

(Belcher, 2011; Otto, 2015)

Styles That Can Hurt

- Being overly controlling

- Trying to "fix" things that are not fixable (sometimes just empathetic listening is the best thing you can do)

- Being inconsolable; expressing feelings is good, but it can be overwhelming to your partner if nothing he/she *does* seems to help comfort you

- Withdrawing from your partner

- Directing your anger at the cancer at your partner

- Being such a "super hero" trying to keep up at home and work that there is no time or energy to just *be* with each other

- Not accepting help

- Being too self-absorbed; sometimes our own needs have to take a back seat to the other person's

- Talking about some things but avoiding the "hot topics" like fear of recurrence or sexuality. It can be hard to talk about these things, but you could write a note or get some help from a counselor. If you don't face the issue, it only gets bigger.

(Spung, 2011; Fergus and Gray, 2009)

Relationship Variables

Communication seems to be the key factor in helping relationships survive and even get closer during cancer. One thing that seems to get in the way of good communication seems to be what researchers call "protective buffering." This means that some people don't share information or feelings with their partner because they don't want to worry the other person.

You know your partner and maybe that's always been your relationship style, but if you've always shared your life experiences, hiding your thoughts and feelings about cancer can make the relationship feel less intimate (Manne, 2007). When spouses avoid talking about the cancer or someone doesn't want to listen, the marriage can suffer (Pasipanodya, 2012).

Caregivers usually want to help and support their loved one, but they may not know how to do that well. It's important to be clear about what you want. For example, if time is limited, do you want the caregiver to sit and talk to you or to clean the kitchen? What do you want the caregiver to know about your health? Have you actually told him/her?

For example, a lot of cancer survivors say that they wish their caregivers knew how tired they really are even months after treatment is over. If that's your situation, have you told your caregiver or shown him/her information that backs up what you are saying? Sometimes caregivers are misinformed and may push you to do more than you feel up to, not because they are being insensitive, but because they think that doing more would be good for you. Sharing accurate information and research with each other can be really helpful.

The Hot Topic—Sexuality

Some people report that their partner has avoided them since their cancer treatment, and they've never resumed emotional or sexual intimacy. Many partners of cancer patients have emotions and fears of their own that never were addressed. More and more, the needs of cancer patients are addressed by medical teams, support groups, chat rooms, and books, but partners of cancer patients are often left without support.

These are some of the issues partners cope with regarding sexuality.

- Many partners are afraid of being too pushy. Spouses may say that they love their partner and don't want to push him/her into something that would be uncomfortable. They are waiting for a sign that the partner is ready for sex again. Meanwhile, the cancer survivor interprets a lack of initiative as meaning that the partner finds him/her unattractive, so they begin avoiding each other. Usually that means less touching overall, less emotional intimacy, and after some time, they end up acting like roommates instead of lovers. If this is your case, let your partner know that you feel shy and uncertain about your body but you are sure that you love your partner and you want to be close again. You can talk about this or write a note, but someone needs to take the first step, and it may need to be you.

- Many partners avoid sex because they're afraid to hurt the cancer survivor. Sometimes the couple has attempted intercourse once or twice and it was uncomfortable and they've been avoiding further contact. If this is your case, try to address your pain issues. See the Special Topics section on Sexuality for many ideas about how to make sex comfortable and enjoyable again.

- If partners are afraid to ask for or initiate sex, they begin avoiding emotional intimacy because feeling close makes them desire sex and they're trying to avoid that. Again, the solution involves talking about your desire to be close again. (Yu, 2015; Brandao, 2014; Badr, 2013)

151

Partner Issues

In the midst of dealing with their own changes, **some survivors forget how much their cancer affected their partner too.** Frequently the worry and additional stress of having you be sick has really had an effect on your partners, family, and friends. If a relationship, particularly a close one, is suffering and you've dealt with your own issues, consider the possibility that your partner or loved one is reacting from depression or stress.

- Some partners have become exhausted and depressed. Your partner may be devastated by your cancer; afraid you will die, afraid to lose you, afraid of being overwhelmed by the bills, overwhelmed with the tasks of keeping life going. Sometimes they are angry that you got support and they got none. One man said, "Every day people ask me, 'How is Judy doing?' No one ever says, 'How are YOU?'" Family members often don't ask for support, and they often don't get it. When the survivor's cancer treatment is over and he/she is better, the partner may be so tired and exhausted from work and worry that intimate conversations and sex are the last thing he/she thinks of.

- Sometimes, too, your partner has become a caregiver, and when you no longer need a caregiver, it's hard to switch roles again. If something like this is going on in your relationship, start by talking to your loved one. Find out about the experience he or she went through. What was it like? How did it feel? What was the hardest part? Who supported them? Just help them talk about the experience. You might give them one of the books for partners or caregivers listed in the References and Resources. Sometimes reading about another person's experience is validating and helpful. If your partner or loved one seems really down, suggest getting a physical. Work on getting healthy again together. If these normal TLC (tender loving care) measures don't start helping in a month or so, or if you discover that your partner is seriously depressed, consult a counselor or psychologist or talk to a doctor about evaluating your partner for depression.

- Some relationships really suffer when one partner gets sick. Some partners are unable to cope and start detaching. This can happen for many reasons. One that occurs many times is a situation where the partner lost a parent, former spouse or sibling to cancer and never really resolved the loss. Having another loved one get cancer is too overwhelming, and the person just shuts down. Another common situation occurs when the relationship was not strong to start with and the partner can't bear the pressure of illness. Any of these serious situations probably needs some professional consultation with a good mental health practitioner.

If you are lucky enough to have a good relationship with your spouse (or other main caregiver), you have a great asset going! Facing cancer together can be frightening, but it can also be a true testament to your love. Doing your best to comfort, encourage, and shelter each other in frightening circumstances is real love. Remember to appreciate each other and rejoice in each good thing!

Friends and Others

How did your friends, other family members, and work colleagues react to your illness? What was your experience like? Were you surprised at how your family, friends, and coworkers reacted? Did you get the help you needed? Were you smothered with concern or left to figure things out on your own? When you were tired, sick, or frightened, did people pitch in to help or seem upset and angry with you for not being yourself? Did your relationships seem to get stronger or were some lost along the way? And how do you feel about all of this now?

It seems the answers to those questions are as varied as the number of people who answer.

- Some people find that family and friends were very supportive and that they are much more surrounded by love than they had ever known. Others go through their cancer experience in a very private way, telling almost no one about the experience.

- Some have found that certain family members or longtime friends faded out of their lives when they were diagnosed with cancer. Others report that some friends or family members completely ignored the fact that they had cancer.

- Some people report an outpouring of caring, donated vacation time, and casseroles from work friends; others get the message that if they can't pull their weight 100%, their jobs are at risk.

- Some survivors have been surprised that they met wonderful new friends during their treatment or that people who had been merely acquaintances before they got sick became like family when they were ill.

Most people experience some wonderful acts of kindness and also experience some big disappointments during their illness.

After treatment is over and you begin recovering your health, it's time to survey your garden of friendship. As with all gardens, it may need tending from time to time. It's easiest to appreciate and nourish the relationships that are flowering beautifully. Many people plan parties or celebrations or trips with their supportive family or friends once their treatment is over. It's easy to love the people who love us and to feel even closer to family, friends, and coworkers who have demonstrated their love.

It's harder to address the parts of the garden that are sickly or full of weeds. Some can be revived with care. Others may need to be pruned. And sometimes people find that their tastes have changed and they want to add new people to the friendship garden. This process of reevaluating relationships is one of the challenges of the time when treatment is over.

Problem Relationships

So what do you do with the problem relationships?

FIRST: Take some time to be honest about your feelings. If your sister-in-law never called and never sent a card through your whole treatment, how do you feel? Are you angry? Are you hurt? Are you relieved (maybe you never felt close to her anyway)? If your spouse kept a heavy traveling schedule and seemed to make excuses to be gone when you needed him/her, how do you feel? Are you resentful? Are you hurt? Are you retaliating now? If your mother or sister or best friend can't stand to talk about your cancer and changes the topic or starts to cry every time you mention it, do you feel more alone, less close, rejected, angry, hurt?

Realize that how people treat you does affect you. You may or may not want to address problem relationships yet— or ever. But if you do want to look at these issues, take some time to list the names of the people you have problems with. Write a bit about what you had expected from them, how they actually reacted, and how you've felt about that.

SECOND: After you've spent some time reviewing what happened and where you are now, think about what you want to happen.

- Do you want to strengthen and renew this relationship?

- Do you want to wait and see what happens?

- Are you ready to let this relationship go or let it move into the once-a-year lunch or holiday card category?

Some of the following stories may sound a little familiar to you; these situations are common. The solutions in the story are options, not necessarily what you should do. If you want to strengthen and renew the relationship, start with yourself. Be very honest about how you feel. Feelings are based on our thoughts and expectations, so take time to write out what you are thinking.

Remember that *you get to choose* how you handle any relationships in your own life.

Nancy's Story—the Frightened Friend

For example, a woman named Nancy reported that her friend Carol had been overwhelmed with a family crisis the year before Nancy was diagnosed with breast cancer. During that time, Nancy had watched and carpooled Carol's children, brought over several meals, and listened to Carol talk about her problems for many hours. Carol had made it through her crisis and the friendship seemed good.

But when Nancy got breast cancer, Carol sent flowers to the hospital, visited once, and then seemed to drop off the face of the earth. When Nancy called Carol, she found Carol rushing to get off the phone. Nancy was understandably hurt, confused, and angry. What she wrote was that Carol was a taker, not a giver; that she was only in the relationship for what she could get; and that Carol really must not have cared about her or she wouldn't have treated her this way.

As we talked about the history of the relationship, Nancy told me about how Carol had been there over the years and the many ways they had helped each other. In light of their history, Carol's reaction seemed strange.

If people react very differently from the way they've behaved in the past, something is going on. What happened? As we talked more, Nancy began to wonder if her cancer had frightened Carol into withdrawing. Nancy knew that Carol's grandmother had lived with their family when she was a child and that her grandmother had died of cancer. She didn't know the details, but began to wonder if something about Carol's childhood experience was so awful that she couldn't face going through cancer with another person she loved.

As she talked, she realized that she loved and missed Carol and was willing to take some action to try to get this relationship back. She realized this would have to be a two-way street, and if Carol wasn't willing to work things out, it wouldn't happen. But she did really miss Carol and she decided to take the risk.

She talked to Carol, casually at first, and then over lunch one day, she brought up the subject of Carol's absence during her cancer treatment. Carol was defensive and embarrassed, but Nancy had rehearsed reacting with kindness. Finally Carol admitted that she had felt afraid and overwhelmed, didn't know what to do or say, and was ashamed that she had left Nancy to face her cancer alone.

Nancy's guess was right. Carol had such frightening memories of her grandmother's cancer that she'd been unable to face hospitals and cancer treatments again. Over several months, they rebuilt their friendship, and Carol went to a therapist to work through some of the old childhood memories that were still terrifying her. Nancy's cancer turned out to be a growing experience for both of them.

Joan's Story—Unable to Face Cancer

What if the other person isn't as receptive as Carol had been? Joan's mother could not tolerate any discussion of Joan's cancer. During Joan's treatment, her mom would come to her house on chemo days, clean, make dinner, and leave before Joan came home. They'd talk on the phone, but the minute Joan would talk about cancer, her mom would change the subject. Even a year after treatment was over when Joan was doing well, her mom could not listen to cancer talk. Joan decided not to push it.

She knew her mom loved her, but could not be an emotional support. Joan turned to friends and a support group to meet her emotional needs and expressed appreciation to her mom for all the practical help she provided.

Ed's Story—Fair-Weather Friends

And then there are the people who truly seem to be fair-weather friends. Ed had been on a golf league for several years and thought he knew the men in the league very well. They'd

157

play every week and then go to lunch. They'd shared stories of family, work, and travel and enjoyed each other's company.

When Ed got sick, the group sent a card to the hospital and that was the last he heard of them. His treatment began at the same time as the golf season. He'd told them he didn't know if he was up for playing. They got a substitute. One or two of the men had called a couple of times, but the majority had not made any contact.

Ed was finished with treatment and approaching the upcoming golf season with mixed feelings. He enjoyed playing but felt hurt that the group had not stayed in contact with him while he was sick.

As we talked, he realized that this had happened to someone before. Another guy had left the league because his wife had been hospitalized and then needed a lot of care. The group had sent a card, but no one seemed to know what had ever happened to him. Ed realized that he had been so wrapped up in his own life at the time that he hadn't contacted the guy either.

As he thought about that other experience, he realized that he hadn't meant to hurt anyone, and the group probably hadn't meant to hurt him. People in the group were Thursday morning friends. They'd never had contact other than that. Ed started to rethink what he wanted in his relationships, and he realized that he had a variety of friends. Some were deep soul connections, some were work-related, and some were activity-related. He finally decided to go back to the league, but he went with more realistic expectations.

Difficult Relationships

The hardest relationships are the ones that have hurt you the most. The spouse who disappeared or reacted with anger or impatience when you were sick. The adult child who rarely called and never visited during your whole treatment. The longtime friend who abandoned you when you needed her support most.

These kinds of reactions from people who should have been there for you are incredibly painful. Some people react with anger. Some are confused. Some are just very hurt. Relationships that felt important and permanent, like with children, siblings, and spouses, are not easily discarded. You may even live with these people. What are you supposed to do when they have hurt you deeply?

Again, start with yourself.

1. **What did you want from this person during your illness?** What did you expect? Were those expectations realistic? For example, if your son lives halfway across the country, hasn't been home in three years, and only calls every few months, you may have wanted him to come home at least once and call every week, but his behavior over several years has shown that that may not be a realistic expectation.

   Did you ask for what you wanted? If not, the other person may not have known or understood what you needed. If you did ask for help and the other person ignored your requests, you have more information about the state of the relationship.

2. **Second, what do you know about the other person?** How has he or she reacted to family problems and illnesses in the past? Some women have reported that their husbands have always responded to family emergencies by throwing themselves into work. Some men have said that their wives throw themselves into housework or turn to girlfriends instead of talking to them during difficult times. It's hard to know whether this is a way of escaping the emotional intensity at home or a way to be supportive by working harder to "produce" or maybe even a way to cope with uncontrollable events by controlling things where they feel more powerful.

   If your spouse has always run to work when needed at home, his/her behavior during your illness may be more understandable. You may need to work to change these patterns, but you know that the behavior is typical for him/her and not about you.

Teenagers might disappear or act out during a parent's illness too. Just when you were hoping to have more help at home or an extra driver to carpool the younger kids around, your teenager decided to go out for a sport, be in the school play, get a part-time job, or, worse yet, hang out with people you don't know or don't like. Some of that is just typical for that age group. Some of it may be a way to feel more independent and get some distance from the reality that mom or dad is sick, which is really frightening. And some of it may just be the teenager doing normal teenage things with normal teenage oblivion about the needs of other people.

Again, thinking about what was going on for the other person can help you to take their behavior less personally and think more clearly about whether and how to address the relationship problems.

Younger children may behave differently too. Some become more clinging. Some revert to behaviors they had outgrown, like starting to suck their thumbs or wet the bed again. Some seem to prefer grandma or the neighbor who is spending more time with them. Their behaviors can worry us, confuse us, make us feel guilty or hurt our feelings. Remember that everyone in the family is just trying to do the best possible to live through this. Love and good communication can help a lot. (See the Special Topics section on Talking with Children.)

Also remember what this other person's personality has been like over the years. People who have a history of depression, anxiety, or mental illness and people who have always been self-centered or workaholic are unlikely to change much because something happened to *you*. If it happened to them, they might have to take notice, but a life-changing event in someone else's life is unlikely to change their lifelong patterns of behavior. In fact, some people like this get angry or even mean when a person who has always met their needs gets sick and is unable to perform all the services they expect.

Be realistic. What has the other person always been like? If this is an unusual change in behavior, their reactions to your cancer may be based on some old fear of theirs that got triggered by your illness as in the examples of Nancy and Carol. But if their reaction is pretty consistent with how they've always behaved, you might have hoped for better, but your hope probably wasn't realistic.

3.   **What do you know about the relationship?** Sometimes when someone really thinks about this, they realize that the relationship has not been good. Maybe it hasn't been bad, but it's been years since they really felt connected. If you and your spouse basically have shared chores and childrearing and you haven't had a real conversation for a long time, it's hard to know what he/she will do if you really need them. Some rise to the occasion while others seem to lack the understanding that you really need their help and support. Some may not really care. Some relationships have been cold for a long time. Friendships can be like that too. You may have been seeing a certain friend or talking on the phone regularly, but what has the quality of your time together been like? Some relationships endure more out of habit than out of mutual satisfaction.

4.   **Look at your own behavior.** If the other person has been distant or mean, have you reacted by distancing even more or being cold or mean yourself? If the other person doesn't try to get closer, do you try? Or do you wait for the other person to make the first move? Do you talk about the problems at a calm time in a calm way, or do you blow up when you can't take it anymore? Do you not talk at all? Don't

blame or condemn yourself. Just be honest. Look at how you react to this person. Look at the patterns that have developed. Sometimes whole patterns can be altered when one of the people in the relationship makes small, conscious changes.

5. **Last, think about what you want.** As with the examples here, you need to start by honestly exploring what you really desire. If you no longer love or feel connected to this person, do you want to stay in this relationship? If you do, why? Are you staying in a relationship for economic reasons? Because you are afraid to make a change? Because you feel as if you'll never find anyone else? Again, don't criticize yourself. Just be honest.

The decision to stay or leave a relationship is always yours, but if you stay because you don't think you are good enough, smart enough, or attractive enough to find something better, go back and work more on loving yourself.

If you do want to renew the relationship, you have to acknowledge that you can only be in charge of your own behavior. You can't make someone love you if they don't, but you can come to the relationship believing you *are* a loveable person who deserves respect.

You do not deserve to be ignored or mistreated. If you need some help to get to that place within yourself, spend some time with a counselor or a pastoral minister to build that strength inside. Then work on what you want to say and how you want to say it. Deep rifts in relationships can be healed if the people still care about each other. You may need to see a therapist together to expedite the process. But if you both want things to be better, it's very possible to make that happen with some time and some support.

If you don't want to stay, take time to think this through. Don't leave a long-term relationship on impulse or because you are angry or hurt. Give yourself some time and talk it through with someone you can trust. If this is a marriage or a job you're contemplating leaving, make sure you get good legal advice before you sever the ties. Particularly after cancer when "chemobrain" is still operating, you need that kind of objective help to make sure that you understand the legal and financial ramifications and are as well protected as possible if you leave.

You might also spend some time with a therapist to make sure that you aren't running away from something that still has value because of fears or hurts that could be resolved. If it's a relationship you know is mostly dead but you really can't completely end it, like with a sister or an adult child, think about how you can avoid or minimize face-to-face contact and insulate yourself from more hurt. A good therapist might be helpful here.

Some Relationships End

The sad truth is that some relationships end. If you've thought it through and you don't want to be in a relationship any more, be honest with yourself. Take some time to decide whether to address this up front with the other person or whether to just let the relationship fade away. You may decide that it's time to actually get the divorce you've been contemplating or to leave your job.

If you have to do something this hard, talk with a pastor or therapist and a lawyer to get some support and practical help. Hard as this is, it is generally better to know and acknowledge the truth than it is to pretend that things are okay when they are not. By acknowledging that a relationship is over, you give yourself permission to grieve and permission to look elsewhere for relationships that can truly help you give and receive the love we all need.

When a relationship ends, we do grieve, even if the relationship has not been good for a long time. We question what we might have done wrong. We blame the other person.

We are confused about how the love or friendship was lost. We need time to talk about and think about the relationship and what it meant to us in our lives.

But whether the mistakes were yours or the other person's or some combination of mistakes and bad circumstances, know that it is possible to go on and live life fully and to create new relationships that will be fulfilling. Keep repeating the mantras of self love: "I am loveable. I deserve respect. I love others as I love myself."

New Relationships Grow

Invest more time and interest in people who treat you with kindness and respect. Shy away from those who seem mean, disrespectful, or self-centered. Give as you would like to receive; but don't keep giving to sane adults if it's not ever reciprocated. Listen to what your best friends say about your new relationships. Our friends often see more clearly than we do.

The truth is that cancer often changes people, and when people change, their relationships are affected. Any kind of change can be scary, and people often don't want to address issues that make them uncomfortable. The good side is that a life-changing experience like cancer can push you into growing stronger and wiser and help you become more focused on what is truly important to you. If you change, the people who know you may need some time to grow accustomed to this new you. After all, they liked the old you. They may not understand that the changes in you are real; they may just think you're moody or that these changes are still part of your illness.

Just like your legs would ache when you were growing in adolescence, your relationships may suffer growing pains as you grow through your cancer experience. And just as in adolescence, you may find yourself leaving some things behind while other things grow and transform into richer, fuller parts of you.

As difficult as dealing with relationships can be, people who have come through cancer treatment have a tremendous advantage. Almost always, cancer survivors have grown in wisdom and compassion. These traits can help you take the time to think through what is happening, view the situation from another person's point of view, and approach the problems in as loving a way as possible. Cancer survivors also generally have a great appreciation for the sweetness and fragility of life, and that often gives them the courage to address issues they would have been scared to approach before.

As you complete your survey of the garden of your friendships, stop to just appreciate all the good relationships in your life. You may make some changes. You may find that wonderful new friends have entered your life. The most important thing is to remember that you are the gardener here. Enjoy the process.

Questions for discussion and journaling:

1. Were you surprised by the support you received during your cancer treatment? What was the nicest thing anyone did for you?

2. Did anyone you expected to support you let you down? How do you understand that at this point?

Power Tool: A Heart Full of Love

Sometimes, no matter how strong you are, you feel as if you can't influence something or someone you are dealing with. When this feeling happens to someone who is already coping with the life-altering specter of cancer, it's normal to feel overwhelmed and overpowered. So if you are feeling overwhelmed and powerless, try this strategy:

- When facing someone or something that seems "impossible," consider what the outcome is worth to you/the people you love/the world. Is it worth the energy you are giving it?

- Be realistic about what could be accomplished in the best of circumstances.

- Now be realistic about the current circumstances. Are you being truthful to yourself?

- If you are still feeling overpowered or overwhelmed, decide to be loving (yes, that's right, loving).

- Approach the person or the situation with a heart full of love. You don't have to love this particular person or situation. Prepare by filling your heart with memories of other love, knowing that you are capable of love even if this current situation is not optimum.

- Know, without a shadow of a doubt, that you are in control of how you approach the person/situation—even though you may not be in control of how it turns out.

- Now LISTEN. LISTEN with a heart full of LOVE. You are the only one who knows what you are doing.

- No matter what is happening before you, try to hold on to the love. Talk yourself through this—you can hold the love.

- Do your best. The outcome you have committed to is to hold a heart full of love.

- Keep going—you won't believe how this changes the way you feel! It's better than any tonic or technique ever invented. ENJOY the results!

SESSION 8

Renewing My Body, Regaining My Strength

Kay Ryan, PhD, RN, HFS, CHES; Jeannie Hannan, PhD, HPS, HFD; Shanda Berg, PT, CLT-LANA; Natalie Dowty, PT, MPT, EdD

Key Points
- Exercise provides many benefits for cancer survivors.
- It's important to follow the guidelines for safe exercise after cancer.
- Choose among many types of exercise to find an exercise program that's right for you.
- You can exercise even with lymphedema.
- Exercise can help you manage fatigue.
- Managing your energy can also help with fatigue.

Healing with Exercise

Exercise, individualized to fit the cancer survivor's circumstances, is not only safe but also beneficial, according to the American College of Sports Medicine (2009). In fact, it can be used as a "medicine" to help you heal. Let's explore what this can mean for you as a cancer survivor, but first let's think about these questions:

- What is your idea of exercise?

- What images do you have when you think of exercise?

- How do you feel when you think of exercising?

Many of us think of athletes sweating and working their bodies to the point of pain when thinking of exercise. Or we think of young people at the gym exercising at a high level of ability and agility. And many of you recovering from cancer may wonder, how can I exercise safely after undergoing treatment and perhaps a prolonged period of diminished activity? Healing with exercise? How can that possibly be?

Perhaps you are still feeling the effects of fatigue and pain from cancer treatment. This can be an exceptionally hard time to believe that exercise is healing. But it is, and the purpose of this session is to discuss the benefits of exercise, types of exercise, how to choose an exercise program, and what to be mindful of when exercising as you regain your strength and health.

Benefits of Exercise

The many benefits of exercise for the general population are well documented, and most of us have heard of them through the media or from our physicians. The great benefit of exercise for prevention of **heart disease** is widely known. Regular exercise can decrease high blood pressure, improve cholesterol levels, lower resting heart rate, and decrease the risk of developing diabetes—all of which decrease your risk of developing or dying from cardiovascular disease.

In addition to these wonderful improvements, regular exercise also decreases the effects of **osteoporosis**, provides greater ease of movement by improving the flexibility of muscles, tendons, and ligaments thereby helping with the symptoms of **arthritis**. Exercise helps with **weight control,** which is a contributing factor in the development of many health problems. Exercise improves **mental well-being** by decreasing the symptoms of depression and anxiety, improving sleep and energy levels. Exercise enhances the **immune system**, assisting your body in warding off illness.

The benefits of exercise can extend beyond the average individual to people who are undergoing treatment for cancer. In fact, the American College of Sports Medicine (ACSM) recommends cancer survivors avoid inactivity (Wolin, Schwartz, Matthews, Courneya, & Schmitz, 2012).

Physical exercise has been shown to improve quality of life during and after treatment for cancer survivors (Valenti, et al., 2008). Exercise is strongly related to the primary prevention of cancer (National Cancer Institute, 2009), and current research is very promising about its role in cancer remission (Ehrman, 2010; Kuiper et al., 2012), while too much leisure time sitting may even contribute to cancer risk (Medscape, July 14, 2015).

Surgery, chemotherapy, and radiation can have serious side effects that impact the quality of life for individuals who have gone through cancer treatment. Some of these side effects are decreased range of motion (ROM)) and strength, decreased immune response because of low white blood cell counts, and anemia—a decrease in red blood cells that can lead to feeling weak and tired, depression, stress, and fatigue.

We know that the physiological benefits of exercise can greatly reduce the negative side effects that can result from cancer treatment. Exercise can improve red blood cell production, increase strength, ROM and endurance, and improve cellular immune function and metabolic function. All of these benefits result in improved quality of life and greatly reduce the symptoms of fatigue.

Exercising at high intensity levels has been shown to decrease immune function, while exercising at safe and appropriate (moderate) levels can enhance the immune system's function (Livestrong.com, August 2013). This makes it very important to exercise at moderate levels of intensity while undergoing and recovering from cancer treatments. Studies done on women with breast cancer have shown that women who exercise moderately 3 to 5 hours per week decrease their recurrence rate anywhere from 30 to 50%, and reduce their risk of death from breast cancer (Galvao and Newton, 2005; Holmes, Chen, Feskanich, Kroenke & Colditz, 2005). Studies also show that survivors of many cancers who engage in regular moderate physical activity may reduce their risk of death by up to 61% (Jeon, et al., 2013) (Kenfield, Stampfer, Giovannucci, & Chan, 2011) (Lee, Wolin, Freeman, Sattelmair, & Sesso, 2014) (Meyerhardt, et al., 2006).

Do you know of any other factor that improves your survival rate by this much? And it doesn't involve drugs or the multiple side effects that go along with them.

Which Exercise Program Is Right for YOU?

Now that you have some motivation to exercise, let's take a look at choosing an exercise program that is healing for you. When investigating which exercise program is the best exercise, the truth is, "Any exercise that you will do."

The most important factor in choosing an exercise program is choosing one that you like, and one that likes you. By this we mean activity that provides only positive benefits. As you examine which exercise program is the right one for you, take into account any health considerations that you have. Following are examples of circumstances and considerations that help you choose exercise that's right for you:

Cancer: The effects of chemotherapy and radiation treatments can affect your body for long after treatments have ended. Some chemotherapies have a cardiotoxic effect. In other words, they can interfere with heart function. So as you initiate an exercise program, it is prudent to monitor your heart rate and stay within recommended ranges. The *best* way to begin is to start out *easy* and pay close attention to how you feel during exercise; build up your endurance/intensity gradually over time. If you have been told that your heart function has decreased because of cancer treatment, you should consult your doctor for safe guidelines to follow for exercise. If you are having symptoms such as chest pain, chest "heaviness" or tightness, or shortness of breath, you are advised to stop exercising and seek medical help immediately.

It may be prudent to see an exercise specialist or physical therapist for an exercise prescription to follow. If you begin an exercise program and cannot seem to progress in strength and endurance, please be sure to talk with your doctor. Check with your doctors to see if they can recommend a cancer exercise specialist. Cancer exercise specialists have advanced education and training to help cancer survivors exercise safely. The personal trainer at your gym may not have that kind of education.

Some known cardiotoxic (harmful to your heart) drugs include Herceptin, Taxol, Taxotere, and Adriamycin. Not every person treated with these drugs experiences heart problems, but if you have had these drugs, be aware that you may be more vulnerable to heart problems even many years after your treatment has ended, so report any physical symptoms to your doctor. Likewise, chest radiation can cause heart problems.

Because of the potential effects of high-intensity exercise on your immune system, remember to exercise at more moderate intensity. When your blood counts are down, it may be best to avoid water exercise as you may encounter more bacteria and viruses in this environment.

Remember: Exercise should cause you no harm. Always drink plenty of water before, during, and after exercise. STOP exercise if you experience any tightness or pain in your chest, dizziness, or shortness of breath. Don't exercise if you are running a fever.

Deep breathing and flexibility/stretching exercises can provide a good low-intensity exercise session on days you are having chemotherapy, or on any day when you feel you have less energy.

In choosing an exercise program, you may also want to consider other chronic conditions you may have, such as these:

Arthritis: People with arthritis need to be mindful of the stress placed on their joints when they exercise. Nonimpact or low-impact exercising is best. Biking, swimming, yoga, and Pilates provide good results with little to no impact on joints. If back problems are an issue, you can use a recumbent bike or elliptical trainer to improve body mechanics, lessening the stress to the spine. Because arthritis leads to stiff and sore joints, a good stretching routine is highly recommended and will provide improvement of this condition.

Osteoporosis/Osteopenia: With this condition, your bone density is lessened and the risk for fractures (broken bones) increases. The incidence of osteoporosis/osteopenia is greater among people who have had chemotherapy. Studies have shown that weight-bearing activities improve osteoporosis/osteopenia. For this reason, walking or running would be better exercise options. Swimming and biking do not offer the weight-bearing benefits to improve this condition. Weight (strength/resistance) training is also beneficial as this adds demands on the bone structure thus improving bone density.

Diabetes: All exercise programs will affect blood sugar levels, so close monitoring is essential as you begin an exercise program.

Heart Disease: If you have risk factors for cardiac disease or have been diagnosed with heart problems, monitoring heart rate and blood pressure with your exercise program is recommended. Remember, if you do not have risk factors for cardiac disease but have received a chemotherapy drug with possible cardiotoxic side effects, it will be more important for you to monitor heart function (heart rate and blood pressure) while exercising during and after chemotherapy. Please remember that late effects from cardiotoxic chemotherapies can arise many years after the treatment is finished.

Other factors to consider when choosing an exercise program include finding the best time of day to exercise. There tends to be a time of day that exercise works best or feels best for each individual. Pay attention to that time of day and exercise at this time as often as possible.

As Marsha Doble says, "I have to exercise in the morning before my brain figures out what I'm doing." Many of us have to actually schedule in our exercise time. This works best. According to Bill Phillips, "Failure to plan is planning to fail." Once you have discovered the best time of day to exercise, schedule it in. It will fast become a part of your routine and something you will really look forward to.

Some might be saying. "Me? Look forward to exercise? Fat chance." So the last tip in choosing and beginning an exercise program is **make it FUN!**

- Find a partner and enjoy each other's company. Your dog makes an excellent walking companion too.

- Listen to music or watch TV while you exercise; take in that favorite program while you improve your health.

- Make exercising interesting; walk around the zoo or museum.

- Dance is an excellent form of exercise. From salsa to swing dance to square dance, it is a wonderful form of aerobic activity and can provide a great social outing as well.

- Diversify. If you become easily bored with the same exercise routine, diversify. Shake it up. One day swim, the next dance, the next a long walk in the woods, and end a long hard week with a nice relaxing class of yoga.

All exercise is good exercise, especially when you enjoy it. Most important, know that any activity that increases your heart rate is exercise. For most people, walking is an enjoyable and relaxing way to exercise. Exercise does not have to be overly strenuous, and remember it is actually less healthy for you if it is "too much." Sometimes people do not start to exercise because they feel it must be strenuous to be of benefit. Nothing could be further from the truth.

According to the American Heart Association (2015), one way to figure out your target heart rate for exercise is to first of all know your "maximal heart rate" and calculate from there.

For someone undergoing treatment for cancer or still feeling the effects of cancer treatment, exercising at 50% of your maximum heart rate is recommended. A chart showing target heart rates calculated at 50% heart rate maximum appears in the introduction to this book. For someone who has recovered from treatment, exercising at 60 to 70% of maximum heart rate is recommended once they are strong enough.

When beginning with any exercise program, it is prudent to start slow and build up as endurance and strength allows. Keep the intensity level moderate. It should feel good both during and after exercise. If you pay attention to your body's response to exercise both during and afterward, you should be able to find the balance of performing enough activity to feel improvement without causing increased fatigue or muscle soreness. The Borg CR10 scale is another way to monitor how hard you are working at exercise (a copy of the scale is included in the introduction of this workbook).

If you are just beginning exercise after treatment, you may want to start at a "1" or a "2." Very gradually over time, let your strength and endurance grow. Eventually you may feel like increasing the intensity or length of your exercise session (or both) to a "3" and maybe even a "4." The best results come from a moderate intensity workout that you enjoy.

Types of Exercise

"No pain, no gain" is perhaps a motto for professional athletes who need extraordinary conditioning to perform, but for everyone else, it is wiser to build up exercise strength and endurance at a pace that allows your body to adapt without pain.

The American College of Sports Medicine Guidelines (2012) suggest that cancer patients return to normal daily activities (observing all safety considerations and precautions as appropriate) as soon as possible following surgery and continue these activities to the best of their ability during and after treatment.

Set small goals at first and build upon successes! As you feel able, remember to include aerobic exercise: any activity that increases your heart rate and is sustained for a length of time (30 minutes is most often recommended to insure improvement in cardiovascular status) is called aerobic exercise. The American College of Sports Medicine recommends that cancer survivors build up to at least 150 minutes/week of moderate intensity aerobic activity (Wolin, Schwartz, Matthews, Courneya, & Schmitz, 2012). That's a 30-minute walk (or some other moderate mode of activity) almost every day!

Common forms of aerobic exercise

- Walking

- Biking

- Running

- Aerobic dance

- Swimming

- Cross-country skiing

- Stair climbing

- Skating

Another type of exercise is resistance training. Resistance training (also called strength training or weight training) is designed to improve muscular strength and endurance. It can provide an aerobic benefit if done in a manner that sustains your heart rate at a moderate working level, but is designed to increase muscular mass, thereby increasing strength.

Resistance training can improve weaknesses that have developed from surgery and treatment of cancer. Often people are left with weakness and muscle imbalances from surgery and cancer treatment. General weakness can occur while undergoing chemotherapy and radiation therapy. Resistance (strength) training can be an excellent way to correct these imbalances and improve overall strength and endurance. ACSM recommends resistance training activities for all major muscle groups at least twice per week. In addition, flexibility exercises that stretch major muscle groups and tendons should be performed on days that you participate in aerobic and/or resistance exercise. (Wolin, Schwartz, Matthews, Courneya, & Schmitz, 2012).

Studies are showing too that resistance training is an important aspect in combating cancer-related fatigue. It can also boost memory in a single session, according to a study by Weinberg et al. (2014).

Other types of exercise that incorporate mind-body awareness are yoga, Pilates, Tai Chi, and the Alexander technique. Karate and judo provide exercise while building self-defense skills. A recent study (Mustian et al., 2013) suggests that yoga can improve sleep quality and reduce the need for sleep medication.

Movement is good for minds and bodies. It can help you feel better and help you to gain strength and health. There are many ways to exercise, and all can be beneficial exercise if you are enjoying it and staying within the guidelines suggested for each exercise program.

Contraindications to Exercise

There are some situations in which cancer survivors should not exercise without first consulting their health care provider or a cancer exercise fitness professional. These situations include extreme fatigue or anemia, initial wound-healing following surgery, cardiopulmonary disease, noticeable changes in swelling, and ostomies.

Lymphedema and Exercise

Lymphedema is a condition that results in swelling of body parts because of damage to or removal of lymph nodes. Cancer survivors may develop lymphedema at any time after lymph nodes are removed or damaged. Exercise can have a positive effect on lymphedema, but certain precautions are very important to follow. Please read the Lymphedema section in the Special Topics area at the back of the book.

The Journey to Feeling Good Again—How to Manage Fatigue

Studies have shown that fatigue is experienced by 72 to 95% of people undergoing cancer treatment. This fatigue is most likely caused by a number of physiological and psychological changes that occur as a result of the diagnosis and treatment of cancer. Cancer-related fatigue has been known to continue for patients long after the end of treatment, sometimes for many years.

Nearly every cancer survivor expresses a similar sentiment: "No one prepared me for the battle that comes after the battle with cancer." While our medical system does an excellent job at treating cancer, patients are often left to navigate the journey from surviving cancer to establishing a meaningful and fulfilling "new normal" way of life, on their own. A key to successfully making the transition to feeling good again is learning how to negotiate the ebb and flow of resiliency and energy resources that come with the recovery process. In addition, harmony with this balance is one of the most valuable spiritual and behavioral gifts that the survival process can offer.

Typically, when you are experiencing fatigue, it is a natural response to rest and to limit your activities. This behavior is appropriate and healing. However, when fatigue is not resolved with rest, **resting too much can lead to decreased activity tolerance**, reduced fitness, and even disability. In addition, resting too much and avoiding safe activity may be more likely to increase fatigue than to make it better.

On the other hand, overworking or pushing through fatigue when energy is low can deplete vital resources that could otherwise be used by the body to maximize recovery. The key is to engage in a balance of the right amount of activity and rest to maximize energy and function without increasing overall fatigue.

So how do you know how much activity is too much activity, and how much activity is not enough? Fortunately there are some tools and guidelines that can be helpful.

The Energy Budget

There is a common analogy among physical therapists, mental health therapists, and patients dealing with fatigue that is very fitting. It is the idea of an energy budget. Most people are familiar with how to account for money or resources when working within a limited budget. Skills for maintaining a balanced budget include planning ahead, prioritizing expenses, anticipating expenses and income, pacing expenditures to match cash flow, allowing for charity, and saving or investing wisely for the future. People who do these things with success enjoy a reasonable standard of living, indulge in modest recreational and material pleasures, provide some support to a church or charity, and save money for the future. If we are doing these things on even the smallest scale, it is a sign of financial balance and security.

The analogy holds true for the way we spend the energy that animates the mind, body, and spirit. In the body, as in the economy, managing the budget becomes particularly important, when resources are scarce or inconsistently available.

Basics of the Budget

- **Pay yourself first.** Just like in investing, this strategy pays benefits in the long run. If you are trying to get an activity into your schedule or trying to progress an exercise program, try doing it first thing in the morning, or when you typically have the most energy. This ensures that you have the energy you need to get the task done and done consistently. Consistency of deposit leads to a steady return on investment.

- **Avoid the overdraft penalty.** When we work so hard that we "crash" later, we create an energy budget crisis. If we go into overdraft, we end up having to pay the energy back with interest. This is not the best use of energy resources. It is better to try to avoid the penalty.

- **Stop overspending.** If there are activities that leave you feeling as if you have been hit by a truck every time without fail, it might be a good idea to try to change, delegate, or moderate that task for the time being.

- **Save for a rainy day.** Plan for the unexpected. This means not letting the tank go all the way to empty, and looking for opportunities to fill your resiliency stores with preplanned coping strategies, healthy pleasures, spiritual meaning, and loving connections. Get the best sleep that you can.

Love Is Rewarding

Getting out of energy debt starts by being very gentle but firm with yourself and by being your own most loving supporter. This is not just sap. Negativity is very energy-expensive. Positive, loving sensations are life-sustaining. They synergize beneficial neurotransmitters (brain chemicals) and stimulate the parasympathetic nervous system. The parasympathetic nervous system is the part of the autonomic nervous system that is responsible for healing and restoration.

Generating habits of positive, encouraging self-talk and positive emotional stimulation can lay the foundation for a good energy budget. This is especially important when you discover that your resiliency is not what it once was. It is important to generate a sense of loving wonder and awe at what is being created in yourself and through you during the process of healing. Some people maintain journals of their progress—lists of things that inspire gratitude or collections of inspirational quotes. No matter what technique is used or what other methods are applied, the bottom line is the same: the most efficient and enjoyable path between suffering and really living is love.

Pacing

Imagine that you woke up this morning and your income was cut in half. What expenses would you cut? Most people cut their entertainment. But with a little ingenuity, you might have even more fun doing things that cost nothing than doing more pricey alternatives.

The same is true of a reduced energy budget. What creative ways could get your needs met and still stay within your budget? Working within a reduced energy budget means that you have less energy to spend than you used to have. You may have less energy than those around you. With practice you will get more efficient with the energy you have.

The first sensation we often feel is the need to grieve the loss of the energy that is gone. This is an ongoing process that requires some energy in itself. It is important to set aside time for this process and to put gentle limits on the impact that grief has on recovery. If grief is taking too much of the energy budget, a counselor may be able to help with the process.

Then you must accept your energy budget as it is: limited. You don't have to like it. You just have to accept it. With that done, you can get down to the business of looking the situation straight in the eyes. This process reads a lot like a General Business course and includes the following:

- **Prioritize life activities**, taking into account what you want and what you need to do. Do this on a daily, weekly, and monthly basis. Focusing on just the top priorities for a time can provide some relief from a sense of being overwhelmed by the tasks of living.

- **Track your fatigue.** Rate and record your fatigue level daily on a scale of 1 to 10, with 0 being "no fatigue" and 10 being "fatigue so great that you feel you need to be bed-bound and need medical attention." Record the range of your fatigue by dividing the 24 hours of a day into naturally occurring blocks of time for recording purposes, such as morning and night. For example, "This morning my fatigue ranged from 2 to 4, and this evening it ranged from 4 to 5 out of 10," meaning that during the daylight hours fatigue ranged from 2 to 4, and after the sun went down it was 4 to 5. Using and recording these numbers on a daily basis helps you track your progress and know when you can do more, as would be the case with consistently low ratings. Steadily escalating fatigue numbers are a good indicator that whatever you are doing is too much. You need to balance activity with rest or consider pacing back. Pushing through fatigue levels that remain persistently above 6 out of 10 may result in exhaustion and a reduced capacity to recover.

- **Break up tasks into smaller units of shorter duration.** For example, wash and core two apples for a baked apple dish for dinner, then put them in the refrigerator and rest while you sit and read the mail for 15 minutes. The relative rest of sitting and reading the mail reduces the fatigue of the meal preparation while still using time productively. This requires, however, that you plan to start the meal preparation considerably sooner. Another example of breaking tasks up might be to trim one hedge per day, instead of doing all of the hedges in one day. It's helpful to achieve a sense of celebration of each small step of the task over a longer period of time. Checklists with the task broken into the smaller component parts are a good way to facilitate a sense of accomplishment and celebration with small tasks.

- **Make a plan.** Lists are very helpful. Organize life activities. Take note of activities that are or have been well tolerated or have caused increases in fatigue in the past. Plan these activities according to available resources.

- **Delegate!** Asking for help is appropriate if it allows you to maximize your activity level. For example, in some cases it is appropriate to ask someone to help with mowing the yard, which may be too energy expensive, so that you can go take a walk—an activity that is more appropriate to your fitness level and energy budget. Let your helpers know you have a plan to recover your ability to be more independent.

Move

Life is dynamic. Our bodies, minds, and spirits were designed to move and, through movement, connect. During illness, we become more static and more isolated. Movement, therefore, is the antithesis of disease. This session on exercise contains many good ideas for how to reintegrate exercise for fitness.

No matter how much or how little you do, try moving with intention and with an internal focus daily. Do not worry about what you look like or if you are doing it "perfectly." Instead, feel deeply your connection with the ground and sense the air around you on your skin. Or perform the simplest movements with profound gratitude and grace.

As your fitness and exercise tolerance improves, gradually "pace up" your activities, slowly increasing the duration, intensity, frequency, and range of your activities. This should be done very gradually. It's recommended that only one of the three variables (duration, intensity, and frequency) be increased per day or at a time.

For example, if the maximum that you can do is to sit up for a few minutes, then make sure to use that ability to sit. Make an effort to avoid lying in bed all the time, or perform one gentle exercise in bed each hour.

If the maximum that you can tolerate is to go on short walks, make a point of taking a 2-minute to 5-minute walk once or twice per day as tolerated. You may be able to add 1 minute to the duration of your walking at a time, gradually day by day. If you cannot move physically at that moment, visualize yourself moving. The goal is to increase the activity by a small amount while avoiding the "crash" that can come after a period of "overactivity." The journey to our best life starts and continues with small but determined steps.

Rhythm of Life

All of us tend to match the rhythm of the pulse of life around us. Nature uses rhythms to help manage energy efficiently. Like a finger humming a vibrato on the rim of a crystal glass, synchronized rhythms reinforce each other.

When we are in synchrony with the rhythms of life, we resonate with the vitality around us. Like the finger on the crystal glass, we find a groove that seems to flow naturally and generate a hum from the friction between our existence and the world around us. Rhythms that are out of sync, however, distort each other or cancel each other out. Often when we are sick or traumatized, we get pulled out of sync with the normal rhythms of our lives. Our own natural and creative rhythms are disrupted by treatment, pain, fatigue, anxiety, and even the efforts of others to help.

We often hear caregivers make the recommendation to patients: "Get back to your routines and you will feel better." While it might not be feasible to do all of the things in the old routine that you used to do, what they are really suggesting is to try to reconnect with restorative rhythms of life. This includes cultivating healthy routines such as attempting to go to bed and get up at a similar time each day, and maintaining some "anchor" practices mentioned earlier, such as exercise, meditation, connections with friends or family, and intimacy, on a weekly or semiweekly basis, as the energy budget allows. Novel or forced behavior patterns are relatively energy expensive.

Rhythms and routines can be important energy-saving techniques. They allow the mind and body to develop habits as a way of accomplishing tasks so that the full measure of focus and energy is not required. If you allow this knowledge to work to your advantage, the result can be similar to the finger on the crystal glass: the lightest touch in steady regularity creates a most pleasing "hum."

Sensitive Detachment

The story is told that when the Buddha sat under the bodhi tree, he experienced an awakening that allowed him to eradicate delusion and perceive existence with simultaneous detachment, deep compassion, and sensitivity. This is revolutionary for a number of reasons, but the important point for us to grasp is that being able to experience opposing perspectives at the same time allows for expansion of consciousness.

When dealing with your own fatigue, you need to acquire skill for listening to fatigue with sensitive detachment. On one hand, you need to become more aware of messages your body is sending you so that you can learn to heed the messages it gives you sooner. You need to be sensitive enough to know when to "pace down," rest, or change an activity before fatigue escalates beyond management, or to the point where you have to pay a penalty. By doing this you save energy.

On the other hand you cannot be so paralyzed by fatigue, or fear of fatigue that you remain inactive. The longer you remain inactive, the less activity you will be able to tolerate. You need to be detached enough to move your body toward progress even though you are tired. You need to detach yourself from the unproductive emotional baggage of fear, guilt, shame, and past failures or success. You need to detach yourself from the fatigue itself. Sometimes it is necessary to detach from results entirely to keep moving forward. Sensitive detachment maximizes your pacing and exercise strategies, so that you can be the best that you can be.

All of these tools—accentuating self-love, pacing, moving with intention, restoring the rhythm of life, and cultivating sensitive detachment—are critical to balancing the energy budget and managing fatigue. But they are also keys to successful living and positive aging. Each is a precious gift and a continuing lesson.

Questions for discussion or journaling

1. What feeling or feelings did you have after reading or hearing the information on exercise? For example, some feel hopeful that they can do more to improve their health; some feel angry that they are told to work harder when they are exhausted; some feel guilty or ashamed that they could do a little exercise but choose not to. What do you feel?

2. How do your feelings affect your thoughts about this chapter? For example, do you just get discouraged or feel hopeful? How do your feelings affect your behavior? Can you do something even if you don't feel like it or do your feelings rule your behavior? Do you want to change that? How might you encourage or even bribe yourself to do something that you don't feel like?

3. When you think about increasing your activity, what small improvement would be possible now?

4. Do you think exercise will be part of the "best life" you are creating? Is this something you want to start now or do you think something else will take priority first?

5. Remember that there are many ways to heal and improvement in any area counts—mind, body, spirit, relationships, work, fun, humor, and others. Which area of your life would you most like to upgrade now? Which area of your life would be the easiest to work on now?

6. Can you identify with the symptoms of cancer fatigue (for example, resting too much then overworking)? Give examples of this in your recovery.

7. What activities in your life are the most energy expensive?

8. Which energy expensive activities can you cut, reduce, delegate, modify, or decrease in frequency?

9.	What activities in your life are the most energy-giving or energy-boosting?

10.	Which energy-boosting activities can you enhance, add, or increase in frequency?

11.	Create an energy budget. Prioritize key life activities on a table. Rate the energy/fatigue levels of each activity from 0 to 10. Use the resulting information to inform how you spend your energy so that you can make the most of your energy resources.

12.	Given what you have learned, what are some of the creative ways you can get your needs met and still maintain a positive balance of energy?

Power Tool: Make Something

When it takes all the energy you have just to get through the day, and you don't have anything left to call on for the things that make life exciting and fun, life can get pretty boring or worse: painful. It's hard to imagine ever "getting your life back"—especially those little things that we used to take for granted. Good intentions start to fade.

It's easy to give up. When you need to get your motivation recharged, try one of these "in the moment" activities. Sometimes doing *SOMETHING* is all it takes to help you feel better.

1. Write a short description of how you would like to be as you deal with this health problem.

2. Pick one or more of the following to help you keep on track:

    a. Find a prayer, poem, or quotation that states your intention. Write it or type it and put it in several places where you'll see it daily (for example, in your wallet or purse, taped to your mirror or your refrigerator).

    b. Find one or more songs that affirm your intention. Buy, rent, or borrow tapes or CDs of the songs. Record them onto a tape or iPod of inspiring music that you can listen to when your intention needs reinforcement. (This can be a great job for friends who want to do something for you.)

    c. Locate movies, short stories, novels or biographies that reinforce your intention. Watch inspiring videos instead of violent TV shows. Read or listen to audio books.

    d. Look through magazines, collections of art, pictures on the Internet, or family photo albums and find photos or artwork that you find inspiring. Make copies and put them in places where you can see them readily.

e. Think of the people in your lifetime that you have admired, both personal acquaintances and famous people. Make a scrapbook of them including a picture and a short description of the quality you so admire in them. Look through your scrapbook for inspiration when you feel low. If you like, you could write paragraphs or short stories about these people and paste them into the book. This book also could become a gift to a favorite child, a dear friend, or a relative.

3. Have a serious conversation with someone you trust. Tell them what you are trying to be. Ask them to watch you and tell you about times when they see you following your intention.

4. Keep a journal. Make an intention at the beginning, writing down what your goal is. Decorate this page in any way that you like, maybe with words, quotations, pictures, or colors that emphasize your intention. Every day or as often as possible, write down what you did that day to follow your intention. Emphasizing your success encourages more success.

5. Buy or make CDs or playlists of music that reinforce the values and behaviors that align with your intention. Play your intentional music in your car, while you rest or do housework, or work on a hobby. Hypnotherapists know that anything you repeat over and over while in a relaxed state begins to take root. Your thinking gradually changes in a painless, nearly effortless way. Music can be a wonderful way to reprogram negative thoughts, establish positive ones, and reinforce your best intentions.

Power Tool: How to Write Your Own Musical Affirmation

by Karen Drucker

There are so many scientific studies that show how writing or saying your affirmations can help manifest those desires. What about singing them? What about taking that great mantra or affirmation that you have been saying daily and adding a simple melody to it?

One of the reasons that I feel that singing your affirmations can be a powerful tool is because music has this wonderful ability to "sneak" past that chattering mind and go straight to the heart. The simpler you can make your affirmation with the words and the melody, the more the mind relaxes and pretty soon you can be singing that affirmation and feeling it change your whole body.

I learned this when my mother told me that her affirmation while she was dealing with cancer was: "I am healed whole and healthy." I turned that little affirmation into a chant for her that said:

> *I am healed whole and healthy.*
> *I relax and visualize.*
> *I am healed whole and healthy.*
> *I am well, all is well …*

She would either sing it herself or listen to the CD I made for her while she would get her chemo infusions. She told me she would sing her chant and visualize the chemicals going into her and healing those cancer cells.

So how do you write your own chant?

First we need to tell that inner critic who is instantly saying "I can't sing" or "I'm not a songwriter!" to leave the room for just a few minutes so I can talk to you. Tell your inner critics (mine is named Zelda) that there is a latte with extra whipped cream on top waiting for them at the Starbucks down the street, and they can come back when you are done.

This can be an amazingly easy process, and I ask you just to have fun with me for a few minutes.

So let's start with a new affirmation. I want you to write 5 short affirmative phrases starting with either "I am" or "I can" or "I feel."

For example: I am beautiful. I feel well. I am worthy. I am happy. I feel great. I can do it.

The only rules you need to follow are these:

- Keep it simple

- Make it true for you (look into your heart and see if what you wrote is really how you feel).

- Stay in the present and the now (when you say I will or I want, it puts the desire in the future. The goal here is to feel like it's happening right now. Write it from an "Act As If" perspective).

- Don't worry about rhyming. Just say whatever is true for you.

The next step:

Now take a simple song like "Row Row Row Your Boat" and put your words with that melody. Stumble around a bit and find the right words to go with it. Again don't worry about rhyming or being perfect, just try to fit those simple phrases with the melody.

See how easy that was?

Another idea could be to do this as a daily practice of checking in with how you feel right now. Just acknowledging how you feel can help to be present in the moment.

Again, using our "Row" song, sing this one with me:

I feel wonderful
and I'm kind of tired
I am happy that I have time off
now it's time to eat ice cream!

You could try this same idea with simple songs like:

- "Edelweiss" from The Sound of Music

- "This Land Is Your Land"

- "Are You Sleeping, Brother John"

- "Lullaby and Goodnight"

You get the idea. You can also take the chorus of one of your favorite songs and just write words to it that apply to you. The key is to ask yourself a question and let the words just flow.

Another example: Question: What do I really want to do today? To the tune of "This Land Is Your Land":

I'm going to take a bath
Then I will take a nap
I'll let someone else do all the dishes
Then I will call a friend
and we will laugh and sing
I am happy to be alive!

The key here is to just let it flow. Let whatever you want to say out of you.

Just get it down on paper, no need to judge, edit, rhyme or be perfect. Just let your creativity come. Again the simpler you can make it (you can even just say one line over and over!), the more the words and melody can stay with you throughout the day or whenever you need it. I find walking and singing my affirmation makes me feel so empowered.

I'll leave you with one more example: To the tune of "Edelweiss"

I am grateful, I am blessed
I am healthy and happy
I am grateful I am blessed
I am living my life in joy!

So live your life in joy and enjoy this process of affirming what you want through music, and keep singing your song!

SESSION 9
Rebuilding My Core

Sister Mary Hogan, OSM, MA

Key Points
- We are all hard wired with an "inner core" that can provide us with great wisdom, but we need quiet, private time to access it.
- Paying attention to your feelings can be a way to access that inner wisdom.
- The inner wisdom can also be tapped by tuning in to your breathing, using active imagination, spending time in nature, and taking time to savor poetry, literature, music, and art.
- Living mindfully (with your attention focused in the present) clears your thoughts to enjoy and appreciate life.
- Even your pain can help you to learn, grow, and live fully.

---

*Tell me, what is it you plan to do
with your one wild, precious life?*
Mary Oliver

The Naskapi Indians live in the forests of the Labrador Peninsula. These simple people are hunters who, because of the rough terrain and brutal weather, live in family units instead of tribes. They are isolated from other Indian families. Because of the reality of no communication, they have no tribal customs and are untouched by culture. They have neither religious teachers nor cultural influences.

In spite of this, they do have a basic view of life. They know within themselves an "inner companion," one whom they call "Mista'peo," my friend, or the "Great Man" within. They understand this indwelling friend as immortal. According to Marie-Louise von Franz, their situation calls them to a life of solitude. They meet their inner friend in the quiet of their lives. No decisions are made without consultation with the

195

"Great Man" within. Dreams, they believe, are given by this spirit, and the Naskapi are careful to follow the instructions of the dreams. The Naskapis know from their own experience that they hold an inner spirit.

The psychologist Robert Moore says we are hardwired with an inner core; it is part of the DNA of every human being. So why is the inner core not as apparent and its gifts not as useful to us as it is to the Naskapi Indians?

There are many reasons for this situation. Although we are hardwired to live 90% of life from the inside, we are confronted constantly with externals as if they were the essence of life. The very existence of intelligence and spirit orients us to something bigger than ourselves. There is more to us than the 10 % external glitter this world offers. The busyness of life may keep us from realizing this truth. Modern life provides little time for quiet and reflection necessary to access the inner core.

Illness, too, can dull the awareness of the existence of the inner core. Dealing with cancer requires lots of energy. Dr. Charles Shields, in his book *Spiritual Survival Guide: How to Find God When You're Sick*, gives us a good picture of what happened to him with the diagnosis of cancer. He says:

> *My first response was immobilizing shock. I could not believe the diagnosis could possibly be true. But multiple confirmations quickly transformed the denial into anger, and I was incredibly angry, with nowhere to focus the fury. I could not be mad at the members of my family; it was not their fault I had cancer. I could not be mad at the people I worked with—it was not their fault, either. So at times I focused on myself: what did I do to bring this on?*
>
> *What should I have done to recognize, to waylay this disease? And I focused on God: Why would God lead me to a doctor only to deliver what felt like a death sentence? I had been betrayed by my own body, betrayed by a personal physician who should have looked for the tumor earlier ... betrayed by God.*

Sound familiar? Often people are blind-sided at the diagnosis of cancer. Initially they feel unable to make the response they wish. The resources of the inner core are limping.

A strong inner core can help an individual not only cope with cancer but also to thrive in spite of the health crisis. But energy is needed to do the work. That is why the *A Time to Heal* program delays this presentation until you have replenished some energy. We will explore the many inner resources you have to nurture your inner spirit. You will probably like some suggestions better than others. That's good! Choose what moves your heart and what gives you life.

Feelings

Feelings are part of our body wisdom. More than 50% of human knowledge is learned from the body. The body is unique in what we call *felt knowing. We know* more through the body than we do from the mind. Knowing through feelings is different from thinking, analyzing, or reasoning. Dr. Eugene Gendlin, a psychologist, discovered that patients who could name and locate a feeling in their body were more likely to recover than those who could not. He worked with his clients to help them honor their feelings and not to disregard them. Each feeling, he said, has a story to tell.

Authors have compared feelings to a phone ringing: it rings because there is a message at the other end of the line. Feelings, too, carry a message. But we must be aware of the feeling before we can listen to its message. Holding the feelings of anger, hurt, despair, and fear in a loving way makes it possible to relate to them, to hear their message. This skill can be learned through practice. Healing can be the outcome. The theologian Johannes Metz in *Poverty of Spirit* says:

> *Something profound happens in your heart when you turn with kindness toward all the circumstances of pain previously repressed. A softening, an opening ...*

197

In the hurly burly of everyday life it is easy to ignore the body and not recognize its part in our healing of mind, body and spirit. Cancer recuperation may be a good time to reconnect with the body and come to know it as your best friend. The body knows what it needs at a given moment.

Probably the most important function of the body is breathing. But we all do that exercise poorly. So let's take a look at how breathing helps us get in touch with the inner core.

Breathing

Since beginning this program we have practiced several methods that involve breathing. The medical field tells us that relaxation helps the healing process. One of the great results of breathing properly is relaxation. Joseph Nassal, author of *Conspiracy of Compassion*, tells how his mother would cover his scratches with "some red liquid" and then breathed on the attendant part. As a child he was convinced that his mother's breath is what made him better, not the red liquid. As an adult he came to see that breathing is not only therapeutic but also a healing spiritual practice.

The Buddhist meditation teacher, Lama Surya Das, teaches a way to use breath to comfort our intense feelings. He suggests, first, to breathe in and say to yourself *I feel_____*(anger, fear, rage, etc.). Next, breathe out and say to yourself *I send compassion to my_____* (anger, fear, rage, etc.). The breath bathes wounded feelings in comfort and calms us over time.

In the second chapter of the Book of Genesis the author tells us. "Then the Lord formed man from the dust of the ground, and breathed into his nostrils the breath of life." For those influenced by the Christian tradition the Gospel of John tells us that when Jesus visited his apostles after the Resurrection "… he breathed on them and said to them, 'Receive the Holy Spirit.'" (Jn 20:22)

If you want to make music with a flute, you blow your breath into it. Breath gives life. With mindfulness, the simple act of breathing can be prayer. The spirit of life resides with us. Breathing integrates mind, body and spirit. Those who have a practice of breathing well are assisting the healing process and are also getting in touch with their inner core.

Active Imagination

Another wonderful inner tool that aids the healing process and touches into your inner core is active imagination. Did you know that your imagination was developed before your intellect? Imagination is the faculty that makes it possible for you to form inner pictures. Images can bring you out of the busyness of the mind into creativity. When you use your senses to see, hear, feel, and taste a scene, you are using your body to pray.

You can use this gift on days you feel the need of support.

- SEE with the eyes of your imagination, a beautiful landscape, or a loved one. Be conscious of how you feel.

- HEAR the voice of someone you love, or your favorite songbird. What is happening inside you is the body-feel of grace.

- SMELL a rose or the sea or … Does something move inside you?

Don't *think* about the scene you are reflecting on. Let your imagination do the work. Close your eyes and see the scene a writer is describing. For example, see the little children, hear their laughter; touch the green grass, feel it and feel the gentle breeze.

If you discover that this form of prayer is helpful to you, you may find comfort in Pastor Charles Shields's book *Spiritual Survival Guide.* Dr. Shields records how he attended to his inner core when he was dealing with cancer. Because of his own experience with cancer, his work strikes an authentic chord.

Those of you familiar with the Bible may remember words that give comfort. In time of sorrow and suffering, for example, it helps to repeat over and over the words of Isaiah 43:4b, "You are precious in my sight and honored, and I love you."

Close your eyes and remember these consoling words. Insert your name: "You are precious in my sight [Donna, or Joe] and honored, and I love you."

We Americans can talk about integration of mind, body, and spirit, but with little realization of what that means. When we repeat these words over and over so that they become a *mantra,* they become part of our body as well as our spirit. Repeating, "You are precious in my sight and honored ..." over and over can provide an amazing comfort and healing.

Nature

Often we lack the awareness to see or to hear the messages in our everyday events. The consciousness of what is going on around us is dulled. Sickness can do that. We miss the gifts right under our noses. Beauty, for example, always touches the inner core. Have you ever reached the top of a hill and discovered a breathtaking view? The awe you experience touches the inner core. Or maybe you like to go to a garden. Do you have flowers, trees in your own yard? That's a place just to be. Nature heals. The smells, the colors, and the beauty all stimulate your inner core and speak of life.

Your enjoyment of nature is not unusual. People from all ages have been renewed by nature. Psalms in the Bible speak of the writer's love and awe of nature. Listen to Psalm 8 and feel what the psalmist felt when he looked up into a starry sky:

> *When I look at your heavens, the*
> *work of your fingers,*
> *the moon and the stars that you*
> *have established;*
> *what are human beings that you*
> *are mindful of them,*
> *mortals that you care for them? V. 3-4*

Mary Oliver, who is noted for her love of nature, wrote about "talking roses" in her poem "When the Roses Speak, I Pay Attention."

200

As long as we are able to
be extravagant we will be
hugely and damply
extravagant. Then we will drop
foil by foil to the ground. This
is our unalterable task, and we do
it joyfully.

And they went on. "Listen, the heart-shackles are
not, as you think,
death, illness, pain,
unrequited hope, not loneliness, but

lassitude, rue, vainglory, fear,
anxiety, selfishness."

Their fragrance all the while rising
from their blind bodies, making me
spin with joy.

Mary Oliver

Every experience adds abundance to our lives if we take the time to become aware of it.

Poetry

Poets are gifted with great imaginations and therefore have a way of reaching inside us.

Meeting truth in our inner being holds the potential of healing the lie that we are of little worth especially now that we have cancer. Mary Oliver's poem "Wild Geese" has a bit of wisdom that touches the heart.

You do not have to be good.

You do not have to walk on your knees

For a hundred miles through the desert, repenting.

You only have to let the soft animal of your body

Love what it loves.

Tell me about despair, yours, and I will

tell you mine.

Meanwhile the world goes on.

Meanwhile the sun and the clear pebbles of the rain

Are moving across the landscapes,

Over the prairies and the deep trees,

The mountains and the rivers.

Meanwhile the wild geese, high in the clean blue air

Are heading home again.

Whoever you are, no matter how lonely, The world

offers itself to your imagination,

Calls to you like the wild geese, harsh and exciting –

Over and over announcing your place

In the family of things.

"You only have to let the soft animal of your body love what it loves." What is it you love? Dr. Lawrence LeShan encourages cancer survivors to do what they love, what they enjoy, because that stimulates the immune system.

Literature

The holy books of the Bible, Muslim's Qur'an, and Hindu's Vedas can open for us the inner richness of the world. The Bible, Old and New Testaments, is full of wonderful stories that challenge the imagination and grace the reader with inspiration and reflection.

Psalms are found in the Hebrew Bible. They are classic expressions of every feeling human beings have had. For example Ps 13 speaks of deep depression:

How long, O Lord?
Will you forget me forever?
How long will you hide your
face from me? V. 1

Or happiness and thanksgiving as in Ps. 138:

I give thanks, O Lord, with
my whole heart;
Before the gods I sing your
praise. V.1

Whatever mood you are in or whatever feelings you are experiencing, you will find a similar expression in the Book of Psalms. They are so human, so in touch with the human experience. You will find comfort there.

Novels can also stimulate your inner core and lead you to reflection. Think of a novel that has challenged you in the past—a story that inspired you to strive for a goal that you thought was impossible to reach. A couple examples of novels that touch many people are *The Shack* by William Young or *The Help* by Kathryn Stockett or *To Kill a Mockingbird* by Harper Lee. Books may be a help to you to strengthen your inner core. Alice Walker, in her immortal book *The Color Purple*, says it all in Shug's comment:

Here's the thing, says Shug. The thing I believe.
God is inside you and inside everybody else. You
come into the world with God. But only them that
search for it inside find it. And sometimes it just
manifest itself even if you not looking, or don't
know what you're looking for. Trouble do it for most
folks, I think. Sorrow, lord.

What novels have you read that moved you and caused you to reflect on some aspect of your life?

203

Music and Art

Music has a special power to tap us into our inner sacred place. Mozart does that for some people; whereas, others prefer livelier music, music that calls for tapping of toes or clapping of hands. There are those who like only instrumental while others prefer songs with words. Our bodies, specifically the bones, remember music even if we forget. Yes, the body remembers. Listening to an Irish Band or a '40s band or a symphony orchestra is a form of therapy for us if we enjoy the music. Listen to what helps you become peaceful, or leads you into quiet.

If you like to sing why not sing out loud? A woman could not sleep one night because of some bad news she had received that day. She said she was in bed trying to solve all the problems when the song, "He's got the whole world in his hand ..." came into her mind. Before she knew it she was singing to herself, "He's got the whole world ..." The song gave her comfort and soon she went to sleep.

Have you ever wanted to play a musical instrument—the piano or the guitar, for example? Now is the time to give it a whirl. You don't have to put on concerts. Playing for your own pleasure is a good thing. Use what *you* like.

Art, too, pulls life out from within us. Do you like to view masterpieces or do you prefer painting a scene you like—even painting by numbers? The joy it gives you strengthens your immune system.

Living Mindfully

Everything, *everything*, speaks to us about the life within— even sports. Psychologists are researching the question of sports and the spiritual life. They tell us that there is a place for sports in the spiritual journey—specifically "the flow." Sportsmen and women say that when they are in "the flow," they have a feeling of wholeness, of total involvement.

Have you ever watched a basketball player preparing to make a free throw? What you see is total, complete presence, wholeness. That is an example of living in the present moment, a spiritual value recommended by all seekers of a deeper life.

The famous Buddhist, Thich Nhat Hanh, refers to this experience as living mindfully. His book *Present Moment, Wonderful Moment* is a compilation of verses to bless the actions of everyday life. People have found great peace and inner strength by using the practice of living in the present moment. When we are in the present moment, all is well. We are in peace, aware that all is well. You may not be interested in sports, but you may learn something about the art of living in the present moment.

One valuable way of living in the moment is to remember the reason God made us according to the Africans: "God made us because God thought we would like it." Like what? Like the beautiful earth, the sky full of stars, relationships with God and other people who so enrich our lives.

When you wake up in the morning a helpful practice is to make the intention to live in the moment that day. Every day is a new creation: the world has not ever seen this day before and will not ever see it again. The new day is a wondrous gift to be lived fully. So the first thing when you wake up in the morning is to express your intention to live fully and mindfully that day.

Wounds

Our wounds, too, can cause us to reflect on our lives. Often they help us discover our personal depth, a depth we did not know we had. The theologian Elizabeth Johnson defines God "as the mystery of absolute love bent on our healing and liberation through the reversals, disappointments, difficulties of life." These reversals and disappointments of life—these wounds—can teach us about our inner strength in ways no other experience can. The poet David Whyte puts it this way in "The Well of Grief":

Those who will not slip beneath
the still surface on the well of grief, turning down
through its black water
to the place we cannot breathe,
will never know the source from which we drink, the
secret water, cold and clear,
nor find in the darkness glimmering
the small round coins,
thrown by those who wished for something else.

A Final Thought

We conclude these reflections with some words of wisdom from Rachel Naomi Remen who has spent her life helping people not just survive but to thrive through the challenges life offers. Live fully and you will grow in consciousness of the rich resources you have in your inner core. Treat yourself with the gift of time to reflect. You are worth it. You will be amazed at how different life will look to you.

As Dr. Remen says in *My Grandfather's Blessing*: "I've spent many years learning how to fix life, only to discover in the end of the day that life is not broken. There is a hidden seed of greater wholeness in everyone and everything. We serve life best when we water it and befriend it; when we listen before we act."

Power Tool: Appreciation

When we are faced with problems, stresses, or disease, our thoughts become dominated by fears. We notice all of the things that go wrong, we focus on all of the unknowns, the "what if's." This is a natural result of stress, but it tends to make things worse by heightening anxiety and leading to depression. One way to stay more balanced is to consciously try to keep things in perspective. The negative thoughts come automatically, but it may take a conscious effort to think of the positives. The goal is to identify something that you appreciate or enjoy every day—even on the bad days.

Here are some ways of doing this that have worked for other people.

- Begin a gratitude journal. On a calendar or in a notebook, write down 3 to 5 things you are grateful for each day. On bad days it may be something very simple, such as seeing a beautiful sunset out your window, the fresh smell of clean sheets. But try to write something each day. People who do this faithfully say that it subtly changes them, making them more appreciative and optimistic.

- Write a thank you note or make a thank you call every day or every week. These are especially nice when they are thank yous to people who have done something special for you—a coworker who always had a joke or a smile, a teacher who encouraged you years ago, a spouse who does everyday tasks faithfully. Be creative. The more you do, the more ideas you will generate about who to thank.

- If you feel dependent on others at times, try to "get even" by doing something nice back for them. Learn a new joke to tell them, tape record music or stories for them to play in their cars while they run errands, fold clothes.

- Say thank you.

- Take time to compliment at least one person every day.

- Remember that most people get a lot more criticism than encouragement. Try to encourage someone whenever you can. Point out what the person does well, the effort they put into their work, the improvement or growth you have seen in them. Young and old alike crave encouragement.

- Give gifts when you can. These don't have to be expensive. Simple things like copying a recipe or making a list of family birthdays and anniversaries can be wonderful gifts. Sending a card with a note, a newspaper clipping, or a joke is great. Flowers, cookies, sharing a pot of homemade soup—all are simple gifts that others appreciate and make you feel good too.

Power Tool: Spiritual Imagery

The purpose of these selections is to assist you to assess your inner core in order to offer peace and hope. Use whatever is helpful to you.

1. Read Isaiah 43:1-4a.

(From the Revised Standard Version)

> *But now thus says the Lord, he who created you O Jacob, he who formed you, O Israel:*
> *Do not fear, for I have redeemed you;*
> *I have called you by name, you are mine.*
> *When you pass through the waters, I will be with you; and through the rivers, they shall not overwhelm you; When you walk through fire you shall not be burned; and the flame shall not consume you.*
> *For I am the Lord your God, the Holy One of Israel, your Savior.*
> *I give Egypt as your ransom, Ethiopia and Seba in exchange for you, because you are precious in my sight and honored,*
> *and I love you.*

Just read these words slowly. Stop and savor their meaning. Let them sink into your being. To make the passage more personal change the words "O Jacob" to your name— Judy or Joe or... It will go like this, "He who created you, Judy, or…." Do the same for "O Israel." Sit quietly with the word. Let God address you with love. Be in the peace of the words.

Maybe you would like to make a mantra out of verse 4a: "You are precious in my sight and honored and I love you." Say it over and over especially when you feel low. That gives voice to the life that is in you.

2. Another passage from the Hebrew Scriptures that helps us meet the living God is from Jeremiah 29:11-14.

> *For surely I know the plans I have for you, says the Lord, plans for your welfare and not for harm, to give*

209

you a future with hope. Then when you call upon me and come and pray to me, I will hear you. When you search for me, you will find me; if you seek me with all your heart, I will let you find me, says the Lord, and I will restore your fortunes and gather you from all the nations and all the places where I have driven you, says the Lord, and I will bring you back to the place from which I sent you into exile.

Read the passage slowly. Stop at words that are meaningful to you. Stay there. Let them give you hope. Meet the God who wants to give you hope even more than you want it.

3. The psalms are also a rich prayer because God taught the people how to pray and that pedagogue is recorded in the psalms. In them we find every feeling a human being has ever had. The psalms are the prayers that touch every human reality. Who does not understand the joy of nature recounted in Ps. 8?

When I look at your heavens, the work of your fingers, the moon and the
stars that you have established; What are human beings that you are mindful of them, mortals that you care for them? V. 3-4

Nature can lead us to prayer. Allow yourself to be moved by the beauty of the budding spring. Write your own nature psalm the next time you are overwhelmed by the grandeur of nature.

4. Regarding Ps. 22, v 1-2, who has not felt the despair expressed here?

My God, my God, why have you forsaken me?
Why are you so far from helping me, from the words of my groaning? Oh my God, I cry by day, but you do not answer;
And by night, but find no rest.

Working through the feelings of despair the psalmist comes to hope and peace as he concludes his prayer in v. 24-31. God taught the people to find God in their feelings whatever the feelings happen to be.

5.   If you like the psalms, I suggest Nan C. Merrill's *Psalms for Praying: An Invitation to Wholeness.* She dedicates her rewrite of the Psalms "to the indwelling Divine Guest whose Voice is heard in the Silence." Here is an example of her work in the rewrite of Psalm 23:

> *O my Beloved, you are my shepherd,*
> *I shall not want;*
> *You bring me to green pastures for rest*
> *and lead me beside still waters renewing my spirit.*
> *You restore my soul.*
> *You lead me in the path of goodness*
> *to follow Love's way.*
> *Even though I walk through the valley of the shadow*
> *and of death, I am not afraid;*
> *For you are ever with me;*
> *Your rod and your staff they guide me, they give me*
> *strength and comfort. You prepare a table before me*
> *in the presence of all my fears;*
> *You bless me with oil, my cup overflows.*
> *Surely goodness and mercy will follow me all the*
> *days of my life, And I shall dwell in the heart of*
> *the Beloved forever*

6.   Prayer of imagination is another powerful way to pray because it uses the senses: seeing, hearing, feeling, and tasting. Let's look at this form of prayer by using Mark Chapter 5:25-34.

> *Now there was a woman who had been suffering*
> *from hemorrhages for twelve years. She had endured*
> *much under many physicians, and had spent all*
> *that she had; and she was no better, but rather grew*
> *worse. She had heard about Jesus, and came up*
> *behind him in the crowd and touched his cloak,*
> *for she said, "if I but touch his clothes, I will be*

*made well." Immediately her hemorrhage stopped;
and she felt in her body that she was healed of her
disease. Immediately aware that power had gone
forth from him, Jesus turned about in the crowd and
said, "Who touched my clothes?" And his disciples
said to him, "You see the crowd pressing in on you;
how can you say, 'who touched me?'" He looked
all around to see who had done it. But the woman,
knowing what had happened to her, came in fear
and trembling, fell down before him and told him the
whole truth. He said to her, "Daughter, your faith
has made you well; go in peace and be healed of
your disease."*

See the beautiful sunny day. Feel the gentle breeze and the crowd of people pressing to hear what Jesus had to say. See the woman approaching the crowd and quietly moving into position. Why would Jesus embarrass her by asking who touched him? She seemed to want to be anonymous. The very attitude of Jesus answers the question. He wanted the woman to know how much he valued her as a person. To help her understand he gently raises her from the ground so that she can look into his face and see there his love for her. Do the prayer again putting yourself in the place of the woman and look Jesus in the face. See his love for you. Have a conversation with him. Allow yourself to feel his understanding of your struggles. Stay there and allow yourself to feel the peace.

7.   Poetry also can open us to the richness of our inner self. See what Mary Oliver's poem "Wild Geese" does for you.

*You do not have to be good.
You do not have to walk on your knees
for a hundred miles through the desert, repenting
You only have to let the soft animal of your body
Love what it loves.
Tell me about despair, yours, and I will tell you
mine. Meanwhile the world goes on.*

Meanwhile the sun and the clear pebbles of the rain
Are moving across the landscapes,
Over the prairies and the deep trees, The mountains
and the rivers.
Meanwhile the wild geese, high in the clean blue air
Are heading home again.
Whoever you are, no matter how lonely, The world
offers itself to your imagination,
Calls to you like the wild geese, harsh and exciting—
Over and over announcing your place
In the family of things.

New and Selected Poems by Mary Oliver.

8.   David Whyte has a gift of touching readers. In "Faith" he says

I want to write about faith,
about the way the moon rises
over cold snow, night after night,
Faithful even as it fades from fullness,
slowly becoming that last curving and impossible
sliver of light before the final darkness
But I have no faith myself
I refuse it the smallest entry.
Let this then, my small poem,
like a new moon, slender and barely open,
be the first prayer that opens me to faith.

Where Many Rivers Meet by David Whyte

Do you know the feeling David Whyte is talking about?

9.   You may be surprised at your ability to express a spiritual experience in painting, experiences that you could not express in words or writing. Try to draw or paint your inner experience.

10.   Music is the language of the soul. It has a universe of possibilities. Listen to what gives you peace, or leads you into quiet. If you like to sing, why not sing out loud. Have you ever wanted to play a musical instrument—the piano or the guitar, for example? Now is the time to give it a whirl.

11. What does the following anonymous reflection do for you?

Cancer is so limited…
It cannot cripple love,
It cannot shatter hope,
It cannot corrode faith,
It cannot eat away peace,
It cannot destroy confidence,
It cannot kill friendship,
It cannot shut out memories,
It cannot silence courage,
It cannot invade the soul,
It cannot reduce eternal life,
It cannot quench the Spirit,
It cannot lessen the power of the Resurrection.

SESSION 10
Adventures and Misadventures in the Supplement Jungle*

Teri Gabel, PharmD, BCPP

Key Points
- Many cancer survivors use herbal medications or supplements.
- These natural substances are still medicine. They may help with some symptoms, but you need to understand how they work, how to use them, and when not to use them.
- Safe use of herbs and supplements requires that you start with a reputable product.
- Understand the "N of One" process for determining whether any herbal medicine or supplement is helping.
- A chart of commonly available natural medicines is included showing what part of the plant is used, the usual dosage, the possible benefits, and the drug interactions or negative side effects that could result.

You Are NOT Alone

More and more, Americans diagnosed with cancer are using complementary medicine. In fact, in one survey, up to 91% of breast cancer patients have used or are using herbal medications and supplements before, during, and after treatment. And many of these patients do not tell their health care providers about their use.

Do supplements and herbal medications help? Yes, no and maybe. Some supplements such as a multiple vitamin are natural to us in periods of physical and mental stress. Others are new to us and some are potentially problematic. Sometimes eating our natural medicines is best because of phytosynergy, the way that all of the components of a food work together. Remember: Not everything natural is good for us. Think of arsenic and strychnine. And too much of a good thing is also potentially dangerous—100% oxygen can be toxic!

*The information in this session is copyright ©2016, Teri Gabel. This information is provided for educational purposes only. It is not meant to diagnose or treat any person or illness.

Lifestyle Changes:

The Mind-Body-Spirit Approach

Nothing we do will work in a vacuum; all the herbs and supplements in the world can't help if we don't "get with the program." Lifestyle changes are a must for the best outcomes to be realized. The mind body spirit approach requires us to get active, to eat right and develop the "I can" attitude, to nurture the spirit and the soul. It's about embracing our lives.

Mind: The "I can" attitude means having an attitude of survival, fight, health, and thanks. Use it or lose it. Playing and learning keep our synapses sparking. If you don't mind, it doesn't matter.

Body: Use it or lose it applies here too. Exercise comes in various forms: Weight bearing, strength, balance training, plus aerobics. Start slowly, go slow, but GO. This also applies to sex.

Spirit: Nurture your spirit and your soul (for example, through humor, nature, pets, prayer, meditation).

Herbs and Supplements for Cancer Survivors

Symptoms such as hot flashes, flushes, insomnia, fatigue, irritability and moodiness, neuropathies, weight gain, vaginal dryness, osteoporosis, and hyperlipidemia (high cholesterol) can all seem like mountains to overcome. While they won't necessarily make symptoms completely disappear, herbs and supplements may be very helpful in turning these mountains into molehills. You'll notice I did *not* say make them disappear. Most natural medicines aim to rebalance and strengthen our bodies, targeting the normalization of the body's functioning not treating specific symptoms. The result of normalization is the decrease of and/or the elimination of the symptoms which result from the body's dysfunction. Generally it is not one herb but a person-specific blending of herbs that is required for the best results.

Herbs and supplements are not risk free. They have great potential benefits—and potential side effects, toxicities, and drug interactions. Respect them. If you choose to use an herb, remember that the doses provided here and on the labels are general guides. Most product doses are based on the 170-pound male. You may need to adjust the dose for your weight. If you choose to use a liquid extract or tincture, it will give a dose in drops. In general, one pump of the dropper will provide that amount. Test it out a few times to double check.

Use an herb or supplement with forethought and planning. Not everything is helpful for all of us. **Start with one intervention (herb or supplement) at a time.** Start these after you have initiated your lifestyle changes and are working that program for a time—to let things stabilize in that area.

Insomnia

Insomnia is most frequently the result of an imbalanced lifestyle, but can be related to a medical or psychiatric problem. Appropriate intervention requires the identification and treatment of the underlying issue. Lifestyle changes or "sleep hygiene" are a must for the appropriate treatment of insomnia. It is a myth that we have to sleep every night, and that we need eight hours of sleep every night. But we do need it most nights, and restful sleep to boot!

The Rules for Good Sleep Hygiene

- Rise and shine and tuck yourself in at the same time every day. The most important of these rules is to get up every day at the same time.

- No activity besides sex and sleep in the bedroom— no reading, no TV, no computers. It is best to remove any electronics from the bedroom. The blue light emitted by these devices can disrupt your sleep even when you are asleep.

- Control the environment: temperature, number of blankets, quiet, darkness.

- Turn the face of the clock away from the bed. The alarm will still go off!

- No caffeine after noon. Maybe not at all if you are sensitive to it.

- No alcohol prior to bed (after 8 p.m. usually).

- Exercise in the morning or early evening not prior to bed.

- If you can't sleep—get up and do something boring. Keep the lights low and do not watch TV, work on the computer, or play with your smartphone. Again, that blue light wakes up our brains.

- Do not try to make up sleep.

- Do not nap for longer than a 20-minute power nap and not after 3 p.m.

- Have a nighttime ritual. Set the lights low, read something calming or boring. Take a bath and sip on warm milk or an herbal tea for sleep. Go to bed when you are tired.

The N of One Process

When scientists test a drug to see if it works or not, they go through a scientific process. If you are going to try a prescribed medication or an herb or supplement, it makes sense to do a scientific evaluation of your own. Otherwise you can end up spending a lot of money on something and not really know how much it is helping. An individual scientific test is called an "N of One" trial; in scientific terms, "N" means the number of people in the study. This study is only about you, so it is "N" of one—and you are a very important ONE.

Step One: Identify and document your target symptom(s) at baseline. What is it that you want to address? Be specific, choose the symptoms that go with the first intervention. Do one thing at a time. For example, for arthritis and a trial of glucosamine, you might target the number of doses of pain medication, how severe the pain is, and the range of motion in the joint you are concerned about.

Step Two: Use a simple linear scale for each symptom:

0 ------------5---------------10, with 0 = not present and 10 = worst pain ever, horrific (you get the picture). Make several of these scales on slips of paper. Rate your symptoms for a week or two before you start taking the drug or supplement. How is it before you start?

Step Three: Start your intervention. As you do your ratings throughout the trial, use the same scale, mark the score, date the slip and put it away in an envelope. Do not look at it again until the end of your trial. Don't look at the other rating slips in the envelope. Use a different scale for each major symptom. For each intervention, the time period between evaluations will vary, don't do it too often or it becomes overwhelming. Usually every 2 weeks is adequate as trials last 2 to 4 months on average. It usually takes several months for the effects of herbs and supplements to be noticeable, so do this for at least 2 to 3 months. It may require dosage adjustments as well. Decide on how often you will rate your symptoms as you go.

Step Four: Outcome of the trial = difference from baseline. How do you feel? What do you think? Now open the envelope. Take out all of the ratings and line them up by date. Are the symptoms getting better over time, getting worse, not changing? Do they indicate improvement in the target symptoms? Is it worth continuing? If not, try something different.

If you see some improvement, but not enough, you may need to change the dose or add something else. But if you don't do this objective kind of rating, you won't know if the intervention is working or not and you may be wasting your money and time on ineffective treatments.

Herbs and Supplements: Make It an Adventure Not a Misadventure

When choosing a product: Do your homework. Research the information that is out there. If the company providing the information is selling you a product, expect the information to be biased. Check collateral sources. The clerk at a health food store is *not* a health care professional.

If the makers of a product claim their product cures everything, run in the opposite direction. If they make claims that your doctor or the medical profession doesn't want you to know about their product, run in the opposite direction.

Use products made by reputable, established companies. The companies listed at the end of this session are but a few of the reputable companies out there. I have no stock in any of them. Check the United States Pharmacopoeia and Consumer Labs webpages for updates and for more information regarding quality products.

Avoid products imported from Asian countries; too much mystery. You will not know exactly what you are taking. Avoid products that contain multiple (more than 5) herbs and proprietary blends. You are paying a lot for things you don't need, often in amounts too small to help you.

Check the label for minimum information such as a tollfree company phone number or at least an address, lot numbers, and expiration dates. It is good to know the genus and species and part of the plant (such as root or leaves) used. The label should indicate standardization (if applicable) and give milligram dose / dosage form as well as the number of capsules, tablets, or drops in a dose.

Summary

Each and every one of you is a unique and wonderful human being. You have your own specific needs, your own answers, and your own blend of herbs and supplements. Don't expect one product to work for everyone. There are no guarantees. Only you can decide if the potential benefit of any treatment, whether prescription, over-the-counter, herbal, supplement or even no treatment, is within your comfort zone. Best wishes.

Natural Medicines

Many agents have multiple uses. Doses and side effects etc. may vary depending on use.

Agent	How it Helps	Side Effects (SE) / Cautions (C) / Contraindications (CI) / Drug Interactions (DI)	Product Information / Dosing
ADAPTOGENS			
B Vitamins Thiamine (B1), Riboflavin (B2), Niacin (B3), Pyridoxine (B6), Folic Acid (B9), Cyanocobalamin (B12)	Assist in nervous system function; maintain vision, skin, blood, and heart health; assist with release of energy from carbohydrates and with metabolism; maintain immune system, and reproductive health	SE: bright yellow urine	Product Info: Variety of formulations and sources Dosing: Use only in combination, supplementation of individual agents can lead to imbalance Sources: legumes, grains, nuts, vegetables, fish, and lean meats and poultry. Generally a B50 formulation is adequate
Rhodiola (Rhodiola rosea)	Increases resistance to chemical, biological, physical stress Stimulates the nervous system, fights fatigue, depression and improves sleep Antioxidant	SE: Dose related irritability, dizziness, jitteriness, insomnia C: Bipolar disorder – could cause a manic episode	Product Info: Root Standardized to 3-5% rosavins Dosing Varies - Follow label directions Adrenal fatigue: 500mg twice a day on an empty stomach
Asian ginseng (Panax ginseng)	Adaptogen; improve immune function; antiviral; antioxidant; anti-fatigue; improve mood; hot flashes; decrease blood pressure; increase sexual arousal and satisfaction (postmenopausal women) May have anticancer activity (breast, ovarian, lung, liver, skin)	SE: Stimulation, insomnia, headache, nausea, gas; less common vaginal bleeding, breast pain, rapid heart beat C: Heart disease, anxiety disorders, Bipolar - cases of mania have been reported; Component can be estrogenic. Do not use in hormone sensitive cancer DI: Additive decrease in blood sugars, blood pressure and blood thinning; additive stimulation; inhibits CYP 2D6 (many drug interactions – increased blood levels); may decrease the effect of immunosuppressants	Product Info: Root Dosing: Start low and titrate up Standardized products use dosages between 100-300mg/day Whole root products may use dosages between 1-3 grams/day Tincture: follow label directions Standardizations 4-5% Ginsenosides Important to find a quality product.

American ginseng (Panax quinquefolius)	Adaptogen; diuretic; may help with chemo brain and fatigue; antiviral; decrease blood sugars; increase the immune system	SE: upset stomach, diarrhea, increased heart rate, insomnia, anxiety C: Component can be estrogenic. Do not use in hormone sensitive cancer DI: Additive hypoglycemia; may decrease the effect of immunosuppressants CI/DI: Significant decrease in the effectiveness of warfarin	Product Info: Root Dosing: Take within 2 hours of food Follow package directions Be sure to get a quality product
Siberian Ginseng (Eleutherococcus senticosus)	Adaptogen; regulate blood pressure; anxiety; insomnia; mood stabilization; antiviral; improve cognitive function	SE: Anxiety, drowsiness, irritability, rapid heart rate in higher doses C: Cardiovascular disorders; may have estrogenic action – avoid in hormone sensitive cancer and other disorders DI: Additive sedation, decrease in blood sugars and blood thinning; may counter immunosuppressants; may increase blood pressure	Product Info: Root and leaf Dosing: Variable – follow product directions Be sure to get a quality product
Indian Ginseng (Withania somnifera)	Anti-stress; anti-fatigue; improves mental function; immune modulation; may increase thyroid production; restorative; may have anti-cancer action	SE: Well tolerated DI: Additive lowering of blood sugars and blood pressure; may counter immunosuppressants No estrogenic effects	Product info: Root and berry Dosing Varies – follow package direction 1 to 6 grams daily in two to three divided doses of the whole herb in capsule or tea form Tea – three times a day Tincture or extract 2-4 ml three times a day
Maitake (Grifola frondosa)	Enhances the immune system; liver health; decrease blood pressure, blood sugar and cholesterol; Beta-Glucan: Anticancer – protect healthy cells, inhibit growth and spread, increase cancer cell death; may increase effect of cancer medications and decrease their toxic effects	SE: none known C: stop 2 weeks before surgery due to effects on blood sugars DI: Can decrease blood pressure and blood sugar monitor response – additive effect May increase INR by increasing free fraction of warfarin	Product Info: Whole plant Dosing: Edible Follow package dosing Consider a medicinal mushroom combination product

Herb	Properties/Uses	Safety	Product Info/Dosing
Reishi (Ganoderma lucidium)	Tones the nervous system; Free radical scavenger; hepatoprotective; antihypertensive; anti-allergy; immune enhancing; Inhibits the spread of many cancers, increases cancer cell death, blocks the development of new blood vessels to tumors; helps with fatigue; bladder health in cancer patients	SE: None known DI: Synergistic with other antihypertensive medications	Product Info: Whole plant Dosing: Stress: five 420 mg capsules/day Hypertension: 55 mg extract three times daily (Max 3 grams TID) Consider a medicinal mushroom combination product
Cordyceps (Coryceps sinesis)	Energy, stimulates the release of glucose; helps adrenals function; antioxidant; increases immune function; Uses in multiple cancer types Anticancer – may increase time in remission		Product Info: Whole plant Dosing: Follow package directions Generally 3 grams a day whole plant formulations Consider a medicinal mushroom combination product
Shitake (Lentinula edodes)	Decrease cholesterol; immune enhancing	SE: May cause gastritis, dermatitis, photosensitivity C: Large doses (4g) for a prolonged period of time may cause eosinophilia	Product Info: Whole plant Dosing: Edible Follow package directions Consider a medicinal mushroom combination product
ANXIETY/MOOD			
Saint John's Wort (Hypericum perforatum)	Mild to moderate depression; seasonal depression; premenstrual moodiness; antiviral; antianxiety; sedative	SE: Nausea, rash, sedation C: Not for use during pregnancy or lactation. Photosensitivity/Phototoxicity can occur with sun exposure Stop use 14 days prior to surgery DI: Do not use with other antidepressants. Induces CYP 3A4, 1A2, 2C9, 2C19, … **Can decrease blood concentration of many other medications, e.g., *oral contraceptives*, cyclosporine, AIDS antivirals, *tamoxifen* Expect drug interactions with this herb.	Product Info: Flowers Dosing: Standardization 0.3% hypericum or 2-5% hyperforin Depression: 300mg three times a day initially may need to titrate dose, evaluate after one month for dose increase Hot flashes: dosing most likely the same Night sweats try bedtime only at first

SAM-e (s-adenosyl-methionine)	Antioxidant; antidepressant; fibromyalgia; migraine; headaches; anti-inflammatory Increases levels of neurotransmitters; Enhanced cellular membrane fluidity	SE: Heartburn, diarrhea, headaches; agitation C: Bipolar disorder – could cause mania DI: Serotonergic antidepressants and other agents – Serotonin Syndrome; Dextromethorphan	Product Info: Synthetic Dosing: Usual starting dose is 200mg two times a day Average: 400-1600mg/day Bioavailability of the tosylate salt is 1% and the butanedisulfonate salt is 5%
Magnolia Tree Bark (Magnolia biondii)	Anxiety; irritability; insomnia; anti-inflammatory; muscle relaxant	SE: Well tolerated C: Stop 2 weeks prior to surgery due to concerns of additive sedation and blood thinning DI: Additive sedation	Product Info: Bark and flower bud Found in herbal blends Dosing: Variable
Neroli Oil (Citrus aurantium L. var. amara)	Decrease menopausal symptoms; decrease anxiety; decrease blood pressure; analgesic	SE: Dermatitis can occur C: DO NOT TAKE BY MOUTH	Product Info: Essential oil Also known as Bitter Orange – different products for oral uses. Recommended route used: inhalation, diffusion
BONES/JOINTS			
Calcium (Carbonate, Citrate)	Good for bones, good for sleep, may decrease hot flashes High calcium and milk intake decreases risk of colorectal cancer	SE: constipation, gas C: Over use of supplement sources may have negative effects DI: Binds with iron	Product Info: Focus: Vegetables, Diary Supplement: Oysters, shells, Synthetic Dosing: 1200-1500mg elemental calcium daily in divided doses Add up the calcium in your diet and only supplement the amount needed to get the daily dose you require No more than 500mg elemental calcium at a time Carbonate formulations with food Citrate formulations with or without food Avoid coral calcium

224

		Product Info:
Vitamin D (D3 - cholecalciferol)	Stimulates active transport of calcium in the small intestine and colon; immune system health; mood May be an inverse relationship of 25-OH Vit D levels and the prevention and survival of some cancers (breast, ovarian, follicular and other lymphomas, prostate, lung, colorectal cancer including survival of metastatic colorectal cancer	SE: Well tolerated in usual doses C: Use with caution in lymphoma and hyperparathyroidism. DI: normal levels improve absorption of calcium and magnesium; may induce gut CYP3A4 decreased levels of several medications including atorvastatin, estrogens, cyclosporine (caution in combination) Medications that decrease vitamin D levels include: carbamazepine, corticosteroids, orlistat and other agents for weight loss, phenytoin	Product Info: Found in: fish, milk, milk products, fortified foods, fruit, beans, vegetables, whole grains, lean meats Dose: 2000 IU /day on average Max 5,000IU/day Higher doses when levels indicate they are necessary Levels: 25-hydroxyvitamin D = range: 30-100 ng/ml Recommended average is 50-75 ng/ml
Glucosamine (2-amino-2-deoxyglucose)	Stimulates the growth of new cartilage, decreases pain over time	SE: Gastrointestinal, mild, generally nausea DI: Additive blood thinning	Product Info: Shellfish and Synthetic Dose: 1500mg daily in divided doses Four month trial Try it alone first, then with chondroitin
Chondroitin	Protect from further breakdown, increase synovial fluid	SE: Mild, nausea DI: Additive blood thinning	Product Info: Use synthetic not bovine Dose: 1200mg daily in divided doses Not very bioavailable
MSM (Methylsulfonyl-Methane)	Osteoarthritis; Pain Naturally occurring source of sulfur May inhibit degenerative changes in joints	SE: Nausea, headache DI: Additive blood thinning	Product info: Synthetic Dosing: 500mg three times a day

CANCER BRAIN

Ginkgo (Ginkgo biloba)	Dementia; tinnitus; atherosclerosis; peripheral vascular disease; chemo/cancer brain	SE: GI upset, constipation, dizziness, headache, palpitations C: Ginkgotoxin in seed decreases the seizure threshold DI: May have additive blood thinning, alters blood sugars May decrease effect of alprazolam May inhibit 1A2, 2C9 and 2D6, may induce 2C19 Do not take with trazodone (one case of coma) No effects on tamoxifen, anastrozole, letrozole	Product Info: Leaves Products should *not* contain the seeds. Do not eat the seeds. Avoid non-standardized products. Dosing: Standardized products (EGb 761 is most studied) (standardized to contain 24% to 25% flavonoid glycosides and 6% terpenoids) Dementia: 120-240 mg per day (320mg)
Huperzine A	Prevention of age related memory problems; neurotoxicity from toxins; increase alertness and energy	SE: Nausea, sweating, diarrhea, dizziness, drooling DI: Additive cholinergic effects	Product Info: An alkaloid (from Chinese club moss, Huperzia serrata and Lycopodium selago) Dosing: 30-100mcg twice a day
Tumeric/Curcumin (Curcuma longa)	Anti-inflammatory; antioxidant; Immune enhancing; gastrointestinal, liver and gallbladder complaints; brain health – may decrease plaques associated with Alzheimer's disease Anti-carcinogenic (breast, stomach, colon, prostate, genitourinary, ovarian, head and neck, lymphoma and leukemia) - Inhibition of tumor growth, to induce apoptosis in cancer cells and may inhibit angiogenesis May protect against DNA mutation and assist in DNA repair	SE: Nausea and diarrhea C: Do not take if have gallbladder issues DI: Additive blood thinning May enhance the cytotoxic effects of tamoxifen, doxorubicin, cisplatin, camptothecin, daunorubicin, vincristine, and melphalan May decrease effects of cyclophosphamide Docetaxel no interaction	Product Info: Rhizome Curcumin – active ingredient Dosing: Best dose unknown Range 440mg to 2200 mg daily of curcuma extract, containing curcumin 36 to 180 mg Found in Curry spiced foods

226

Brahmi (Bacopa monnieri)	Improve learning; anxiety; memory problems; allergic conditions; irritable bowel syndrome; nerve tonic; cardiotonic; diuretic Modulation of acetylcholine release, choline acetylase activity, and muscarinic cholinergic receptor binding Mast cell stabilizer for allergies	SE: Nausea, dry mouth, fatigue	Product Info: Dosing: Cognitive Function 300 mg brahmi extract per day for 12 weeks
Green Tea (Camellia sinensis)	Polyphenols, caffeine Antioxidant, antibacterial, weight loss, decrease (total and LDL) cholesterol and triglycerides, raises HDL, increases body utilization of glucose - augments the activity of insulin, help treat headache Cancer prevention – information varies Green tea extract with l-theanine may improve memory and attention in mild cognitive impairment*	SE: Primarily due to caffeine content and are usually dose related – stimulation, gas, nausea, vomiting, insomnia, agitation, confusion C: Rare cases of liver toxicity DI: Primarily caffeine related. Additive stimulation; additive effects on blood pressure; blood thinning (primary concern) but may counter the effects of warfarin due to vitamin K content (large doses); decreased blood levels of nadolol;	Product Info: Leaf, leaf bud and stem Dose: Standardized Extract: 80% polyphenol and 55% epigallocatechin content - 1-2 capsules/day Tea: 2-5 cups a day, one cup = 60mg caffeine avg. Usual dose of caffeine/day for alertness and headache = 250mg To decrease cholesterol 10+ cups/day or 375mg/day of theaflavin-enriched green tea extract Caffeinated and Decaffeinated teas, many extracts are decaffeinated
Gotu Kola (Centella asiatica)	Enhance memory; increase intelligence; delay aging; rejuvenating for nerve and brain cells; decrease stress	SE: Nausea C: Pre-existing liver disease-are cases of liver disease developing – unclear if due to contaminants DI: Additive sedation	Product Info: Dosing: 600 mg three times a day or 60mg extract three times a day
EYES			
Lutein (and zeaxanthin)	A carotenoid Prevention of age-related macular degeneration (AMD), cataracts, retinitis pigmentosa, Breast and colon cancer.	DI: Beta-carotene may decrease absorption	Product Info: Fruits (kiwi fruit, grapes, orange juice Vegetables (broccoli, kale, squash, zucchini, spinach) Enriched eggs, Marigold extract Dosing: (44 mg of lutein per cup of cooked kale, 26 mg/cup of cooked spinach, and 3 mg/cup of broccoli)

	Retinopathy; improve visual acuity and night vision; venous insufficiency; anti-inflammatory; lower blood sugar: antioxidant	SE: None noted C: High in chromium - increased risk of chromium toxicity if use with brewer's yeast, cascara, or horsetail or chromium supplements DI: Additive blood thinning and lowering of blood sugar	Product Info: Fruit and leaf Dosing: Standardization 25% anthocyanosides Retinopathy and Improving night vision: bilberry extract 160 mg two times a day
Bilberry (Vaccinium myrtillus.)			

HEART/CARDIOVASCULAR/CHOLESTEROL/BLOOD SUGARS

	Anti-microbial activity; antiviral; immune enhancing; antioxidant; anti-inflammatory; decreases blood sugars and lipids; decreases blood pressure; Anti-cancer: increases detox of carcinogens, inhibits proliferation and increases cancer cell death; decreased risk of colorectal and gastric cancer and multiple myeloma; Keeps vampires away!	SE: Dose related. Upset stomach, odor – breath and body, gas, diarrhea DI: Additive blood thinning and lowering of blood pressure; inhibition of CYP2E1 (several anesthetic agents); may induce 3A4(data is inconclusive) but to be safe – avoid using medicinal amounts of garlic with AIDS antivirals, especially non-nucleoside reverse transcriptase inhibitors (NNRTIs); chemo agents: etoposide, paclitaxel, vinblastine, vincristine, vindesine; oral contraceptives	Product Info: Whole clove Dosing: Standardization 1.3% alliin General use: 1 - 4 cloves/day (1 fresh clove has 1% alliin) 4 grams of fresh garlic (1% alliin) => 18.3mg allicin 1mg alliin => 0.5mg allicin Garlic extract 600mg containing 1.3% alliin => 3.6mg allicin Hyperlipidemia: garlic extract 600-1200 mg/day in three divided doses Prevention of colorectal and gastric cancer: fresh or cooked garlic 3.5-29 grams weekly ***Heat destroys active constituents and necessary enzymes. If used in cooking, crush/dice the garlic, let sit for 15 minutes prior to use. Add to dish last.
Garlic (Allum sativum)			

Omega 3- Fatty Acids Fish Oil Omega-3's: EPA (eicosapentaenoic acid) and DHA (docosahexaenoic acid)	Antioxidant; anti-inflammatory; decreases lipids, especially triglycerides; colon cancer prevention; good for the central nervous system; chemo brain; treatment of cachexia due to chemotherapy	SE: Upset stomach, halitosis, fishy after taste C: Doses larger than 3 grams/day may suppress the immune system; hypomania in bipolar and depression; fish sources can contain heavy metals and other toxins watch the products and types of fish DI: Additive blood thinning and hypotension; orlistat may decrease absorption; estrogens may decrease the effect of triglycerides	Product Info: Cold water fish: Tuna, salmon, herring, trout, sardines Other sources of omega-3's include nuts, seeds Dosing: Keep in the freezer to decrease fishy after taste Look for a combination of milligrams of EPA+DHA = as close to a 1000mg per dose as possible, try for 1-2 capsules or tablets in a dose. Usually 1-3 grams daily divided with meals *Not more than 6 grams a day without HCP monitoring.*
Co-Enzyme Q10 (Ubiquinone)	Antioxidant; heart health (heart failure, hypertension); respiratory disease; fatigue; hepatoprotectant; brain; gums; muscles May decrease cardiotoxicity associated with doxorubicin (Adriamycin) chemotherapy	SE: Well tolerated, can see upset stomach, nausea, vomiting, diarrhea DI: Additive decrease in blood pressure; may increase levels of vitamins A,E,C; may have vitamin K like action – monitor INRs; omega-3 fatty acids may decrease CoQ-10 effects – take separately; statins decrease CoQ-10 levels; smoking decreases CoQ-10 levels Low levels associated with increased risk of melanoma and metastasis	Product Info: Fermented beets in sugar cane with certain yeast strains Dosing: Varies, safe to 1200mg/day Take with food Divide doses greater than 100mg 100mg three times a day for migraine prophylaxis 100-200mg/day for statin myopathy 100-200mg/day for doxorubicin cardiotoxicity, diarrhea (no decrease in effectiveness)
Red Yeast Rice	Decreases cholesterol May increase HDL, improves circulation, spleen and stomach health	SE: Muscle pain C: Rhabdomyolysis Same types of risks as prescription "Statins" Monitor carefully	Product Info: Rice fermented with monascus purpureas yeast Dosing: Start 600mg daily can increase to 600mg twice a day. Then to 1200mg twice a day if necessary.

Supplement	Benefits / Uses	SE / DI / C	Product Info / Dosing
Broccoli extract (Brassica oleracea var. italic)	Decreases progression of coronary artery disease; decrease cholesterol; decrease calcium deposits; immune enhancing; anticancer Sulforaphane and Indole-3-caribinole (I3C) – active constituents for cancer prevention	SE: None reported DI: Induces CYP 2A6 and 1A2 resulting in lower blood levels of medications metabolized by these enzymes. Check for possible drug interactions before use. Ingestion of sulforaphane may be inversely related to some cancers (prostate, leukemia, liver) I3C use as an isolated supplement may increase risk of cancer – contradictory evidence. Level of risk is unknown at this time.	Product Info: Above ground parts Broccoli Sulforaphane and Indole-3-caribinole are found in other cruciferous (Brassica genus) vegetables as well - Brussels sprouts, cabbage, cauliflower, kale, kohlrabi, mustard greens, rapeseed, turnips (head of cabbage = 1200mg of I-3-C) Dosing: No specific dosing Eat raw broccoli and other veggies Broccoli extracts – follow package directions I3C products: 200-300mg/day depending on use. Follow package instructions
Vitamin E Alpha-tocopherol (natural) dl-alpha-tocopherol (synthetic)	Antioxidant; heart health; can decrease hot flashes slightly; free radical scavenger; cancer prevention (lung, oral, colorectal, gastric, prostate, pancreatic); immune enhancing; Alzheimer's disease Cisplatin peripheral neurotoxicity may be decreased by Vitamin E during and after treatment, without interfering with medication effectiveness	SE: Nausea, gastritis, diarrhea, fatigue, weakness; high doses – increased risk of bleeding and stroke C: Fat soluble vitamin and is stored in body fat; can antagonize vitamin K Concerns that high doses (400IU and greater) may increase risk of prostate cancer. Use high doses only under the direction of a health care provider (HCP) DI: Additive blood thinning; may decrease beta-carotene levels; may interact with chemotherapies requiring the generation of free radicals (debated); Medications that decrease vitamin E levels: carbamazepine, phenytoin, orlistat and other weight loss products	Product Info: Nuts, seeds, whole grains, vegetable oils, eggs, animal fats, meat, poultry, fruits, and vegetables Dosing: 200-400 IU daily in general 400IU max for unhealthy people 800-1000IU for healthy people (consult HCP first) Conversions: mg to IU: 1 mg of alpha-tocopherol is equivalent to 1.49 IU of the natural form or 2.22 IU of the synthetic form IU to mg: 1IU = 0.67 mg of the natural form or 0.45 mg of the synthetic form Only half of a dose of synthetic vitamin E is used in the body you will need roughly 50% more IU of dl-alpha-tocopherol vs natural alpha-tocopherol Natural E – with or without food Synthetic E – with food

230

	Uses	SE / C / DI	Product Info
Lycopene	A carotenoid Prevention of atherosclerosis, cardiovascular disease, and cataracts Decrease progression of cancer (prostate) and decreased risk of (lung?) CA Potent antioxidant	DI: Beta-carotene may increase absorption ***Avoid if established prostate cancer – conflicting data, may worsen	Product Info: Fruits (tomatoes) watermelons, pink grapefruits, apricots, pink guavas) Vegetables Dosing: 15mg twice a day
Resveratrol (Vitis vinifera)	Uses – atherosclerosis; lowering cholesterol levels and increasing HDL; anti-aging; anti-inflammatory; may prevent breast, colorectal, thyroid, stomach, pancreatic cancer; prevent the spread of liver cancer	SE: None C: May have estrogenic activity – avoid in estrogen sensitive cancers DI: Additive blood thinning; may inhibit CYP 3A4 (and 2D6?) increased levels of many medications; may weakly induce CYP 1A2 decreasing levels of some medications	Product Info: Red wine, red grape skins, purple grape juice, mulberries, peanuts, blueberries, bilberries Eucalyptus and spruce are also sources Dosing: Trans is the primary active form Follow package instructions Low bioavailability Occurs as cis and trans stereoisomers, trans is most active
Beta-glucan	Hypercholesterolemia; diabetes; cancer; HIV/AIDS; Immune enhancing; anti-stress during chemotherapy	C: Autoimmune disorders DI: Decreased effect of immunosuppressants	Product Info: Cell walls of plants, fungus, algae Dosing: 3-10grams daily in divided doses
IMMUNE ENHANCING			
Astragalus (Astragalus membranaceus)	Adaptogen; antioxidant; antiviral; increases immune function; decrease blood sugars; anti-inflammatory; may decrease GI and hematologic side effects of some chemotherapy; may protect the liver; uses in multiple cancer types	SE: Minimal C: Autoimmune diseases DI: May counter immunosuppressants	Product Info: Root Dosing: Varies Cold 4-7 grams a day in divided doses

Echinacea (Echinacea angustifolia, E. pallida, E. purpurea)	Non-specific immunosuppressant actions May help with chemo induced leukopenia	SE: Nausea, vomiting, diarrhea, dry mouth, headache, dizziness C: Cross- allergy with ragweed, autoimmune diseases DI: May affect other medications in the liver – inhibition May increase absorption of other medications (alprazolam) Watch with immunosuppressant therapy	Product Info: Roots and above ground parts Dosing: 900mg – 3600mg daily in 2-3 divided doses Capsules, tablets, extract, tea For colds – start as soon as notice symptoms and stop when cold resolved
Ascorbic Acid (Vitamin C)	Antioxidant; decreases histamine levels; suppresses bronchoconstriction; normalizes fatty acid metabolism (anti-inflammatory action)	SE: Dose related - gastrointestinal distress, flatulence C: could increase the development and precipitation of kidney stones in large doses DI: Decreased effectiveness of bortezomib	Product Info: Dosing: Start low and increase the dose as tolerated Drink plenty of fluids Allergies: 1-2 grams three times a day Normal Supplementation: 500mg-1000mg a day Bolus doses of 2000mg for acute cold/allergy symptoms – buffered form recommended, short-term use only

LIVER/KIDNEY

Selenium Trace mineral	Glutathione peroxidase – scavenger for waste products, helps keep liver healthy May prevent prostate cancer but data is mixed, Cancer – colorectal, lung, gastric (M>W) Prevention of post-surgical lymphedema Improvement in immune function	SE: C: Caution with long term high dose use (200-400mcg/d), may increase risk of type II diabetes Excess: nausea, vomiting, stomach pain, nail changes, fatigue, irritability, alopecia, and weight loss → muscle tenderness, tremor DI: Cisplatin may decrease selenium levels, additive blood thinning **Do not supplement if you have prostate cancer – discuss with HCP first	Product Info: Brewer's yeast, cereals, seafood, vegetables Dosing: RDA: 55mcg CA prevention: 200mcg daily Upper limit is 400mcg Dietary intake is affected by soil content
Milk Thistle (Silybum marianum)	Liver protectant; increases glutathione; helps clear toxins form the body and liver; antioxidant and anti-inflammatory; promotes DNA repair; may prevent cancer (prostate and ?); may decrease spread of many cancers	SE: Well tolerated DI: May inhibit the metabolism of other medications – monitor for changes in side effects/toxicity (i.e., Indinavir)	Product Info: Seeds – crushed, ground, milled Dosing: Standardized to 70-80% silymarin Liver protection 12-15g (200 - 600 mg silymarin/ day in divided doses) Hormone sensitive cancer – use product from seeds only

232

			Product Info:
Dandelion (Taraxacum officinale)	Anti-inflammatory, liver and kidney health; Tonic; Anticancer	DI: May inhibit 1A2; May increase lithium levels; Additive diuretic effects, hyperkalemia	Leaves, root; Package directions; Tincture, capsules, and tablets; Tea

MENOPAUSE/HORMONAL SYMPTOMS

			Product Info:
Sage Common Sage (Salvia officinalis) Spanish Sage (Salvia lavendulafolia) Dan Shen (Salvia miltiorrhiza)	Dries secretions; decreases hot flashes (breast and prostate cancer); antioxidant; anti-inflammatory; CNS depressant (calming); anti-acetylcholinesterase activity; hypoglycemic	SE: Mild and dose related. Typically they include nausea, and stomach irritation C: High blood pressure and seizure disorders; may dry milk production In large doses some chemicals (thymol) in sage are known to be pro-convulsive, hepatotoxic and neurotoxic in nature (less in Spanish sage) *If S officinalis is successful and you are using a lot of it, change to Spanish Sage. DI: Additive decrease in blood sugars, additive sedation; may decrease the effectiveness of high blood pressure medications and anticonvulsant medications	Use leaves, extract, or tincture NOT concentrated sage essential oil by mouth Dosing: Tea: one teaspoon of leaves in one cup of boiling water, let steep for 10minutes, strain and drink. Adjust strength as needed Tincture forms are available: 1:1 concentration, follow product directions, put it in water. Extract: 150mg three times a day Works fast and can have a long duration of action. Regimen: Taken just prior to bed for night sweats, three times a day for hot flashes, as needed Can combine with chamomile and other flavored herbal teas for flavor
Black Cohosh (Cimicifuga racemosa)	Decreases the severity of hot flashes; memory problems; depression; mood swings; vaginal tissue fragility and dryness Its mechanism of action is unknown, most current data indicates that it is *not* estrogenic	SE: Nausea, headache, dizziness, weight gain and rash. DI: Not for use with hormone replacement therapy Can use with tamoxifen Do not use isolated formononetin (specific phytoestrogen) products	Rhizome and root Dosing: Menopausal symptoms: Dried root – two 500mg capsules or tablets a day or Standardized form: Remifemin® available in 20mg strength. This extract tablet form is standardized to triterpene glycosides. Tincture: 1:5 one teaspoon or 1:1 20 drops (may be more effective) - Taken three times a day Trial of three to four months Duration: 6 months, then re-evaluate

Flaxseed (Linum usitatissimum)	Antioxidant; Phytoestrogens – Lignans; Source of omega-3 fatty acids; may improve CVS and or decrease risk; anti-inflammatory	SE: Diarrhea (crushed seeds) – start with small amount and work up to a therapeutic dose; bruising C: Not if pregnant DI: Additive blood thinning and decrease in blood sugars Does *not* interact with tamoxifen OK for use after estrogen positive cancer	Product Info: Crushed Seed and seed oil Do *not* use raw unripe flaxseeds Dosing: Crushed Seed: 3-5 tablespoons a day, sprinkle on and in other foods. Used this way you reap the benefits of the fiber also Oil: 1000mg capsules up to three times a day – not for menopausal symptoms, no phytoestrogens in the oil (is anti-inflammatory) Trial: 3 – 4 months, then reassess
Soy (Soya bean)	Antioxidant; cardiac health –may decrease LDL and total cholesterol and maintain HDL; may help menopause symptoms (decreased hot flashes, night sweats); insomnia; may help with osteoporosis Phytoestrogen – isoflavones (genistein, diadzain, others)	SE: Constipation, bloating, nausea, diarrhea C: Dose related concerns; *risks/benefits can vary with population, age group and cancer/cancer subtypes studied;* gut metabolism differences may also be important; may be differences in positive and negative effects depending on the phytoestrogen involved CI: *Avoid concentrated isoflavones pills in:* estrogen sensitive cancers, endometrial cancer, bladder cancer or high risk of bladder cancer and prostate cancer. DI: Decreases the effectiveness of tamoxifen; additive lowering of blood sugars and blood pressure	Product Info: Soy beans, soy foods Dosing: Keep to 1/3 of total protein intake or less Cholesterol: 20-50rams of soy protein/day Hot flashes: 20-60 grams/day soy protein (34-76 mg isoflavones) Source Isoflavone content Soy flour 2.6 mg / gram Fermented soybeans 1.3 mg / gram Soymilk 0.4 mg / gram Soybean curd 0.5 mg / gram, Soybean paste 0.4 mg / gram Soy sauce 0.016 mg / gram Soy whole food sources *in moderation* are OK for breast cancer survivors. Soy foods combined with other fruits and vegetables may decrease the risk of prostate cancer (i.e., 2-4 glasses of soy milk/day)
Hops (Humulus lupulus)	Vasomotor symptoms; insomnia; antianxiety; anticancer actions (breast, prostate, ovarian)	SE: Topical allergic reactions to hops dust C: Stop two weeks prior to surgery due to additive sedation; may worsen depression CI: Not recommended in hormone sensitive cancer – risk unclear DI: Additive sedation	Product Info: Dried, female flowering part (strobile) Dosing: Standardized extract

234

Name	Uses	SE / C / DI	Product Info / Dosing
Maritime Pine Bark (Pinus pinaster) (Pycnogenol©)	Decrease vasomotor symptoms; antioxidant; anti-inflammatory; Improve CVS; insomnia; improve cognitive function	SE: Well tolerated C: Discontinue 2 weeks prior to surgery DI: Additive blood thinning and decrease in blood pressure; decrease the effect of immunosuppressants	Product Info: Extract from the bark Standardized to 70 ± 5% procyanidins Dose: Vasomotor symptoms: 30-100mg twice a day Cognitive function: 150mg/day Allergies: 50mg twice a day
Saw Palmetto (Serenoa repens)	Anti-estrogenic; Decreases symptoms of benign prostatic hypertrophy, effect on size is not known; May inhibit prostate cancer cell growth Anti-inflammatory, antiseptic	SE: Dizziness, headache, nausea, diarrhea DI: May decrease effect of estrogens and OCs, additive blood thinning	Product Info: Ripe fruit Dosing: BPH: 160 mg twice daily or 320 mg once daily of a lipophilic extract containing 80% to 90% fatty acids (phytosterols)

NAUSEA AND VOMITING/DIARRHEA

Name	Uses	SE / C / DI	Product Info / Dosing
Ginger (Zingiber officinale)	Anti-inflammatory; antispasmodic; motion sickness; migraine; nausea and vomiting with chemotherapy/surgery; lower high blood sugar and high blood pressure; may increase insulin levels	SE: Abdominal discomfort, heartburn, diarrhea; a pepper-like irritant effect in the mouth and throat; may cause some sedation or drowsiness DI: Additive blood thinning, lowering of blood sugar and blood pressure	Product Info: Root Dosing: Cook with it Candied Ginger – actual candied root only Whole Root products: 500mg several times a day Studied Ginger extracts: Eurovita Extract 33; EV ext-33 170 mg three times daily or Zintona EC 250 mg four times daily
Probiotics	Immune function Role in rheumatoid arthritis Fighting inflammation Mental Health	SE: Well tolerated C: Use only with HCP guidance if you are immunosuppressed – cases of GI infection with use of probiotic yogurt and supplementation	Product Info: Yogurt and Kefir with live active cultures Tablet, capsule, powder, and other products Dosing: Follow package instructions

SKIN

Alpha-Lipoic Acid	Co-enzyme; antioxidant; decreases blood glucose; improves insulin resistance; decreases peripheral diabetic neuropathy, may decrease vascular complications of DM; supports skin health	SE: Upset stomach, rash DI: Additive hypoglycemia	Product Info: Red meat, spinach, yams, potatoes, broccoli, beets Dosing: On an empty stomach – 1 hour before or 2 hours after a meal Peripheral neuropathy 600-1200mg/day 5% cream twice a day
Arnica (Arnica fulgens)	Topical: Anti-inflammatory; used for bruises and muscle strains	SE: Possible irritation, especially if sensitive to ragweed C: Used on unbroken skin, not to be taken internally. Very toxic internally.	Product Info: Flower Dosing: Topical ONLY Homeopathic (30X) or Usually a maximum content of 20-25% tincture (1:10) or 15% (1:5) of the oil
Calendula (Calendula officinalis)	Anti-inflammatory; antispasmodic; stimulates tissue granulation; enhances wound healing; may be helpful in mucositis due to radiation and 5-fluorouracil; decreases fever; may inhibit HIV replication; antibacterial; antitumor	SE: Possible irritation, especially if sensitive to ragweed C: Not for use on deep wounds CI: Not for pregnancy – abortifacient DI: Additive sedation	Product Info: Flowers Dose: Ointment: 2-5 grams of herb in 100 grams of ointment Flower oil in concentrations of 0. 02% to 0.1%, are considered safe for use Tea: one cup three times a day Liquid extract, 1:1 in 40% alcohol, 0.5-1 mL three times a day Tincture, 1:5 in 90% alcohol, 0.3-1.2 mL three times a day

SLEEP

Valerian (Valeriana officinalis)	Sedative and hypnotic; decreases the time to fall asleep and helps maintain sleep GABA-ergic – direct receptor agonism and decreased GABA metabolism Actions with adenosine and 5-hydroxytryptamine-1	SE: Stinky, nausea, sedation, excitability, headache, cardiac disturbances C: Pre-existing Liver disease-are cases of liver disease developing – unclear if due to contaminants; stop two weeks prior to surgery DI: Additive CNS depression	Product Info: Root and Rhizome Dosing: Anxiety: 200mg two to three times a day Insomnia: 400-2000mg at bedtime Regimen: Taken at bedtime as needed, can take smaller doses during the day for anxiety

236

Herb	Actions	Safety	Product Info / Dosing
Chamomile (Matricaria recutita Chamaemelum nobile)	Relaxes, allows you to drift off; antispasmodic; antianxiety; anti-gas; anti-inflammatory; wound healing	SE: Upset stomach, rash C: No large doses in pregnancy Rare cross allergy with ragweed (swish and spit test: make a strong cup of tea, swish cool tea in mouth and spit. If your mouth is tingly and itchy do NOT use chamomile) Stop two weeks prior to surgery DI: Additive blood thinning is possible	Product Info: Flower heads Dosing: Tea: steep tea bags in a cup of boiling water for 5-10 minutes, use throughout the day for anxiety, at bedtime for sleep, more tea bags = stronger tea Combine with sage for a bedtime toddy for night sweats
Passionflower (Passiflora incarnate)	Insomnia; anxiety; neuralgia; menopausal symptoms; analgesic; antispasmodic	SE: Dizziness, sedation, confusion, unsteadiness C: Discontinue 2 weeks prior to surgery CI: Do not use with benzodiazepines (lorazepam, clonazepam, alprazolam, diazepam, etc.) DI: Additive sedation, blood thinning and lowering of blood pressure	Product Info: Above ground parts Dosing: Anxiety: 45 drops of passionflower liquid extract (1:1 in 25% alcohol)/day (0.5-1ml three times a day average) or Tincture: 0.5-2 ml three times a day (1:8 in 45% alcohol) Tea: one cup two-three times a day Anxiety 500-1000mg three times a day Insomnia: tea or other at bedtime
Lavender (Lavandula angustifolia)	Insomnia; anxiety; relaxing; depression; headache; stomach issues; analgesic; antispasmodic; high blood pressure; may have anticancer action; decrease pain with dysmenorrhea; anti-inflammatory Oil: possible estrogenic and anti-androgenic actions	SE: Oral use (not the Essential Oil): Constipation, headache, increased appetite Topical: possible dermatitis (rare) C: Discontinue oral and topical use 2 weeks prior to surgery DI: Additive sedation (i.e., with benzodiazepines) and low blood pressure	Product Info: Flowers, leaves, essential oil (EO) Dosing Depression: tincture (1:5 in 50% alcohol) 60 drops a day for 4 weeks then re-evaluate Agitation: inhalation route is recommended Migraines: 2-3 drops EO on upper lip for inhalation if too strong use diffuser Relaxation/wellbeing: EO drops up to 3 ml alone or combination in bath water or use an air diffuser

Melatonin	Insomnia; circadian sleep disorders; jet lag; may improve immune function Anticancer – breast, brain, lung, prostate, head, and...; antioxidant; radioprotective (from radiation and radiotherapy; protects against adriamycin cardiotoxicity and increases its antitumor action; immunomodulatory; oncostatic effects; decrease chemotherapy related side effects (cachexia; thrombocytopenia; asthenia; neuropathy, and...) and possible increase in remission rates	SE: Generally no worse than placebo; drowsiness, headache, irritability, nausea, hypotension, mild anxiety, daytime sedation, confusion have been reported. Potential is greater with large doses. C: May decrease seizure threshold use with caution in seizure disorders *Decreased melatonin levels due to light exposure at night may play a role in resistance to tamoxifen – supplementation with melatonin may reverse this. DI: Additive blood thinning and sedation; chronic caffeine consumption may decrease endogenous melatonin production; may decrease the effect of immunosuppressants Potential interaction with some chemo-therapeutic agents – need to use caution, check for DIs prior to using; may interfere with immunosuppressant therapy	Product Info: Synthetic not from animal pineal glands Dosing: 0.3–5mg at bedtime for sleep – start at low doses and titrate up Rapid release – for difficulty falling asleep Sustained release – sleep maintenance Antioxidant: 10-20mg/day Doses in cancer vary Use in large doses with assistance of a HCP

238

Questions for Discussion and Journaling

1. Have you ever tried an herbal or natural medicine supplement?

2. How did you make the decision to try it?

3. What was your experience like? How long did you take it? How did you evaluate its effectiveness?

4. Would you do anything differently if you decided to try a natural medicine now after reading this chapter?

Suggested Resources

Books

Cooperman, Tod and colleagues. *ConsumerLab.com's Guide to Buying Vitamins & Supplements: What's Really in the Bottle.*

Duke, James A. *The Green Pharmacy Herbal Handbook: Your Comprehensive Reference to the Best Herbs for Healing.*

Hobbs, Christopher. *Herbal Remedies for Dummies.*

Tyler, Varro E. *Herbs of Choice: The Therapeutic Use of Phytomedicinals.*

Tyler, Varro E. *The Honest Herbal: A Sensible Guide to the Use of Herbs and Related Remedies.*

Internet Resources for Natural Medicine

NIH, National Center for Alternative and Complementary Medicine, http://nccam.nih.gov/

National Cancer Institute, Complementary and alternative medicine in cancer treatment: www.cancer.gov/cancertopics/pdq/cam/cam-cancer-treatment/patient

Thinking about CAM: A guide for people with cancer, www.cancer.gov/cancertopics/cam/thinking-about-CAM

Memorial Sloan-Kettering Cancer Center, Complementary therapies to ease the way during cancer treatment and recovery www.mskcc.org/cancer-care/patient-education/resources/complementary-therapies-ease-wayduring-treatment-and-recoveryand www.mskcc.org/aboutherbs

Cancer Council Australia, Complementary and Alternative Therapies www.cancer.org.au/about-cancer/treatment/complementary-therapies-and-cancer.html

MD Anderson Cancer Center, mdanderson.org/cimer

National Institutes of Health, Office of Dietary Supplements www.ods.od.nih.gov

American Botanical Council: Herbalgram, www.herbalgram.org

Herb Research Foundation, www.herbs.org

Consumer Labs (subscription), www.consumerlabs.com Food and Drug
Administration, www.fda.gov

Dr. Duke's Database, www.ars-grin.gov/duke and www.greenpharmacy.com

Medical Herbalism: A Journal for the Clinical Practitioner, www.medherb.com

Pharmaceutical Information Network, pharminfo.com

US Pharmacopoeia, www.usp.org

Natural Medicines Comprehensive Database, www.naturalmedicinesdatabase.com

Linus Pauling Institute, www.lpi.oregonstate.edu

Suggested Reputable Companies

Bioforce, Eclectic, Quanterra, Schwabe, Solaray, Enzymatic Therapy, Nature's
Herbs, Nature's Way, Phytopharmica, Solgar Gaia, HerbPharm, Vitamin
World, GNC, Spring Valley

Power Tool: Humor

Fear, anxiety, and depression are normal responses to a cancer diagnosis, but as you have already learned, those emotions stress your body and your spirit.

One of the best antidotes to stress is a good laugh. Not only does it feel good, but laughing also releases muscular tension, changes your perspective, gives you a little distance from disturbing situations, and creates a whole new chemical condition in your body. Laughter can be very healing both physically and psychologically.

Researchers have found that humor has a major effect on blood vessels; people have better blood flow after watching a comedy and reduced blood flow after watching a violent show. Other writers such as Norman Cousins and Bernie Siegel have documented the benefits of using humor in the fight against pain and illness.

To use humor for your own health, experiment to find things that strike you as funny. We all have our own senses of humor. All humor helps from the mild chuckles to the deep belly laughs that bring tears to your eyes. Here are some ways to start:

- Begin a collection of things you find funny and share them with your family and friends.

- Cut out cartoons and quips, save Internet email jokes, and make a scrapbook.

- Rent or purchase humorous videos and books. Netflix funny movies.

- Write down the funny things people say or do (grandchildren are a major source of humor).

- Collect goofy bumper stickers.

- Learn some new jokes and tell them to others.

All of these activities brighten your mood, and the chemical changes they promote can have healing effects.

SESSION 11
Where Am I Going Now?

Stephanie Koraleski, PhD, and Kay Ryan, PhD, RN

> **Key Points**
> - There is much about the causes of cancer we know and don't know.
> - The things that you have some power to change may benefit your health.
> - This section is meant to help you plan to begin creating your "best life" after cancer, one doable step at a time.

During treatment many people say they just can't wait to get back to normal again. Within a few months after treatment, many realize that will not happen. Life changes, but it won't go back to the old "normal." Too many things have happened. You have grown and changed. You are not the same. So where do you go from here?

Stay Healthy and Cancer Free

The biggest concern on everyone's mind is how to stay healthy and cancer free, or if you are dealing with chronic cancer, how to keep it stable or put it into remission. At this point in research, no one knows exactly what causes cancer. The theories and current evidence suggest that cancer develops based on some combination of genetics, environment, lifestyle, and psychological factors. You did *not* cause your own cancer; you are not that powerful. But after you have been diagnosed with cancer, it makes sense to survey the aspects of your life where you have some control and work to make them as health promoting as possible.

Genetics is out of the scope of our control, and for the most part, the total environment we live in is influenced by forces beyond your personal control. Likewise, you are not totally in control of the content of the air you breathe, the water you drink, or the chemicals in the food you eat, the products you use, or the clothes you wear.

You can take action if you feel strongly about these things, though. You can work to make your own home environment as healthy as possible, especially by monitoring the purity of the products and foods used in your own home. But even with these efforts, genetics and environment are huge elements, not really under the power of any of us as individuals.

There are factors that are much easier to influence, however. Several of the sessions in *A Time to Heal* have focused on individual lifestyle factors such as nutrition and exercise. One session focused on nurturing and maintaining a healthy spiritual orientation. Another discussed developing healthy relationships both with yourself and with other people. This session will focus on developing and taking action to implement the healthiest possible orientation toward your life. And this is something that only you can do for yourself.

Personality and Personal Style

Is personality or personal style associated with cancer? Early research on cancer and psychology looked to see whether people with certain personality types were more prone to cancer than other types of people and whether traditional psychotherapy could be helpful to the health of cancer patients. Early research that you may run across seemed to indicate that there was a "Type C," or cancer-prone personality. These were people who were almost too nice, who were not assertive, and when they were diagnosed with cancer, they accepted their diagnosis in a meek way (Temoshok et al., 1985, 1987).

Other early research seemed to show that people who had a lot of grief, loss, or depression in their lives and who had additional losses later in life might be more prone to cancer (LeShan, 1966). At this point in time, with much more research having been done, those earlier studies don't seem to hold up. The most recent research says there is not enough data to say that personality traits or depression are direct risk factors for cancer or cancer survival (Nakaya, 2014; Bleiker et al., 2008; Price et al., 2001).

244

Psychological factors alone do not cause cancer.

You may have read that being stressed, depressed, or grieving the death of a loved one might have caused cancer and been scared by that. After all, if someone you love dies or you lose a job or a relationship you care about, grief and depression are normal reactions, and you can't go back and undo those things anyway. If you have read things that attribute your cancer to something you did in the past, think about putting those articles and books away.

The current statistics say that 1 in 2 American men and 1 in 3 American women will develop some kind of cancer in their lifetimes. Cancer is far too common and the body of research at this time doesn't support the theory that personality or personality characteristics cause cancer.

Cancer and Stress

Many people look back at their lives prior to cancer and decide that stress caused the cancer. What does the research say?

Actually, the evidence is mixed. On the one hand, some studies suggest that stress may affect the immune system and/or may trigger cancer growth in some cells. Some doctors have believed that feelings of hopelessness and helplessness (Everson, 1996) were associated with cancer. One author noted that the increase in breast cancer paralleled the number of working women and conjectured that that might be due to the increased stress of juggling multiple roles and gender discrimination (Rosch, 1996).

One Swedish study asked 1,400 women if they'd had stress lasting a month or more in the previous five years. Some twenty-four years later, the women who had reported high stress had twice the risk of breast cancer even when other factors were ruled out (Helgesson, 2003). Recently, studies with fruit flies and mice have shown that while stress does not necessarily cause cancer, it can affect the release of particular chemicals that may spur cancer growth or deactivate the systems that normally prevent cancer growth (Wu, 2010).

There is also, however, a lot of evidence supporting the idea that stress does not cause cancer (Dalton et al., 2002).

We used to believe that stress weakens the immune system and that's how stress contributes to cancer, but more recent research has shown that mice genetically engineered to have no functioning immune system don't show a huge increase in cancer, and people who are on immune-suppressing drugs for other medical conditions show only a small increase in certain types of cancer that are associated with infections—for example, stomach cancer and *h. pylori* infection, liver cancer and hepatitis, lymphoma and Epstein Barr, or cervical cancer and human papilloma virus. And so, while the jury may still be out about the relationship between your immune system and cancer, there are other reasons to strive for a healthy immune response.

Reviews of thirty years of research found no direct cause-and-effect relationship between stress and cancer (Garsson et al., 2004), and several studies have shown that people under high stress, for example, parents whose children are very ill or have died, have no higher rate of cancer than the general public.

On the other hand, some evidence supports the idea that stress may promote cancer spread (Antoni et al., 2006). It seems that chronic stress through its effect on neuroendocrine responses has been shown to promote cancer growth in lab experiments. More research is needed to understand exactly how this might work in human cancer growth (Moreno-Smith et al., 2010).

The bottom line is that we know that living in uncontrolled stress saps the joy from our lives and is associated with a variety of health problems. The best course of action is to use the tools in *A Time to Heal* to learn to manage your stress and to calm your mind and your body every day.

Research by Candace Pert and others has shown that psychological factors can influence body chemistry. Whether you are under stress or deeply relaxed, the chemistry of every cell in your body can be affected. **Therefore, improving your psychological environment can actually have the effect**

of improving the body's internal chemistry. We've already talked about the value of meditation or the relaxation response. Both men and women with a variety of cancer types showed less stress-related gastrointestinal and heart symptoms, less confusion, more vigor, and less depression and anxiety after a short course in mindfulness-based stress reduction. The Power Tools in *A Time to Heal* and the information in session 4 can help you reduce stress too. Taking the time to give your cells a break from stress is a healthy choice that is under your control, and you've seen that it doesn't take long.

Psychologist Dr. Lawrence LeShan has worked with cancer patients since the 1950s when very few drugs were at all effective against cancer. Dr. LeShan's work over time showed that the most effective psychological strategy cancer patients could employ was to develop a vision of a life that they would really love and then to actively work toward making that life a reality.

Other researchers documented better outcomes in patients with a "fighting spirit" who based their decisions on what seemed right to them rather than just accepting what they were told. Dr. Bernie Siegel noticed that many of his patients who were long-term survivors had not been model patients; in fact, they were the ones who insisted on getting the information they wanted and doing things in ways that seemed right for them. In other words, cancer patients with better outcomes seem to share the psychological trait of really being themselves.

Shakespeare's famous line, "To thine own self be true," seems to be the best psychological advice we can give to a person recovering from cancer.

Fight for Your Life

What does this mean? It means **give yourself a life you love.**

How do you do that? Dr. LeShan and his colleague Dr. Ruth Bolletino outline five steps:

First, identify what it is that turns you on. What have you enjoyed most? When did you feel most alive? When were the times when you woke up excited to face the day and went to bed feeling tired and satisfied at night? What kinds of activities do you most enjoy? What types of contact with people have been most satisfying for you? Do you like working alone or are you a team player? Are you more turned on by ideas or facts?

What were the highlights of your life? Which experiences have you treasured most?

Second, given the reality of your current situation, how can you begin to get more zest and fulfillment in your life now? If you can't do everything you want, that's okay, but how can you begin to get a bit and then a bit more of the life you want? The goal is to take it step by step to make your life more and more what is truly good for you.

Third, identify the things that keep you from creating a life that would be the best for you. The list might include practical limitations, beliefs you have, concerns about how other people would react—anything that keeps you from going after what you really want. Pay particular attention to the things that cause you a lot of stress. Write those down, too, so you can make a plan to deal with them or at least to take breaks from the stress.

Fourth, make a specific plan to upgrade your life to reflect the unique person you are. This plan should be specific, have concrete goals, and specify a time frame for each step. It could include building in more of the things that fulfill you and finding ways to decrease or minimize the barriers that are holding you back, especially if those barriers are inside you (such as outmoded beliefs or fears about what people would think). You may also want to put in some specific ways to manage stress.

Fifth, take action to implement your plan. Set specific dates for accomplishing each step and be true to yourself. Make the commitment and follow through. If you change your timeline, that's okay, but set a new timeline and follow through. Prove to yourself that you are worthy of respect. Keep the commitments you make to yourself.

What does this look like in action?

Karen's story: Karen was 42 when she was diagnosed with breast cancer. She had married young and never had the chance to go to college. She got pregnant quickly and had three children who were in their teens and early 20s when she was diagnosed. Karen had always worked cashiering in a grocery store and really hadn't questioned whether this was what she wanted to do; she'd just felt lucky to have the salary to help with raising her children.

Karen was shocked at her diagnosis, but she was a practical person and did what she needed to do for treatment. As her treatment ended, a favorite aunt of hers died and left Karen a small inheritance. For the first time in her life, Karen took time to think about what she wanted. She had always wanted to be nurse. Her parents couldn't help her with college when she was younger, and because she was in love, she decided to get married instead of working her way through school. Then the babies came and she'd never had the money or time to go. She was afraid she was being selfish taking the money from her aunt to go to school instead of saving it or investing it in her kids' education. She talked with her husband and with a counselor. Her husband told her that they hadn't been expecting this money, it was a gift to her from her aunt, and he wanted her to use it for something that she really wanted. Her counselor encouraged her as well. She was terrified that she wouldn't be smart enough to compete with the younger students. She didn't think she'd fit in. But despite all of her fears, she enrolled in two classes.

Karen found that she loved school. She continued her cashiering job, but spent all of her extra time studying. Her family reported that she seemed more alive and animated, even though there were times when she was really busy and they'd had to pitch in. There were a few rough times when her husband or her kids felt a little shortchanged because mom wasn't always around to make their lives run smoothly. But no one was truly suffering and, though life was busier than before, everyone seemed to be okay. Karen was terrified when the first set of tests came up and shocked when she got all *A*'s and *B*'s.

Karen finished nursing school with a cum laude added to her degree. She got a job at a nearby hospital and loves her work. She describes her journey as "finding a piece of myself that I thought was lost; it was like coming home." Karen's cancer was diagnosed 15 years ago, and currently she's happy, healthy, and cancer free.

What if you don't have an unfilled childhood dream or an aunt who will leave you an inheritance? How do you do this then? Think about things that have meant something to you—times when you've felt most alive.

Larry's story: Larry had been an art major. As a young man he had worked a variety of jobs that allowed him time to paint. When he'd met his future wife, he'd decided that he need to make more money, so he took a job in sales, and the painting was relegated to a small studio in a corner of the spare bedroom. But when the kids came, that extra bedroom was needed, so the studio had been packed away. Over the years, Larry always thought that "someday" he would get back to his painting. Someday never came.

After his cancer treatment, Larry identified painting as something he always loved but never had time for. It had been so long since he'd painted he really wasn't sure he could do it again. Larry made a plan to try painting again to see if he liked it. He didn't have a lot of money or space and couldn't afford to invest in all of the materials he'd had before, so he felt a little blocked. He also felt a little foolish dabbling in this old "childish" hobby, as he called it.

But then he found an advertisement for an art program for cancer patients sponsored by a local hospital. All of the materials were provided and the class was a one-day event. He signed up for the class. After some initial awkwardness, Larry reconnected with his painting that day. The teacher was an instructor at a local community college and told Larry about some other non-credit classes he could take. Larry took one, then another, and over the course of a year, he felt that he had not only revived his artistic skills but he'd also had fun and made some new friends.

The changes in your life don't have to be big things.

Margene's story: Margene realized that she is always surrounded by people at her job and at home. Her plan recognized her need for some solitude. She started a practice of daily meditation, and once every month or two she schedules a day at a nearby retreat center, just to have time to think and pray in the quiet.

Ed's story: Ed said he had always enjoyed working with children, especially working with his sons in scouting. But after his kids were grown, he found himself always with adults. He decided to call the local branch of the Boy Scouts and see if they needed some help. He found out that they were really short on adult men to be troop leaders. Many of the boys in the area had single moms, and the troops were struggling to find dependable men to work with the boys. Ed offered to help and ended up becoming the new troop leader. He loved helping the boys learn skills, take field trips, and even took them camping with some help from a couple of parents. Ed felt that helping with the young scouts was not only wonderful fun for him but was also making a difference in the lives of the kids. He loved having the opportunity to teach the boys some things they wouldn't have been able to learn from their moms.

What is it that you've loved in your life? What seems to be missing? You don't have to make major changes; it's fine to start small. You've always wanted to go to Europe? Start by checking out some books from the library; study and plan the dream vacation you'd like to take someday. Do you wish you'd taken music lessons as a child? It's not too late.

What Makes You Happy?

What if you don't even know what you want? Start by thinking about times when you have been happy, felt alive, or been really engaged in life.

Gayle's story. Gayle was a mother of three adolescents who worked at a clerical job full-time. During her cancer treatment, Gayle did what she needed to do medically, but said she felt really noncommittal about her life. She said she wasn't really unhappy but she wasn't happy either. She felt

251

that she was just reacting to whatever her job, husband, kids, family, or social groups needed or wanted. It had been a long time since she'd thought about what she wanted.

She talked with a therapist for several weeks about what would interest her, and the work was slow. She looked at what she had enjoyed as a child and a teen; she couldn't remember much. Her childhood memories were mostly about the family needing to take care of her father who'd been disabled in an accident at work. Her mom had gone to work; they were poor; dad couldn't be left alone.

What Gayle realized was that she'd spent a lot of her life trying to keep other people happy, and she really had never had much chance to figure out what she really liked. With the help of her therapist, she began with small things. Gayle's homework was to start noticing what she liked and didn't like. This was difficult for Gayle. Her normal response was that everything was "fine" or "it doesn't matter." The therapist kept repeating: "It does matter. You matter. What you want is important."

The therapist suggested this: "Start with my office. Look around and just notice one thing you like and one thing you don't like." She didn't have to tell her answers.

Gayle started noticing what she liked and didn't like in food, in clothes, in furnishing. She noticed songs on the radio that she liked and ones that she didn't. She started listening to the news, the neighbors, and even the pastor at church and noticing what she agreed with and what she didn't. Over time, Gayle found that she did have opinions whether she chose to express them or not.

She remembered that as a young girl she had really liked bowling on the couple of times she had gone with friends, but she hadn't done it since she started dating her husband because he didn't like to bowl. One afternoon she went to the bowling lanes by herself and bowled a game. She felt self-conscious being there alone and awkward holding the ball; it had been a long time. Even though she didn't score very well, she went home feeling as if she'd done something important. She'd gone someplace alone, spent a little money on herself, and done something she wanted to do. And she realized that the world hadn't fallen apart because she'd taken a couple of hours for herself.

That was the beginning for Gayle. She kept doing small things and listening to herself. Last time she talked with her therapist, she was still working at the same job and still very involved with her family. She had also joined a bowling league with her work friends and was enjoying having a night out. She was thinking about taking some classes at a community college. She sounded alive. And she is still cancer free. **Sometimes the things that are blocking us are things in us**—like the fear of upsetting our spouse or taking time away from our parenting.

Sometimes the fears are more practical, like being afraid to leave a hated job because it pays well or carries insurance. These are big issues and it's not easy to dismiss them. But if you don't address these fears, you condemn yourself to the same old doldrums you've been in.

Sometimes there are ways to work with or around the issues and find new resources or opportunities. Sometimes people ultimately decide to stay in their current situation but also add something that makes life more fun.

Al's story. Al was in a job that had become boring to him, but he was 63, had a good salary, and was concerned that he'd have difficulty getting a new job and health insurance after his cancer treatment if he quit. He also thought about being close to retirement and collecting his pension; he'd been with his company many years. Al decided that he would stay with his job, but he didn't have to stay bored. He thought about what he needed to do to break his boredom.

Ultimately he decided that he would start planning his retirement present to himself. He had always wanted to visit Ireland where his parents had been born. He decided that he would study about Ireland and really prepare for the trip. He checked out books from the library, rented travel videos, and listened to Irish music. He talked about his plans during breaks at work and found out that other people in the company had visited Ireland. He had lunch with some of them and learned more. One of these women was becoming a good friend. In a few months he realized that he had a new outlook on life because he was interested in something and that newfound zest even made his job better.

Take a Deep Look at Your Life

Sometimes taking this deep look at your life is very hard. Some people get discouraged at this point and realize that there are big problems in their lives. You find that you are working at a job you hate or working for someone you don't respect; every day seems like slogging through quicksand. You may find that you are in a relationship that is eating you alive. Some survivors find they have been married to spouses who were alcoholic or having affairs. Several had children who were mentally or physically disabled or using drugs. Several say that their lives were so difficult and so unhappy that they really didn't care if they lived or died.

It's very difficult to confront these issues, but **it is essential for your own health that you take action to make your own life better.** With complicated issues like these, you might want to get some help from a counselor or psychologist. Even if you don't have much money, there are counseling resources available at low cost, and you and your life are worth the money, time, and energy it would take to get some help to make your life better.

A Caregiver's story. Marcia felt trapped and exhausted. Her husband, Joe, had been treated for an aggressive cancer. The stem cell transplant he'd had left him very weak and too fatigued to return to work. In addition, he seemed to be mentally foggy and, though he could be safely left alone, he was lonely and anxious and wanted her to be with him all the time.

Marcia had little time for herself and felt guilty leaving Joe. When he'd been in treatment, she'd been with him through every doctor's visit and every hospital stay. It had become a habit for both of them to arrange their lives around Joe's medical needs. One day Marcia felt a heavy tightness in her chest. When it didn't go away, she got very frightened that she

254

was having a heart attack. She got herself checked out at the hospital, and the doctors told her that her heart seemed fine, but she was having an anxiety attack.

Marcia was embarrassed at first and then realized that the anxiety attack was a wake-up call. She knew she needed some time to relax and take care of herself. She'd become isolated from her family and friends. Getting Joe through his treatments had been so time-consuming that she had given up nearly all her outside contacts.

Marcia talked with a counselor at the Cancer Center where Joe had been treated. In those conversations, Marcia realized that she had been thinking and fearing that Joe would die. She was afraid to leave him alone and, in the back of her mind, she'd thought that she would have the time to do whatever she wanted after Joe was gone. She saw Joe as a person who didn't have much time left, so she felt that she should be with him and make his life as comfortable as was possible.

What Marcia came to realize was that she was vulnerable, too. The reality was that Joe was doing relatively well, his cancer had not recurred, and, although he had some significant side effects from treatment, in all likelihood he had a long time to live. She began to think that she might not get the time she'd been planning on to do what she wanted. These thoughts led to some sadness and then to anger and resentment—and then she felt guilty for being angry and resentful of Joe who, of course, could not help being ill.

Marcia realized that if she didn't take care of some of her own needs, she'd become more and more resentful of Joe, and she knew this wouldn't be good for either of them. With much thought and a lot of courage, she started to talk to Joe about her feelings and the things she wanted to do. She wanted to attend her niece's wedding in another town. She wanted to visit her sister in another state. She wanted to go back to the volunteer work she'd dropped two years before when Joe was diagnosed. She told Joe she loved him and she would make sure that he knew where she would be and would arrange for someone dependable to be with him if she would be gone for longer times, but that she really needed to take some breaks.

Joe cried and said he knew he was a burden. He was afraid that she hated him and wanted to abandon him. Marcia was shocked by what he said. She had never wanted to leave Joe; she didn't know he was afraid of that. And, since Marcia had really thought this through with a counselor, she didn't get undone by Joe's tears and fears. She was able to answer that she loved him and would never leave him, but it was hard for her to deal with his illness without any breaks and that she really needed to connect more with her family and friends and get back to some of the things she'd loved in her own life.

It was a hard conversation, but Marcia reported that it was really good for both of them. Joe was reassured that she did love him and had no intentions of leaving; she was able to say what she needed and he did understand and agreed to try once he knew that she wasn't disgusted with him and wasn't trying to abandon him.

Marcia did get to the wedding and went back to her volunteer group. Joe was very anxious at first, but got more comfortable over time. Watching Marcia get involved in things again seemed to peak his interest, too, and he decided to start attending an exercise-based support group for cancer survivors, which was helping him build his energy back and also helping with his anxiety.

Marcia thought they were both benefiting from some time with other people. They both had new experiences to share and their conversations improved because they had more to talk about.

Put Intention into Action

Some people find that they have become more assertive about their own wants and needs after cancer treatment. Some of you may already have started dreaming about the life you would love to live. Others may be hesitant to even admit that there is something you have longed for that is more or different than your current life. What needs to change?

It may not be easy to make changes, but it's important. And when you begin to make changes, it's important to set dates and make commitments. As we all know, we can have lots of good intentions, but unless we take action, they never come to fruition. So, when you start to make changes, sit down and write out a timeline.

Larry in our previous story wanted to get back into art.

He started by making a **specific** plan that looked like this:

- By 5 p.m. next Friday I will have acquired a brochure for noncredit art classes.

- By Sunday night, I will have picked out a class.

- I will mail my registration for the class at work on Monday morning.

Your immune system understands actions, not intentions. When you act, you show respect for yourself. Remember back in session one we talked about treating ourselves the way we would treat a dear friend who had a traumatic accident? If you tell a friend you are going to do something, you need to say when it will happen and you need to follow through. Did you ever have anyone make you a promise when you were a child and then not follow through? If so, you probably remember. It's very disappointing and disappointments make us sad and sap our energy. Plan your actions in small, doable steps. Take one small step at a time. You can always reevaluate.

You don't have to begin with a five-year plan. Just commit to taking the first step or two. Your plan may be to try something new, for example, to attend a lecture on a topic you think might be interesting or to go to a demonstration class at a yoga studio. In the nutrition session we talked about trying a new food or new recipes. You might commit to trying one new thing each week for a month and write down which day of the week you'll do that. In the exercise section, we talked about the value of movement. Maybe your commitment will be to walk for 20 minutes a day 3 days this week. Name the days that you will do that and have an alternate plan to do it indoors if the weather is bad.

You don't have to promise to do something for a year; start with trying something new for a day or a week and seeing how you feel about it. And you don't have to change everything!

Start with one or two things that you'd like to try this week or this month. Decide what they are and then make the plan of what you'll do and when you'll do it. Once you've accomplished that, evaluate and make the plan for the next step.

Remember Candace Pert's research. Our cells carry our emotions. Candace Pert tells us that "our biography is our biology." In other words, give your cells "live" messages by building the biography you would love to have. Give your cells positive emotions to bask in!

The most precious gift you will ever have is the gift of your own life. When you give a gift to someone, what you hope is that they will really like it and enjoy using it. Your life is a gift. Work to love it, preserve it, and enjoy it. **Start your plan now.**

Questions for discussion and journaling:

1. Remember that the plan you make for the next step in creating your best life needs to be concrete. For example, the goal might be "I'm going to spend more time having fun with my friends and family." But the action needs to be specific. For example, "I will plan one social event per week. I will have confirmed a social event for the following week before I go to bed on Sunday night." The hardest thing for people to understand is that they need to take specific action to make their goals happen. What is one thing you would like to try? Write a specific plan for that with times and dates.

2. What do you need to have your "best life."

3. Notice how different people's needs and desires are. In your group, recognize the uniqueness of each person and how one person's plan may be perfect for him/her, but would not fit for you. Write about your own uniqueness.

Power Tool: Make a Plan

1. Go back through your memories and notes in your journal. Identify what makes you feel most alive.

   _____

   _____

   _____

   _____

   _____

   _____

2. Given the reality of your current situation, how can you BEGIN to get more zest and fulfillment in your life?

   _____

   _____

   _____

   _____

   _____

   _____

   _____

3. Identify the barriers (the things that keep you from creating the life that would be best for you). Remember that the barriers may be thoughts or feelings like guilt or fear. Be honest with yourself.

   _____

   _____

   _____

   _____

   _____

   _____

   _____

4. What does your best life look like?

_____

_____

_____

_____

_____

_____

5. Make a specific plan to make ONE aspect of your life better. Include your next steps with dates, times, and ways that you are going to make sure these next steps are going to happen.

_____

_____

_____

_____

_____

_____

_____

6. ONE STEP AT A TIME. What is YOUR FIRST STEP? Be very specific and keep your promises to yourself!

_____

_____

_____

_____

_____

_____

_____

Example:

1. Go back through your notes in your journal. Identify what makes you feel most alive.

    I feel most alive when I am painting something beautiful. I have always wanted to take a class to learn how to use different art media.

2. Given the reality of your current situation, how can you BEGIN to get more zest and fulfillment in your life?

    I have a full-time job and I have a family to care for. I don't have a lot of time for me, but I could probably find a way to go to a class once per week.

3. Identify the barriers (the things that keep you from creating the life that would be best for you).

    I feel like I have already let my family down while I went through cancer treatment. I do not want to seem selfish by taking more time away from them.

4. What does your best life look like?

    My best life certainly includes art. I love to create beauty and it makes me so happy that my family notices the difference.

5. Make a specific plan, including your next steps with dates, times, and ways that you are going to make sure these next steps are going to happen.

    I am going to find an art class that fits into my life and schedule. I am going to take a class starting this summer. I am going to ask my best friend to come over and watch my children while I am at the class. I am going to set aside one hour on Saturdays to paint.

6.   ONE STEP AT A TIME. What is step number one?
      Be very specific and keep your promises to yourself!

By Friday, I am going to call the community college and ask for a summer schedule of art classes. This weekend, I will figure out which class I want to take, and I will arrange child care by Sunday evening. On Monday, I will register for the summer art class that best fits my schedule.

CONTRACT

I, _____, promise to take action to construct my best life.

I will begin on _____ (date).

By decreasing the things that drain my energy, I will take these specific actions to lessen the energy drain:

_____

_____

_____

By increasing the things that cause me to be happy, I will take these specific actions to increase my happiness:

_____

_____

_____

The specific goal I am setting to construct my best life is:

_____

_____

_____

My FIRST STEP is:

_____

_____

_____

I will have this first step completed by:

_____ (date) _____ (time)

I will honor myself by keeping my promises I make to myself. I will check in with myself to evaluate my progress on_____ (date of each month).

I will succeed in creating my best life because I deserve to be happy, healthy, and fulfilled!

_____ Signed

_____ (date)

CONTRACT

I, _____, promise to take action to construct my best life.

I will begin on _____(date).

By decreasing the things that drain my energy, I will take these specific actions to lessen the energy drain:

_____

_____

_____

By increasing the things that cause me to be happy, I will take these specific actions to increase my happiness:

_____

_____

_____

The specific goal I am setting to construct my best life is:

_____

_____

_____

My FIRST STEP is:

_____

_____

_____

I will have this first step completed by:

_____(date) _____ (time)

I will honor myself by keeping my promises I make to myself. I will check in with myself to evaluate my progress on_____(date of each month).

I will succeed in creating my best life because I deserve to be happy, healthy, and fulfilled!

_____ Signed

_____ (date)

SESSION 12
Happiness Is...

Kay Ryan, PhD, RN

"Life is not about waiting for the storm to pass, life is about learning to dance in the rain."
Eleanor Roosevelt

Key Points
- A cancer diagnosis might change your ideas about what would make you happy.
- Although freedom from pain and cancer-related symptoms can add to happiness, there are no absolute "musts" for happiness. There are happy people in every possible circumstance. Happy people live life FULLY!
- Having unrealistic expectations about what would make you happy can make you feel disappointed and less likely to be happy.
- Being kind and being grateful come up frequently in the research as practices that encourage happiness.
- Creating your best life is accomplished by taking one step at a time. What would make you happy and what is your next step?

Introduction

While many cancer patients are just happy to be alive after treatment, others feel that they may never be happy again. Fear, uncertainty about the future, and changes in health, memory, and relationships leave some people feeling empty and unhappy. Some frantically seek the happiness that they once had or were content to "wait" for, while others find their views on happiness radically different from their "precancer" ideas.

The purpose of this session is to examine what happiness is and isn't, what seems to make people happy, and how to go about building happiness at home and in your life's work.

Definitions

It is important to define what happiness means to each of us before we look at how we might go about looking for it. How you see happiness is definitely a product of your individual background and experiences. Take a look at some of these ideas:

- To some, life is one long search for happiness.

- Some people see happiness as a "condition" that they either have or they don't.

- Others define happiness as a moment of bliss.

- Still other people see happiness as a profound, enduring feeling of contentment, or capability, or centeredness that leads to overall well-being.

What is happiness to you?

The Research

Who do you think is happier: men or women? According to several research studies, American men would rate themselves as "happier." This seems to be a curious finding to many women. While there are no definitive reasons identified for this difference, it is possible that the definition of happiness may partially explain this finding. It could be that men, as a group, rate their happiness in terms of the "right here, right now" idea of happiness, while women tend to assess a longer view of their life and circumstances before giving a rating to their happiness.

Mindfulness (intentionally focusing on the here and now more than on the past or future) is increasingly making its way to the top of strategies that help people become happier.

Americans take more antidepressants than people in other countries. What makes Americans seek ways to medicate their unhappiness more than other people? Are we less happy? Do we just "feel" life more intensely? Is our hurrying or multi-tasking making us unhappy?

Some say Americans take more pills to feel better. Some experts speculate that we expect more out of life and, thus, are easily disappointed. Others would say that we just don't want to suffer and we have the resources to do something about it. While there are definitely appropriate uses for medicines such as antidepressants, it seems important that we think about what we expect out of our lives and what we intend to do if we don't get what we expect.

You may think that some people were born with a happy personality. It is likely we have all met someone who wasn't! Is happiness a matter of personality? Is happiness a trait that exists in the DNA? Actually, there is some evidence that supports the existence of a happy personality. However, this does not seem to be a prerequisite to a happy life.

Does money make us happier? Interestingly, one of the leading researchers in the field of happiness (Dr. Ed Diener) has found that happiness seems to decline as income increases.

Sometimes good health is seen as an important ingredient for happiness. Freedom from pain and cancer-related symptoms can certainly add to happiness, according to recent studies. Another possible ingredient is the pursuit of goals. While these factors can contribute to happiness, none of them are mandatory. In fact, there are happy people in every possible circumstance; HAPPY PEOPLE LIVE LIFE FULLY!

The Grant Study

A famous longitudinal study conducted to verify the role of lifestyles and risk factors on men's health and happiness was the Grant study. This study looked at traditional risk factors, such as smoking and drinking, as well as behavioral and life factors from childhood through adulthood.

The conclusions of the study took many by surprise when scientist George Vaillant announced that we should "worry less about cholesterol and more about forgiveness…that the feelings of safety, security, and being held outweighed other risk factors." In fact, the study concluded that social connectedness was the ultimate predictor of future health—and that "Happiness is love. Full stop."

Daniel Gilbert, author of *Stumbling On Happiness* says happiness is sabotaged by what we are taught to think will make us happy. He says we also overestimate what we think will make us unhappy. We need to get past those misunderstandings and let our natural tendencies guide us to happiness.

"Happiers"

One study examined the qualities that separated happy from unhappy people in medical school. Researchers found that there were seven "happiers" that sustained people over several years:

- A well-balanced lifestyle

- Pursuit of goals

- Maintenance of relationships

- Accentuation of the positive

- Having a religious belief system

- Having honest feedback (real friends)

- A sense of purpose

Happiness after Cancer

Let's take a good look at our lives before cancer. Were you happy? Did you think you had a shot at true happiness? Were you searching for "something" or were you waiting?

Since the moment you heard those terrifying words—"you have cancer"—how has your life changed?

- Did you hear yourself saying: "I want my life back"?

- Did you find yourself seeing nature in a whole new way?

- Were you surprised at who planted themselves at your side and who suddenly became distant?

- Did your priorities shift about work, relationships, money, achievement, prayer?

- Do you think you will feel healthy again?

- Do you think you can be happy?

Perhaps you have lasting problems related to your cancer and/or treatment. According to a study on survivorship, there are several side effects of cancer treatment that can get in the way of happiness for cancer survivors:

- Lingering sleep problems

- Sexual problems

- Pain

- Cognitive problems

- Disrupted work life

- Fatigue

- Decreased sense of overall well-being compared to healthy peers

And so, while the cancer may be gone, complications may compromise quality of life among survivors.

On the Plus Side

A study on survivorship identified "happiers" uniquely experienced by survivors that included:

- A healthier perspective of what is important in life

- Psychological growth

- Spiritual growth

- Strengthened relationships

- Balancing of life's positives and negatives

- A sense that life is better (quality) than before cancer

Choices We Make That Make a Difference

There is a famous research study conducted on young men who were graduating from Harvard. Each new graduate was asked to rate his relationship with his mother and then with his father as one of these four choices:

- Very close

- Warm and friendly

- Tolerant

- Strained and cold

Thirty-five years later, the same group of men were found and asked about their current health status in middle age. It was found that 90% of those men who had not been warm and close with their mothers had developed serious diagnosed illnesses in middle age (mid-50s), compared to only 45% of those who had rated their relationships with their moms as warm and close. Nearly the same findings were true for the self-rated relationships with their fathers and development of serious illness in middle age.

At first blush, you might conclude that early relationships have irreversible effects on a person's later health status, but there is more to the story.

Dr. Dean Ornish analyzed dozens of similar studies and developed a much more encouraging theory. He believes that it's the pattern of relating that accounts for the later illnesses. In fact, he states that when young people have strained or painful relationships with their parents, they are likely to develop "armor" that keeps them from getting close to others (and protects them from being hurt). While this armor probably does preclude them from entering into risky things like relationships, it also prevents closeness, intimacy, and deep loving with an open heart.

If this pattern continues, it is likely to culminate in loneliness and illness, which go hand in hand. Dr. Ornish believes that we can decide to change—to open our hearts, and only an open heart can be nurtured.

How can we open our hearts even more? Cancer survivors say over and over that the hardest thing about being in treatment was that they HAD TO accept help from other people. They were used to helping others but not being on the receiving end.

What if a way to look at the cancer journey would be to consider how much love you were shown during those tough times? **Gratitude** comes up again and again in the literature as a way to enhance our happiness. Some of you may have learned something you didn't know before: that others do care, that they will help, that you can trust others more than you thought. And this is a gift to the "others" too. Recall how good it feels when you can help someone you love. Accepting help with gratitude is a gift to the help-giver as well as a blessing to the person being helped!

Personal Negativity and the Law of Attraction

Let's look at the reinforcing nature of personal negativity. Researchers have found that people who are negative tend to have low self-esteem, low family support, low social support, low quality of life, high distress, and poor immune response. Of interest, people who are viewed as negative tend to attract other negative people to them at the same time that their family and friends might be distancing themselves. The opposite is also true: positivity, connection, and happiness attract the same virtues and strengthen the immune system. Of course, immune system response isn't everything, but what is the down side of happiness and connection?

In his book *Cancer as a Turning Point*, Dr. Lawrence LeShan outlines his approach to surviving cancer, which is based on strategies that tell your immune system that your life is worth fighting for. He appeals to cancer survivors to add zest to their lives and to find a happy life. It would seem that choosing positive connections would be a great place to start! A key finding in stress research is that happy memories are just as "health promoting" as actual vacations. It seems that the body doesn't know if we are really there or just imagining! In fact, we could make the whole thing up (a fabulous fantasy), and our immune system would still work overtime on our behalf.

Renowned positivity researcher Dr. Barbara Fredrickson says that "positivity transforms us" and that a 3:1 ratio of positive emotions to negative emotions will help us thrive and flourish. What positives? Paying attention to simple pleasures might boost our ratios in troubled times.

Connections for Survivors and Caregivers

Do certain connections matter for our health and happiness more than others? The answer is overwhelmingly "YES"! In three separate studies, the following connections topped the list:

- Feeling close to family

- Being connected to good friends

- Belonging to a faith community

- Feeling that you are an integral part of a good marriage

The most influential factors for positive adjustment among cancer patients were found to be perceived social support and healthy coping strategies. Two major themes have emerged for healing among cancer survivors:

- A search for positive aspects of the cancer experience and

- An understanding and replacing of unachieved expectations and goals. And beyond understanding is an emerging emphasis for self-compassion, according to the research.

Along with these themes, cancer survivors who adjusted well found that their most important values became generosity, forgiveness, pleasure, and spirituality.

Rewiring Our Brains to Be Happy?

In an exciting area of recent happiness research called neuroplasticity, Dr. Rick Hanson claims that we can train our brains to be happier by savoring the smallest positives in our lives amidst the struggles and difficulties. In *Hardwiring Happiness: The New Brain Science of Contentment, Calm, and Confidence* (2015), Dr. Hanson shares his recipe for turning everyday good experiences into new (happier) brain pathways and structures using the acronym HEAL:

H: Have a positive experience (the smallest thing will work, such as sit in a comfortable chair or think of something/someone you love, immerse yourself in listening to a child laugh or watching a hummingbird fly, remember a beautiful moment or a soul-touching song).

E: Enrich it (try to stay with the feeling of the positive experience for 5 to 10 seconds by really savoring it).

A: Absorb it (soak it in and make the experience a part of you forever).

L: Link the positive experience to negative experiences (optional: if you choose, you can decide that when something negative pops into your head, possibly from the past, that you are going to think of the positive experience instead).

According to the principles of neuroplasticity, our brains are remodeled constantly by our experiences. Cancer survivors have had their share of negative experiences. However, we can also provide intentional experiences that rewire our brains to see the good in life as well. Gratitude, mindfulness, and love are the kinds of positives we can choose to experience to heal our brains and "hardwire" them for happiness!

Your Story—How do you see it?

Before Cancer:_____

_____

During Cancer Treatment: _____

_____

Survivorship:_____

_____

- **Can you think of a positive aspect of the cancer experience?** While no one wanted to have cancer, you are different because of it. Are there any ways that the person you are now is better than the person you were before? Are you more understanding, compassionate, kinder? Do people come to you because they know you are strong? Do you find more pleasure in the little things of life?

- **Can you forgive yourself for unachieved expectations or goals?** Did anything about the cancer experience change your priorities or make you more clear about what is and isn't important to you? Can you love the person who learned those lessons?

- **And finally, do you find yourself to be a little more generous—a little less impressed with "things"?** Maybe you forgive a little easier or are more spiritual because of all you've been through.

Every survivor has their own path and will grow in different ways at different rates. However, it seems very likely that you WILL grow from the experience of cancer. Be open to the process and treat yourself kindly. You deserve to be happy!

What cancer cannot do:

Cancer is so limited—
it cannot cripple love,
it cannot shatter hope,
it cannot corrode faith,
it cannot destroy peace,
it cannot kill friendship,
it cannot suppress memories,
it cannot silence courage,
it cannot invade the soul,
it cannot steal eternal life,
it cannot conquer the spirit.
–Anonymous

What cancer CAN do:

It can enable love,
it can encourage hope,
it can help you find your faith,
it can drive your search for inner peace,
it can make you aware of friendships,
it can give you meaningful memories,
it can give voice to your courage,
it can strengthen the soul,
it can give you a glimpse of eternal life,
it can rekindle the spirit.
        –K. Ryan

Living Life

Humans probably weren't programmed to be happy ALL the time (cavemen needed to want more—seek better in order for the species to progress). In fact, it was useful to be suspicious in order to stay alive. However, dwelling in the past is a big problem for us when it comes to being happy. For that matter, it really is better to forgive and forget if you are trying to find happiness.

What makes us happier: having fun or being kind? There is strong evidence to suggest that being kind is the best way to be happy, and kindness is even more powerful if we are using our signature strengths.

- What are you especially good at? (I can't sing, but I have rhythm!)

- Are you good at carpentry, baking, gardening, shopping?

- Are you an organizer?

- Are you a good listener?

- Are you a wonderful parent, grandparent, spouse, son or daughter, aunt or uncle, sister or brother, or friend?

I am especially good at:

_____

(fill in the blank)

The key to health and happiness is dependent on HOW we see the future we wish to create, and WHAT WE DO to bring about that future we wish to see, according to author (McAdams in *Spirituality and Health* magazine).

Recipe

Happiness Guru Dr. David Myers has found extensive support for the following well-being recipe:
A healthy lifestyle, Committed relationships,
And the giving and receiving of acceptance.

Steps Toward Happiness

In 2009 Gretchen Rubin published *The Happiness Project* in which she detailed a year of trying out monthly strategies to become happier. Her approach combined hard research with conventional wisdom, and she concluded that her personal "happiers" had been there all along. For Gretchen, intentional life changes such as exercise, organization, making time for love, friendships, and playing were positive steps, and she is still identifying more steps to happiness today. It would seem that there are a great many paths to happiness.

In *The Extra-Ordinary Healing Power of Ordinary Things,* Larry Dossey, MD (2006) laid out fourteen natural steps to health and happiness. His advice includes being optimistic; finding the power of music; seeing the value in dirt, bugs, and tears; and embracing mystery and spirit.

The Way to Happiness

Christiane Northrup, MD, is quoted as saying, "There is no way to happiness, happiness is the way." His Holiness, the Dalai Lama says, "It's all very simple—just be nice." Mother Theresa shared this advice for happiness: "Be kind and merciful, let no one ever come to you without leaving better and happier."

280

Cancer as a Turning Point

Dr. Lawrence LeShan (author of the book *Cancer as a Turning Point*) makes this vital point:

- You are wiser now. Cancer can truly be a turning point in our lives.

Other wisdom keepers tell us:

- Cancer cells can't stand to go slow… so slow down, relax, enjoy your life.

- Be happy for this moment. This moment is your life. [Omar Khayyam]

- Be open to healing, hoping and being. Life is glorious!

- Develop survivor pride. And when the time is right for you, help others.

Here's the message: Create your BEST LIFE—NOW.

Here's how: You can create your best life from what you have learned.

- Cancer has given you a chance to learn that there are miracles in every second of every new day.

- There isn't so much that is really important except relationships and being a good person.

- It's worth remembering—we're not in charge. We're in service.

- Perhaps you have a new appreciation for life.

- Perhaps you can own the strengths in you that have surfaced on this journey.

Perhaps you are ready to share them.
"May you heal and help others…" Charlene Costanzo

Miracles

And what if it would take a miracle for you to be happy? In *A Course in Miracles,* it is assumed that miracles are natural—and something is wrong if they AREN'T happening! Robert Henri reiterated the natural phenomenon of happiness in his writing: "There are moments in our lives, there are moments in a day when we seem to see beyond the usual. Such are the moments of our greatest happiness."

Moments

Rose Kennedy knew all about those "moments" when she said: "Life isn't a matter of milestones, but of moments." It is the greatest of gifts that happiness can be found one moment at a time. Remember the best times of your life: Were they milestones or moments? It's up to you to decide—to intend to be happy. It's important to remember to use your best gifts (your strengths), to be compassionate and truthful with yourself, to be in the moment (mindful of the positives), to be grateful, and to be open.

The most important things

Three things in human life are most important:
The first is to BE KIND,
The second is to BE KIND,
And the third is to BE KIND!
—Henry James

Questions for discussion and journaling

1. What is my intention for being happy?
2. What is my next step in pursuing my happiness?

Power Tool: Be the Music

Have you ever needed to escape—even if it's just for a few minutes—into another place and time? Remember that your immune system doesn't know if you are really in a wonderful tropical place, or just imagining it!

Sometimes you have only 4 minutes, and you can't concentrate on recreating a wonderful scene—so that's when it may just work to "become the music."

All the same meditation techniques apply:

1. Find a place to relax.
2. Sit in a comfortable position.
3. If your mind wanders, gently and lovingly bring it back to the music.
4. Focus on the music.
    Some people love music with words,
    Some people love music with just one instrument,
    Some people love orchestras …
    This is your power tool, so you decide what music you want to "be."

Suggested music: Karen Drucker, *A Time to Heal*, A compilation of inspirational, healing music to support *A Time to Heal*, a holistic wellness rehabilitation program for cancer survivors. To order the CD, go to www.mytimetoheal.org

Special Topics

Body Image
Cancer and Sexuality
Chemobrain
Cure, Healing, and Palliative Care
The Lymphatic System and Lymphedema
Spontaneous Remissions and Miracles
Talking to Children about Cancer

Body Image

Stephanie Koraleski, PhD

After cancer treatment is completed, many survivors say, "Everyone thinks I'm doing fine and I look good to the outside world, but on the inside I feel very shaky. I feel like I've lost my confidence."

You may look in the mirror and not really recognize the person you see. You see someone who may be bald; might have gained or lost weight; whose skin and coloring may look different; whose body may show scars or radiation marks. You are told that some of the changes are temporary, like hair loss, but some will be permanent. Even small changes can have a big impact on you because, after all, it's YOU! You look at this person in the mirror and wonder, "Who are you? Can this really be me?"

Your self-image is very personal to you. Most of us do care about our personal appearance and the reactions other people have to us. While some people look great in the shaved-head rock star look, others feel totally uncomfortable without hair and maybe without eyelashes. Some feel comfortable with the strangers in the grocery story who ask if they are cancer survivors or share their own stories; others feel totally invaded when someone comments on their chemocap or baldness.

However these changes feel to you, know that your feelings have been shared by many, many other people. Body image includes all of our thoughts and feelings about our entire body and the way it functions. In our culture, women are bombarded with messages about appearance and often have body image issues even when they are well, but cancer only exacerbates that.

Men are, on the one hand, told not to obsess about their appearance, but on the other hand get tons of messages about what it takes to appear strong, rugged, and virile. Distress over body image is the most common concern reported by women with breast cancer. (Fingeret 2014), and men are not immune from body image issues either.

You might have lots of different reactions to these changes in your body.

- You might be scared or shocked. Even if you had what you thought would be a minor surgery, you may have been shocked at the way your body looked or felt after surgery. Your post-surgery, post-treatment body may not look or feel like the you that you knew.

- You might be angry. You didn't ask for this, and you might be furious with all of the procedures and treatments you had to endure.

- You might be sad. It can take some time to process your grief over the changes, and often survivors can't even begin to process their feelings until the treatment is over.

- You might feel powerless. Sometimes it feels as if these huge changes have happened, and there is nothing you can do about them. You can feel hopeless or helpless about all if it.

- You can even feel guilty. Some people say they think they should just be thankful to be alive and cancer-free, and they feel guilty for feeling less than positive about the whole experience

- You may feel scared. Some survivors worry that the changes in their appearance might make them sexually unappealing. If they are single, they worry that they will never find someone to love them like they are; if they're in a relationship, they worry that their partner won't be able to accept their new appearance. Sometimes they are afraid to undress in front of their partner, and they start to avoid intimacy.

- You may worry about how other people react to you based on your appearance.

If you have ever had any of those feelings, you are normal. Those feelings are very, very common to people who have undergone cancer treatment (Preston, 2010)

The relationship with yourself is one of the most important relationships you have. It can't help but be affected by the experience of cancer and treatment. No matter what your relationship with yourself was prior to the cancer, cancer upset the balance.

Even after the treatments are over, things don't go back to normal. You have changed. You may have always been able to pull extra energy out of your toenails to give your all at work or make a family event extra special. Now you may sometimes find yourself struggling to stay awake, losing concentration, or just plain unable to do one more thing. It can be unsettling to be living in a different you; you don't know what to expect.

So. You have changed. And to get on with life in a positive way, you need to work at having a good relationship with this new you. How do you do that?

Many people find that talking with other survivors helps. Learning how others have coped, and being around their strength, humor, and wisdom can help you learn to adapt to the changes.

Exercise has also been found helpful in improving how survivors feel about their bodies. Regaining strength and muscle tone may help you feel healthier and often improves mood (Fong, 2012; Penttinen, 2011).

The American Cancer Society suggests that you attend their Look Good, Feel Better program, which offers workshops on managing hair loss, skin and nail care, cosmetics, and personal style.

But to deal with the root of the problem, you may have to go back even further and process what happened to you.

Many people got the cancer diagnosis and found themselves in surgery a week later. There may have been little time to think through what would happen. Did you get time to have your feelings? Did you get time to say goodbye to the affected part of your body? That may sound funny, but if a friend or neighbor you had known for years was going to move away, you would have said goodbye. You may even have had a party for him or her. But when you lose a body part, you often don't have the time and may not even think about saying goodbye.

Some people find it helpful to take time to give some attention to the breast or prostate or other body part that was lost. You can do this by journaling or talking with a friend or even by sitting quietly and thinking this through. Some do this with a therapist or in a support group.

But basically you are doing what you would do for a friend who had to leave. You would talk about the history of your relationship, how you got to know each other. You might talk about the things you have done together. If you are really good friends, you might even talk about the times you disagreed or fought with each other and then reconciled. And you will express the love and affection you have, and will always have, for each other.

You may feel funny talking or writing to your body, but think about this. Your body has been with you from the moment of your birth. It has grown and changed over time and has been a big part of who you felt yourself to be.

As you think about what's been done to your body and where you are now, you may want to take some time to also think about what your body has meant to you. Were you the child who was always strong and coordinated? Were you always thin and tall? Were you the kind of person who had perfect attendance and great health through most of elementary school? Were you the *Jeopardy* winner every time because your brain was so sharp?

One patient, a six-year colon cancer survivor with a colostomy, told me how much he had underappreciated his colon. He said, "I never would have even thought about the satisfaction you get from just going to the bathroom. I really miss that, and I still find myself wanting to just go to the bathroom and have a bowel movement in the old way." He thought that sounded silly, but it's not silly at all.

Every sensation in your body, every part of your body, was specially designed to help you live a good life. All were and are important. So what does it mean that you have to remove or dramatically alter one of these parts of your body to save your health? One breast cancer survivor cried in gratitude, saying she had a whole new appreciation of an old Biblical verse: "no greater love is there than this, to lay down your life for your friends."

She said she realized that her breasts had been an expression of love her whole life, and now they were indeed giving up their lives to sustain the rest of her life. She decided to write a letter of gratitude in her journal to express her appreciation for these wondrous parts of her body that were no longer with her.

In other words, your lifelong relationship with your body was precious, and you deserve time to remember it, savor it, and grieve your losses. The same goes for any other part of your life, your body, or your experience that has been lost through cancer treatment.

Nurture Yourself

In the very first session, we talked about nurturing yourself as you would nurture a friend you loved who had been hurt. This is the way to regain your sense of who you are and to rebuild your confidence. You also learned about the research on resilient people. The "at risk" people who had someone appreciating them and affirming their strengths were able to overcome their circumstances. You need to have those "alternative mirrors" that highlight your strengths, goodness, and beauty, especially when you don't feel so beautiful.

You won't regain your equanimity by telling yourself you are ugly and focusing on what is no longer there. You will heal and find your strength when you focus on being kind to yourself and your body. Remind yourself of your strengths and your courage. Even if you are having a bad day, there is a lot that you are doing right. Focus on that. Be kind to your body. Touch yourself lovingly. As you apply lotion or vitamin E oil to your scars, massage it in with love—just as if you were putting baby lotion on a precious child.

Appreciate the strength and courage your body has shown as you've gone through surgery and treatments. Say to yourself what you would say to your best friend in a similar situation. Even though you have no guarantee that you'll always be well from here on out, do know that your body is doing the best it can to keep you alive and well. Tune into yourself and listen to what your body needs. Does it need the help of more rest? Better nutrition? Exercise? Is it starving for attention and affection? Listen to your body and attend to it lovingly like you would to a friend you love who is recovering from an injury.

In a way, this is like starting a new relationship. Think of your body as being a bit afraid, a bit embarrassed for being less than perfect. Worried that you won't like it anymore. Do your very best to prove to your body that it is precious to you. Do we reject soldiers coming home from the war because they have wounds or scars? Or do we embrace the soldiers and shower kisses and hugs on them repeatedly telling them how much we hoped and prayed for their safe return, praising their courage and persistence, assuring them they are loved and wanted?

Your body has just been through its own war, and it needs your assurance that you will still love and care for it even though it's changed. With your love and attention, healing will happen. You'll learn more about what this changed body needs and wants. And as you talk and spend time together, most likely, you will learn to love, cherish, and respect this new body and even find that it is stronger in many ways than it was before.

One woman was considering reconstruction, but ultimately decided against it after she read stories about the Amazon warrior women—one-breasted women because they would cut off a breast so they could be better archers. She thought she could be better focused on the targets of her own life when her one-breastedness was a daily reminder of how precious her life was to her. She realized that, for her, seeing the scars of her surgery reminded her of her own courage and strength, and she liked those qualities she had discovered in herself.

We are not suggesting that you avoid reconstruction because that is a wonderful option for many women, but we hope that when you see the reminders of your own cancer in your body that you, too, can let them remind you of how precious your life is and how strong and courageous you have been getting through treatment.

Love Yourself

Whatever decisions you make about the targets for your own life, let the first commitment be to love yourself. You may need to start with getting to know this new you, but as you focus on the strengths and wonders you possess, it's a short path to love. Like the airlines say, in an emergency, take care of yourself first, then attend to those who need your help. This is the Time to Heal, love and respect yourself first. Then, from that well of nurturing, you will have the energy to invest in creating a life you love.

Cancer and Sexuality

Melissa Dahir, DNP, IF

This your time to heal because sexuality is a fundamental part of the human lifecycle. When the cycle is broken, your identity, personal relationships, and quality of life are compromised.

According to the World Health Organization (2002), sexual health is a state of well-being and includes physical, emotional, social, and spiritual dimensions. Issues with sexual functioning (known as sexual dysfunction) will likely occur at some point in everyone's life. In fact, you may have experienced symptoms of sexual dysfunction prior to being diagnosed with cancer.

Multiple factors can contribute to sexual dysfunction, and the cause can be physical (inability to achieve an erection or pain with intercourse), emotional (anxiety, depression, or poor body image), or interpersonal (shifting from a sexual relationship to a caregiver/survivor relationship).

Survivors have an increased risk for sexual dysfunction, especially when the cancer involves sexual or pelvic organs and the treatment compromises your body's ability to produce hormones (estrogen in women and testosterone in both men and women). The most common sexual complaints among women are vaginal dryness, pain, and feeling less attractive. For men, the most common complaints include erectile dysfunction and lack of sexual desire (Ussher, 2015).

The ways in which we view sexuality are largely dependent on our upbringing, religious beliefs, past sexual experiences (including abuse or trauma), and unrealistic expectations. In our society sexuality remains taboo because it is portrayed as something dirty or wrong. As a result, sexual health discussions are often avoided from adolescence to adulthood. When sexual issues are not addressed, it may leave you feeling anxious, depressed, or self-conscious. It can also lead to low self-esteem, relationship conflict, and a poor quality of life.

Several professional organizations at the national level believe health care providers should screen their patients for sexual dysfunction because it normalizes conversations and sends a message that sexuality is healthy for you and your partner (Ford, Barnes, Rompalo & Hook, 2013). Unfortunately, there are many barriers to optimal sexual health for patients including those without cancer.

Most health care professionals fail to discuss sexual health due to a lack of knowledge or limited time during the office visit. Some medical professionals assume that sexuality is no longer a concern after being diagnosed with cancer, especially among older adults. As a result, sexual health screening rarely takes place in the oncology or primary care setting. Patients may not initiate discussions because they are uncomfortable or worry about embarrassing their doctor. Others believe there are no treatment options available.

The reality is there are several medical and nonmedical treatment options, and if your doctor is not familiar with treatment, he or she may be able to refer you to a sexual medicine expert.

Cancer, Women, and Sexuality

You are not alone because 93% of women with various types of cancer are very concerned about their vaginal health and sexual functioning (Carter, 2015).

The main categories of female sexual functioning include desire, arousal, lubrication, orgasm, and pain. Sexual dysfunction rarely occurs as a single symptom. Rather, there is usually a domino effect in which multiple problems coexist. For example: vaginal dryness inhibits vaginal lubrication and this leads to pain with intercourse, pain with intercourse makes it difficult to orgasm, and the combination of symptoms decreases sexual desire (Feldhaus-Dahir, 2009).

Women often experience the following sexual changes due to cancer treatment:

- A lack of sexual desire or interest

- Vaginal dryness or inability to lubricate during sexual activity

- Thinning of the vaginal tissues

- Shrinkage around the vaginal opening or narrowed vaginal length

- Urinary frequency, leakage of urine, or burning with urination

- Pain with intercourse, intimate touching, or self-stimulation

- Delayed or absent orgasm

- Feeling unattractive or less feminine

Survivors have better cancer-related outcomes due to improved screening techniques and advanced medical treatments. However, the prognosis for sexual functioning is poor, especially when the treatment suppresses your body's ability to make hormones. As a result, women commonly experience vaginal dryness, burning, itching, or tearing in addition to pain during sexual activity (Lester, 2015; Schover, 2015). For example, chemotherapy, radiation, and surgical removal of the ovaries can induce ovarian failure, and it can trigger early menopause in young women. The lack of estrogen can cause the vaginal tissues to atrophy and thin, or make existing vaginal symptoms worse.

Adjuvant endocrine therapy also creates a hormone imbalance and increases the risk for sexual dysfunction. Adjuvant endocrine therapy is an oral medication prescribed to women with hormone receptor positive breast cancer, and there are two types of therapy: (1) selective estrogen receptor modulators (SERMs) such as tamoxifen are prescribed to premenopausal women; and (2) aromatase inhibitors (AIs) such as Arimidex (anastrozole), Femara (letrozole), or Aromasin (exemestane) are prescribed to postmenopausal women.

Both SERMs and AIs have increased breast cancer survival rates because they inhibit or block your body's ability to produce estrogen. On the down side, survivors often experience hot flashes, vaginal dryness or pain with intercourse, and as a result, some patients may not take the medication as prescribed (Baumgart, Nilsson, Evers, Kallak & Poromaa, 2013).

If you are suffering from side effects of cancer treatment, you need to talk with your oncologist or health care provider because there are several medical and nonmedical treatments available (this will be discussed later in the section).

Vaginal estrogen can relieve dryness or pain with intercourse. Research suggests that vaginal estrogen is safe to use in women with cancer, but more studies are needed to confirm safety in women with estrogen receptor positive (ER+) breast tumors. At present there is no official position on the use of hormones with ER+ breast cancer, and that is why you may get different opinions from one doctor to another.

Some oncologists strongly advise against the use of vaginal estrogen, and others are fine with prescribing estrogen when the symptoms are severe and quality of life is poor because they believe the risk for recurrence of cancer is minimal. Therefore, if cancer treatment has affected your sexual health and quality of life, discuss the pros and cons with your oncologist. Once you have all the facts, the final decision is up to you.

Testosterone replacement is an off-label treatment for female sexual dysfunction, and it appears to be safe in all female cancer survivors. Testosterone is a good alternative if you do not feel comfortable using vaginal estrogen because it doesn't appear to raise estrogen levels in your blood or increase the risk for recurrence of breast cancer (Glaser, 2010; Witherby et al., 2011).

Different forms of testosterone replacement include cream (applied to the vagina, inner thigh, or forearm), vaginal suppository, oral pill or lozenge, injection, or subcutaneous pellet (inserted under the skin). Testosterone can improve sexual desire, decrease vaginal dryness and irritation, increase vaginal lubrication and response to orgasm, and reduce pain with intercourse. In fact, testosterone may offer you relief of other symptoms such as fatigue, anxiety, depression, difficulty sleeping, hot flashes, and joint pain (Glaser, York & Dimitrakakis, 2011).

Testosterone can also improve sexual health quality of life. A recent study supported the use of vaginal testosterone in women with breast cancer taking AIs (Dahir & Travers, 2014). A low-dose vaginal testosterone cream was applied to the vaginal opening once daily, and after four weeks of treatment, survivors reported the testimonials:

- *I never knew I had options. I hope you can help more women like me.*

- *After using the cream I was almost pain free—thank you for that.*

- *I no longer use Vagisil and I feel like my vaginal tissues have healed.*

- *The testosterone cream caused moisture in my vagina in 24 hours of use. Prior to using the cream, there was no moisture.*

- *I was really happy I did this. I always enjoyed cuddling with my husband, but I am feeling like I am more alert and aware of my sexual thoughts.*

Self-care

- Vaginal hormones are important to maintain healthy urinary and vaginal tissues. A lack of estrogen can cause the vaginal tissues to atrophy and thin. As a result you may experience vaginal dryness or burning, leakage of urine, vaginal itching, or pain with intercourse.

- A lack of testosterone can contribute to vaginal dryness and decrease sexual desire. The ovaries produce 50% of your body's testosterone, and cancer treatments that suppress testosterone production can increase the risk for sexual dysfunction. This includes surgical removal of the ovaries, chemotherapy, and radiation.

- Some women say that penetration is not possible or they feel like something is "in the way." The use of a lubricant can temporarily increase vaginal moisture and minimize pain with intercourse, and they can be purchased from a local pharmacy or grocery, or on the Internet. It is important to know that all lubricants are not created equal, and warming lubricants can increase vaginal irritation. Choose a lubricant that is water-based and glycerin-free such as Slippery Stuff (also known as FemGlide), KY Liquid, or Pre-Seed. Another safe alternative is a silicone-based product because it stays fluid until it is washed off. You may want to purchase this type of lubricant if you are using dilators to stretch the vaginal opening or relax the pelvic floor. Be sure to use silicone-based lubricants with caution around slippery surfaces such as floors or bathtubs because it could increase the risk for a fall.

- An over-the-counter vaginal moisturizer such as Replens or K-Y LIQUIBEADS can also relieve vaginal irritation and reduce pain with intimacy or pelvic exams. Both products are inserted vaginally and do not contain hormones. Replens contains polycarbophil, and it has the ability to retain up to 60 times its weight in water. Replens produces a moist film over the vaginal tissues and delivers continuous moisture for up to three days. It is common to have a grayish-colored discharge as dead cells slough away and should resolve with regular use.

- A lack of vaginal hormones elevates the vaginal pH, which can increase this risk for vaginal infections (yeast or bacteria) and urinary tract infections. If you experience vaginal burning or itching; paper cut tears around the vaginal opening; pain during or after intimacy; or burning with urination, see your health care provider. If an infection has been ruled out, the symptoms are probably due to a lack of hormones around the vaginal opening.

- If vaginal irritation or pain with intercourse is not resolved with lubricants or vaginal moisturizers, talk to your oncologist or health care provider about other treatment options such as vaginal estrogen or testosterone replacement. As previously discussed, the use of vaginal hormones is generally not an issue in most types of cancer, but historically women with ER+ breast cancer have been advised against the use of vaginal estrogen. In addition, the use of vaginal estrogen and AIs is generally not recommended because local estrogen may interfere with the medication's ability to suppress estrogen in your body, but clinical trials suggest the combined treatment does not pose a risk and more research is needed. If the symptoms are severe, you may accept the possible risks and that is okay because the ultimate decision is up to you.

- As previously discussed, testosterone is an alternative to estrogen replacement and it has not been associated with serious adverse side effects when used in appropriate doses. Testosterone is not just a male hormone, and it is important for sexual functioning in women because it supports sexual desire in addition to vaginal lubrication and sensation. Testosterone can increase vaginal moisture and decrease pain with intercourse. It can also relieve other symptoms such as hot flashes, night sweats, joint pain, mood disorders (anxiety, depression, irritability), and issues with sleep (Glaser et al., 2011).

- Ask your doctor about a physical therapy referral. Physical therapists offer individualized treatments to reduce pain and help you function better within your daily life. This includes relaxation techniques, skin rolling to break up scar tissue, and exercises to maintain strength. In addition, pelvic floor physical therapists have specialized training to treat tight pelvic floor muscles, and this therapy can reduce pain during sexual activity.

- There are several relaxation techniques you can try on your own. This includes meditation or yoga, listening to soft music, guided imagery, or diaphragmatic (deep) breathing. Alternative treatments such as acupuncture, massage therapy, or hypnosis can also be helpful (Chang et al., 2015).

Cancer, Men, and Sexuality

It is not uncommon to feel less of a man if your cancer treatment has affected sexual functioning. Although these changes are uncomfortable, do not feel embarrassed to discuss these issues with your health care provider or partner.

Men often experience the following sexual changes due to cancer treatment:

- Difficulty achieving or maintaining an erection (erectile dysfunction)

- Decreased length of penis

- Curving of the penis (known as Peyronie's disease)

- Diminished quality of orgasm

- Dry ejaculation (orgasm without semen discharge)

- Leakage of urine with orgasm

- Decreased or absent sexual desire

Cancer treatments can interrupt sexual functioning especially when the cancer affects pelvic organs (colon, rectum, prostate, bladder, or testicles). Treatments that lower or inhibit your ability to produce testosterone can lower sexual desire and cause erectile dysfunction (ED). This has been associated with anxiety, depression, and low self-esteem.

The following treatments can lower your testosterone level: surgical removal of the testicles, chemotherapy, radiation, and hormone therapy (decreases testosterone production) for prostate cancer. In addition, surgical removal of the prostate or bladder can damage or remove certain nerves, and radiation can interrupt blood supply to the nerves, which can make it difficult to achieve an erection on your own.

Aside from cancer treatment, medical conditions such as diabetes, high blood pressure, and high cholesterol can increase the risk for ED. It is also common for men to experience changes in sexual functioning as they get older. In fact, you may have noticed a decline in sexual functioning prior to being diagnosed with cancer. ED can occur at any age, and the risk significantly increases after age 60. In fact, 67% of men at age 50 suffer from ED, and the risk increases to 89% for men at age 75 (Shiri et al., 2003).

Some survivors feel less of a man or a loss of identity due to sexual dysfunction and the psychological impact of cancer. This can affect your mental health, body image, and sexual functioning. Coping with a diagnosis of cancer and the unwanted side effects can leave you feeling tired, anxious, or depressed. This can further contribute to sexual issues and cause strain in your relationship.

If sexual dysfunction has affected your quality of life, talk with your oncologist about treatment options because you may need a referral to a sexual medicine expert.

Self-care

- Dry orgasm is common after surgery or radiation for prostate, bladder, or testicular cancer if the glands that make semen are removed. You will produce sperm, but you will orgasm without ejaculate fluid because the sperm absorbs back into your body. Some men say that a dry orgasm feels normal, but others say it is less intense.

- Men with prostate cancer have a high risk for sexual dysfunction. Studies suggest that 50 to 80% of men have erectile dysfunction during the first year. A radical prostatectomy (surgical removal of the prostate) can delay recovery of erections due to nerve stretching, thermal damage or nerve tissue injury while controlling bleeding, and inflammation due to surgery in general. Some urologists use a "nerve-sparing technique" (also known as the robotic surgery), and this could decrease the risk for ED. However, it can take up to two years for the nerves to heal even when this technique is used.

- Penile rehabilitation should be started as soon as possible for prostate cancer survivors to preserve the ability to have spontaneous erections. Please note: penile rehabilitation can also be used for other types of cancer as well. The goal is to increase blood flow to the penis so that you can eventually have an erection on your own. A urologist will initiate this type of rehab, and treatments include oral medications such as Viagra, a vacuum erection device (also known as a penis pump), penile injections, and urethral suppositories.

- As previously mentioned, various cancer treatments can cause sexual issues, so if you cannot have erections on your own, there are several options such as

  - PDE-5 inhibitors such as Viagra (sildenafil), Cialis (tadalafil), or Levitra (vardenafil)—oral medications to help you achieve an erection or increase hardness of erection. You can take the medication 20 minutes before sexual activity, and if you take them on an empty stomach, you will have a better response. The down side is that they can be expensive and will not work for severe ED, especially if your testosterone levels are very low. NOTE: If you have high blood pressure or heart disease, it is okay to take these medications, but they should NOT be used if you are taking any medication that contains nitroglycerin.

- A vacuum erection device (VED) can be purchased online or through a urology office. The VED works by placing the penis in a vacuum cylinder and squeezing the pump to increase pressure within the penis. The pressure draws blood into the penis to create an erection. A tension ring placed at the base of the penis secures the erection for up to 30 minutes. The VED can be uncomfortable and takes practice, so don't get frustrated.

- Muse is a suppository that contains a prostaglandin, also known as alprostadil. If you did not get an erection with Viagra (sildenafil)–type medications, you can try Muse alone or in combination, as this may offer better results. The suppository is placed inside the urethra (at the tip of the penis) after urination because it is easier to insert. The medication can make you feel dizzy or lightheaded, so do not use if you have low blood pressure. The benefit to Muse is that it is not invasive, but it does not always produce an erection and can cause mild burning in the urethra.

- Penile injection therapy is a nonsurgical option if you do not have results with other treatments. The injectable solution usually contains phentolamine, papaverine, and prostaglandin E1. The combination injection is often referred to as "tri mix" and is available from a compounding (specialty) pharmacy. These medications dilate blood vessels in the penis and cause the penis to engorge. Caverject (alprostadil) is another type of injection that only contains prostaglandin E1 and is available by prescription at your local pharmacy. Your urologist will teach you how to inject the medication at home. A small needle is used to inject the medication into the side of your penis. Don't panic. The needle is small, and you should get an erection in 5 to 10 minutes. The effects should last for about one hour so be sure to inject the prescribed dose and slowly increase as directed because injecting too much could cause a prolonged erection that is painful, and you may need surgery to release the blood.

- A penile prosthesis is a procedure in which a urologist surgically places a pair of bendable rods within the erection chambers of the penis. The rods are connected to a pump outside the body. When you press on the pump, it will transfer fluid from the reservoir to the cylinders in the penis, thereby causing inflation and result in an erection. Pressing on a deflation valve at the base of the pump returns the fluid to the reservoir, and the penis will return to a normal flaccid state.

- Testosterone levels decrease with cancer treatments such as radiation, chemotherapy, and hormone therapy for prostate cancer in addition to natural aging. Men with low testosterone have symptoms of fatigue, low libido, issues with erectile functioning, decreased muscle strength, sadness, and loss of enjoyment in life. Ask your doctor if you are a good candidate for testosterone replacement. Prostate cancer survivors are usually advised against testosterone replacement because it could increase the risk for recurrence of cancer, but some doctors agree that quality of life is also important when symptoms are severe. A blood draw can check your testosterone level. If it is low or low normal, your doctor may prescribe a cream or gel that you will apply on the inner thighs or under arms.

Some urologists and sexual medicine experts offer additional routes of testosterone replacement such as a testosterone injection that lasts about 2 to 3 weeks or a testosterone pellet (Testopel) that is inserted underneath the skin and slowly dissolves over 3 to 5 months.

Men and Women Take Note

- Feel free to engage in sexual activity if you have the desire. Many cancer survivors worry that chemotherapy will affect their sexual partner, but medical evidence suggests there is no increased risk. However, you should avoid intercourse while healing from genital surgery. You should also avoid sexual contact if you have a low white blood cell count (neutropenia) due to the risk for infection or low platelets (thrombocytopenia), which can increase the risk for bleeding (Goncalves & Groninger, 2015). Please consult your oncologist if you have any additional questions or concerns.

- Sexual dysfunction can make you feel less masculine or feminine. It is important to have open communication with your partner and discuss the changes you are going through. This may feel uncomfortable or embarrassing, but avoiding the topic will likely cause strain in your relationship. If open communication is not easy for you, consider writing a note or sending an email to your partner.

- The physical and emotional effects of cancer can lead to psychological distress. Feelings of anxiety, depression, and fatigue can impact sexual functioning (Usshler, 2015). These feelings are situational, and you may need to take an antidepressant during this time. Some antidepressants such as Prozac (fluoxetine), Zoloft (sertraline), Paxil (paroxetine), Lexapro (escitalopram), Cymbalta (duloxetine), and Effexor (venlafaxine) can delay ejaculation for men, delay or inhibit orgasm for women, and decrease sexual desire in both men and women. These medications may improve your emotional well-being, but the negative sexual side effects could cause you distress. If you are experiencing unwanted sexual side effects caused by antidepressants, talk to your doctor about trying a different medication. Wellbutrin (bupropion) is a good alternative because it can have a positive effect on sexual functioning, and it can be taken alone or in combination with another antidepressant. NOTE: If you are taking tamoxifen for breast cancer, talk to your oncologist before starting a new medication because antidepressants can compromise the cancer drug's effectiveness, and this could increase the risk for recurrence of cancer (Binkhorst et al., 2013).

- Don't forget about your partner's feelings. You partner may be avoiding sexual activity due to fear of upsetting you or worry it would be selfish to think about their own sexual needs. In addition, your partner may have lost the desire for sex because they are focused on your health and survivorship.

- If sexual intercourse is not possible, there are other ways to keep a close connection. Talk to your significant other about alternative ways of showing affection such as hugging, snuggling, kissing, or massage. Depending on your comfort level, you may want to try "outercourse." This is an intimate activity between a couple that has all the benefits of mutual touching without vaginal penetration. This is where a male partner places his penis in between a woman's thighs and approaches in a spooning position (feel free to use a lubricant to reduce friction). Other options include oral intercourse, or both partners could self-pleasure at the same time while lying side by side.

- If you had colon or bladder surgery, you may have an ostomy to empty urine or feces. It is common to worry about sounds, smells, or the bag coming off during sexual activity. The following suggestions can improve your sexual experience: avoid foods that produce gas or light a candle, irrigate the ostomy bag before sexual activity and attach a new bag. In addition, men can wear a comfortable T-shirt and women can wear a camisole or corset to cover the bag during sexual activity.

Final Thoughts

Patients are diagnosed with cancer earlier in life with newer screening techniques, and they have better cancer-related outcomes due to advances in medical treatments. But as the number of aging survivors increases, the risk for sexual dysfunction also increases, and the sexual consequences of cancer treatment can impair quality of life and cause strain in your relationship. You need to know that sexual health discussions are often avoided because your health care provider does not want to offend you or does not want to take the focus away from cancer.

In addition, your doctor may not inquire about sexual issues due to time constraints or a lack of training in sexual medicine, but that does not mean you have to give up. There are several medical and nonmedical treatments to improve sexual functioning, and sometimes you have to be your own advocate.

In closing, everyone has the right to a satisfying sexual life, and this requires a positive and respectful approach from all members of the health care team to ensure the best possible outcome (WHO, 2002). The health care team must work in collaboration to ensure ongoing sexual health assessments because sexual functioning can change throughout the course of cancer treatment. Therefore, optimal sexual functioning is possible with an integrative approach. This includes you, your partner, oncologists, urologists, gynecologists, general practitioners, sexual medicine experts, nurses, physical therapists, and mental health therapists. This is your time to heal. Don't be silent because your sexual health is important, and there are several treatment options available.

Questions for discussion and journaling

1. How has cancer affected your sexual functioning? Did your oncologist or another health care provider talk to you about the possible sexual side effects to cancer treatment before you started treatment? If not, how did this make you feel? If you had additional information, would this have changed your approach to treatment?

2. Looking back, at what point along the cancer journey would you have felt open to discussing sexual health issues? Would you have been offended if your oncologist talked about sexuality immediately after your cancer diagnosis, or would you have been open-minded?

3. Have sexual issues due to cancer treatment affected the intimate relationship with your partner? If so, what can you do to express the changes you are going through? Are you embarrassed or ashamed to discuss your feelings? What could make the discussion easier for you?

4. How has sexual dysfunction affected your emotional well-being? Do you feel self-conscious? Are you experiencing anxiety or depression? What have you done to address these feelings?

5. What self-treatments have you tried to deal with sexual dysfunction? Were they effective and would you be willing to share with others? If they were not effective, are you willing to try other treatments?

6. Did you receive conflicting information about the safety of using hormone replacement such as estrogen or testosterone? If so, how did this make you feel? Did you talk to your health care provider about risks and benefits of using hormone

replacement? If quality of life is important, did you communicate your feelings? How can you put your needs first?

7. If your questions about sexual health treatments were not answered, did you get a second opinion? If not, would you be comfortable seeking a sexual medicine expert on your own? Are you afraid your oncologist would be angry or abandon you if you talked to someone else?

Chemobrain: Clearing the Fog

**Joyce Swanson, MS. LMPH, NCBTMB and
Lisa Merrifield, PhD**

One big source of stress for cancer survivors can come from feeling as if their minds aren't working the same way.

- Are you having difficulty concentrating and remembering details?

- Do attempts at multitasking result in overload?

- Do you often feel confused as if your brain is in a fog?

- Are you constantly losing things?

If this sounds familiar, there is hope! These symptoms have a name, and there are things you can do to help your brain to work more effectively again.

People look forward to the end of cancer treatment so that life can get back to normal. Our picture is often that reaching this point in recovery will be accompanied by the *Rocky* theme as we reach the top of the steps. Goal accomplished. Except that as we reach those steps with our fist pumping in the air with excitement, we might lose one of our running shoes, stop halfway up because we cannot remember why we are running to the top, become distracted by a group of pigeons who fly by, and have difficulty finding the words to ask someone for directions.

These are just some of the symptoms of a condition commonly referred to as "chemobrain." Some researchers prefer to call it "cancer-related brain fog" because even cancer patients who have not had chemotherapy can show signs of some cognitive (mental) changes. Up to 75% of cancer survivors report having at least some of these symptoms (Gordon, 2014).

Chemo brain is also reported with targeted therapies like Herceptin and hormonal therapies and even after surgery but before chemotherapy happened. Researchers think this may be related to the effects of inflammatory cytokines or to an immune response to the cancer itself (Gordon, 2014) For years, cancer survivors have reported thinking and memory problems that can occur after cancer treatment. Many people with memory problems still score well on cognitive tests, which left doctors to wonder whether chemobrain actually exists (Nelson, 2014).

It has been difficult to document what actually happens because the effects are subtle and often don't show up on standard neuropsychological tests, but cancer survivors often report problems with memory and concentration, finding the right word, slowness in their thinking and responding, being less coordinated, difficulty making decisions, inability to handle multitasking, decreased math or language skills, and other problems with brain functions. As new information has been discovered, we now know that chemobrain is real and is experienced by up to 74% of cancer patients (Janelsins, 2011).

At this time, researchers believe that a variety of factors put people at increased risk for cognitive problems. These include the length of treatment, the dose of chemotherapy, increasing age, estrogen deficiency, hormonal therapies, presence of the APOE genetic mutation, and certain kinds of chemotherapies and other treatment drugs. Other factors, such as poor diet, pain, sleep disturbance, menopause, and/or anemia can also contribute to cognitive problems. At this point, researchers say that up to 40% of cancer patients receiving chemotherapy complain of memory and attention deficits.

Research with rats at the University of West Virginia (2008) reported that rats on chemotherapy also lose memory, but when the researchers added injections of a specific amino acid to the chemo regimen, memory loss was prevented. The researchers do not know yet if the drug is safe in humans, but research is ongoing. There is also ongoing research to determine what types of rehabilitation programs might be most helpful.

Despite the many questions, it is clear that the symptoms associated with chemo brain can be a very frustrating and debilitating side effect of cancer treatment. Only in the last few years have medical professionals really started to take notice. A UCLA study in 2006 found that chemotherapy causes changes to the brain's metabolism and blood flow that can linger at least ten years after treatment.

Dr. Daniel Silverman and his colleagues used positive emission scans to show that the brains of subjects who had undergone cancer treatment were working harder to perform memory tasks than those in the control group who had not undergone treatment. Specifically the PET scans revealed that blood flow to key areas of the frontal cortex and the cerebellum were affected (Silverman, 2006).

In a more recent study, chemotherapy patients were matched with cancer patients who did not need chemotherapy. Those who did have chemotherapy reported more cognitive complaints, and their functional MRIs showed their multitasking brain activation decreased from the start of treatment until 6 months after treatment (Deprez 2014).

So how long does chemobrain last?

For many patients, the problems are significantly better two years after treatment; for some, the problems are longer lasting. Dr. Karen Syrjala and her colleagues at the Fred Hutchinson Cancer Research Center started a study of chemobrain survivors of stem cell transplants in 2004. After the transplant, these folks who had had intense chemotherapy had significant reductions in cognitive performance, but within a year after treatment, they seemed to have improved in most ways. When they followed up with these same people in 2011, they found no difference between the survivors and the regular population in high-level multitasking, but the survivors were still lower in information processing speed, memory, and motor coordination. (Syrjala, 2011).

In her book, *Chemobrain: How Cancer Therapies Can Affect Your Mind,* noted science journalist Ellen Clegg cuts through the scientific jargon and explains how chemotherapy works at the most basic biological level. As an objective journalist, she gives voice to the medical professionals who remain skeptical of this condition while she provides cancer survivors with the knowledge to understand and cope with the aftermath of treatment. She includes many tactics and strategies for dealing with cognitive problems, multitasking, and other skills associated with reentering the workforce and daily life.

If this interests you, read on as we review some of the possible causes, common symptoms and possible strategies regarding chemobrain.

Factors that may contribute to this effect include

- Aging

- Depression

- Menopause

- Fatigue

- Medications

- Emotional upheaval associated with cancer

- Physical debilitation

- Sleep disruption

- Low blood counts

- Stress

- Anemia

- Fatigue

- Lack of fluids or minerals, or other metabolic problems

Some signs and symptoms of chemobrain are these:

- Confusion; being unusually disorganized

- Difficulty completing tasks and multitasking

- Difficulty concentrating

- Difficulty finding the right word

- Difficulty learning new skills

- Difficulty comprehending what people are saying

- Fatigue

- Feeling of mental fogginess

- Short attention span

- Forgetfulness; short-term memory problems

- Taking longer than usual to complete routine tasks

- Trouble with verbal memory, such as remembering a conversation

- Trouble with visual memory, such as recalling an image or list of words

Try some of these basic strategies for managing chemobrain:

- Take intermittent naps.

- Write things down: keep a log or checklist containing daily reminders.

- Ask people to repeat information.

- Carry around a small pad so you can easily write down reminders for yourself.

- Take on one task as a time.

- Have someone accompany you to your doctor visits. Don't be afraid to ask questions.

- Use external aids such as lists, notes, personal calendars, Post-it notes, timers, and friends/ spouses.

- Take special care to plan and organize activities.

- Use color coding to help your brain sort drawers or tasks.

- Take notes. Write down lists of things to do. Write down your appointments. This seems simple, but it's actually a whole brain activity and using your whole brain instead of just trying to memorize by repetition seems to help the brain function better. When you write things down, you are thinking of the item, physically writing it, seeing it written, putting the list in your purse, pocket, or wallet, remembering to take the list out and look at it, and rereading the list. This means that several parts of your brain are involved, and that seems to help the brain recover function.

- Put things away in the same place, for example, the planner always goes in the purse, keys always go on a special hook or one place on the desk. Getting in the habit of putting things in the same place can help when memory fails.

- When you need to remember something, like a name or a PIN number, try to make a story about it. The brain seems to remember stories better than random numbers.

- Eliminate distractions when you need to think. Turn off the TV, shut the door, do one thing at a time.

- Play a musical instrument. Listening to music can also help with whole brain function.

- Practice relaxation exercises to decrease stress. Stress further aggravates memory issues.

- Increase physical activity.

- Join a support group.

- Laugh often.

- Exercise your memory like a muscle.

- Stimulate your mind. Brain strengthening mental activities can include doing crossword puzzles, playing a musical instrument, painting, cooking, woodworking, and gardening.

- Learn something new. This may take a while, but the act of learning new things builds new connections in the brain just like regular exercise can build muscle in your body.

In the past few years, there has been a surge in resources associated with keeping our brains in top shape. One example is *Keep Your Brain Alive: 83 Neurobic Exercises to Help Prevent Memory Loss and Increase Mental Fitness* by Lawrence C. Katz, PhD, and Manning Rubin. These simple brain exercises involve doing something familiar in unexpected ways. This stimulates the brain's natural ability to create brain nutrients called neurotrophins, which in turn help to keep our brains younger and more flexible.

Examples include "brushing roulette" (brushing your teeth with your nondominant hand), "blazing new trails" (taking a new route to a familiar place), and taking brain breaks. Working crossword puzzles, doing Sudoku, reading mysteries, playing card games and board games and fixing things around the house are common examples of things that keep your brain active. Lateral thinking puzzles are another possibility.

Try some of these thinking puzzles:

1. Three babies are born on the same day, same year, same mother and father. How is this possible?

2. A girl who was just learning to drive went down a one- way street in the wrong direction but didn't break the law. How is this possible?

3. How can you throw a ball as hard as you can and have it come back to you, even if it doesn't hit anything, there is nothing attached to it, and no one else catches or throws it? (Answers are at the end of this session.)

A simple and effective health break is to take a walk. Physical exercise produces BDNF (brain-derived neurotrophic factor), which acts like Miracle-Gro for the brain. Cross lateral movements (right hand crossing the midline and touching left knee, left hand crossing the midline and touching right knee) help to stimulate both sides of your brain. Learning to juggle, dancing, and many aerobic movements are other ways to cross the midline.

Even more simply, when you use a calculator, put it on your nondominant side so that you have to cross the midline to use it. If that sounds like much too activity for you, handshakes and high-fives cross the midline and also provide the added benefit of connection and celebration.

Balancing activities can help to develop the cerebellum, which is located at the back bottom of the brain. The cerebellum, also known as the little brain, is involved in thought coordination and controls how quickly you can integrate new information and thinking on your feet. Although the cerebellum represents only 10 percent of the brain's volume, it houses about half the neurons. Only recently has its role in processing speed become clearer.

After chemo, we might feel as if we are back using one of the first computers that was developed. While our brain still does most functions, the process can be very slow and frustrating. Low activity in the cerebellum is associated with slow movements and thought processes, trouble learning new information and routines, confusion, and difficulty with details, planning and follow-through.

So to upgrade to a higher speed, balance exercises are the ticket. Many exercises, such as standing on one foot, are simple. The balance games and yoga poses on the Wii Fit are fun and great for your brain. It is very important to do these exercises in a safe manner. Please consult your physical therapist or other medical professionals to find the best and safest way to add this to your daily routine.

Finally, novelty and laughter stimulate the brain in yet another way, so if you combine physical movement with learning—something new that causes you to laugh—it's a bonanza of brain benefits.

To get started, list the activities that are presently in your routine. Include general exercises, balance activities, and puzzles that challenge your brain.

_____

_____

_____

_____

_____

_____

Now, think about some ways you could add to this list. Write down a few that you are willing to do in the next week to exercise your brain.

_____

_____

_____

_____

_____

If the previously mentioned low-tech tips and tricks have resulted in less than full relief, you might consider the more high-tech approach known as neurofeedback. Neurofeedback refers collectively to biofeedback techniques that reflect brain function. Individually, the techniques may be identified as hemoencephalography (HEG) biofeedback, EEG Neurofeedback, Quantitative EEG Training, or LENS. They are different but related, and all can be helpful in improving the symptoms of chemobrain or brain fog.

Neurofeedback has been demonstrated to be helpful in improving mood, reducing anxiety, increasing energy, and strengthening memory in people who are struggling in these areas as well as people who just want to improve their functioning. It is also often tremendously helpful in restoring restful sleep. Fortunately, a history of prior treatment for cancer does not appear to block the beneficial effects of neurofeedback or affect a person's ability to hold onto their improvements.

At this point in time, there is adequate research to demonstrate that neurofeedback techniques can be effective, but not much in the way of comparing the different techniques in terms of which one would be "best" for brain fog in any particular person.

All of the techniques involve electronics and some kind of sensor placed on the head. These sensors pick up information about different aspects of brain function and feed it back to you, thus enabling you to modify your brain's activity. For example, you can learn to deliberately increase the blood flow to certain brain areas that are known to be underactivated in people who experience depression. Or you might focus on training the brain waves in an area of relatively slow activity to go faster.

As the brain waves speed up, often you feel less slowed down in your thinking. It also appears that sometimes just disrupting the status quo can help the brain manage its energy in a new and different way, leading to improvement in symptoms. An experienced clinician can choose the technique that best meets your needs and current abilities.

You can read more about neurofeedback on the website for the International Society for Neurofeedback and Research (www.ISNR.org), which includes research papers and a directory of clinicians who provide neurofeedback services.

Remember that chemobrain (brain fog) generally improves with time as your physical health and functioning get better. Be patient with yourself because your body has been through a lot as you've been diagnosed and treated for cancer. The surgeries, medications, pain, stress, and other treatments were hard on your body. It takes time for everything to get back to full functioning.

Did you remember that there were going to be answers to the questions in the chemobrain section? Do you remember what your answers were? Either way, here are answers to the lateral thinking puzzles.

1. They are triplets.
2. She is walking.
3. Throw the ball up into the air.

Cure, Healing, and Palliative Care

Cathy Barnes, RN, MSN

The experience of cancer can be transformative. Cancer nurses often see people with cancer evolve, grow, change, transform, and heal. Patients often give credit to their physicians, nurses, and cancer treatment for making them well. But *you* are part of the self-healing process.

In her book, *Anatomy of the Spirit,* Caroline Myss, PhD, discusses the differences between curing and healing. She states, "Healing and curing are not the same thing. A cure occurs when one has successfully controlled or abated the physical progression of an illness" (p. 47).

Curing is passive and is outside of the person's control. The patient gives his or her authority over to the physician, and treatment is prescribed. Chemotherapy, surgery, and radiation are all curative therapies for cancer.

Almost all cancer patients and their families hope for cure and that is usually the first goal of treatment. More and more, the therapies to treat cancer are successful in curing cancer. But even when the cancer is cured, sometimes people are not healed. Sometimes hearts and spirits have been battered by life or by the cancer treatment itself. That's when we need to put more active effort into healing.

Healing is active. "It's an internal process that includes investigating one's attitudes, memories, beliefs with the desire to release negative patterns that prevent full emotional and spiritual recovery," according to Myss. Healing is personal. No one can heal on behalf of someone else. Talking does not heal, but taking action does.

Healing requires unity of mind and heart (Myss, 1996). Connecting heart and mind is at the root of wholeness. These insights are some seeds for creating an inner landscape of connection and balance between mind and heart healing. Myss suggests:

- Think love. Live in appreciation and gratitude.

- Be consistent: live what you believe.

- Change is constant. Every life goes through phases of difficult change as well as peace. Learn to go with the flow rather than try to stop change.

- Never look to another person to make you happy. Happiness is an internal, personal attitude and responsibility.

- Life is essentially a learning experience. Every situation, challenge, and relationship contains some message worth learning.

- Positive energy works more effectively than negative energy in each and every situation.

- Live in the present moment, and practice forgiveness of others.

- Make a conscious and willing choice to heal.

These actions that we take might be focused on healing old memories, healing relationships, healing wounds in our spiritual life, or healing hurting parts of our bodies. It's up to you to decide where to focus your healing actions.

Because healing is active, you are the only authority on the kind of life that would bring you greater meaning, enthusiasm, zest, and excitement. You are the only one who can define what healing is to you.

Getting Help along the Way

The cancer experience is a journey that often forces people to encounter issues of mortality, survival, and things that give substance and meaning to life. Because of this reality, people can often see the beauty of the rose even while being aware of the thorns.

Human life is fragile. This awareness becomes real as people with cancer consider issues of dying. This section is written in hope of making the unfamiliar territory of living life fully until you die slightly more comfortable. Terms such as "palliative care" and "hospice care" will be explained to describe individualized care that can be provided to facilitate the best care and quality of life from diagnosis until cure or death.

In recent years, the public and professional mindset has changed from viewing death as a failure to recognizing it as a natural universal experience. Viewing death as a part of the life cycle has provided the health care community an opportunity to improve the quality of life and the quality of dying for individuals and families facing life-threatening illness.

With this new view, the pattern of **referral to palliative care has changed from the last days of life to the time of initial diagnosis of disease. In some areas of the country, palliative care is offered from the start of diagnosis; in other areas of the country, palliative care may not be offered until you are diagnosed with advanced, recurrent, or metastatic disease.** With earlier referral, the members of the palliative care team (nurse, physician, social worker, clergy/chaplain) have the opportunity to more completely address the physical, social, and spiritual needs of patients and their families.

Palliative care is a model of care that focuses on easing suffering. It is *not* necessary to give up more aggressive life-sustaining therapy (chemotherapy or radiation) in order to receive palliative care. The goal of palliative care is to incorporate compassionate care measures even as aggressive life-sustaining care is still being implemented. To do this, palliative services are available in hospitals, clinics, hospices, and home care agencies. Palliative care might focus on relieving pain, keeping your muscles strong, or dealing with your anxiety.

Palliative care and hospice are not the same. While both palliative care and hospice focus on providing comfort and managing symptoms in a compassionate way, they are different. Palliative care can be offered while a patient is still actively fighting cancer, so you can be having chemotherapy, radiation, or other forms of treatment and have palliative care at the same time.

The hospice model of care was developed to address the special needs of dying people and their families. The modern hospice movement began in England in 1967, through the work of Dame Cicely Saunders and her colleagues at St. Christopher's Hospice in London. The hospice movement began in the United States in the mid-1970s, and hospice care became a Medicare benefit in the 1980s.

Currently, patients in a hospice program can no longer receive life-prolonging therapy, and it is required that they be certified by a physician as having a life expectancy of 6 months or less. This sometimes presents a problem for people who are living with a chronic condition, whose life expectancy is unclear, or who, for a variety of reasons, do not want to be "labeled" as dying.

The palliative care and family-centered care provided through hospice care is still needed, but barriers presented by rationing of hospice programs (based on prognosis) and the requirement of denying life-sustaining therapies deprived many individuals of the benefit of such quality and compassionate care.

Today's model of palliative care offers skilled and compassionate care to individuals regardless of prognosis or use of therapy, and you can have palliative care at any time. In looking at the relationship of hospice care and palliative care, hospice care is a program through which palliative care is intensified as a person moves closer to death. Ideally, patients and family members living with a serious, chronic, or progressive disease can receive palliative care throughout the course of their disease and its treatment. As people become closer to death, they can transition smoothly into a hospice plan of care.

Palliative care reflects a "whole person" philosophy of care in which the physical, social, emotional, and spiritual aspects of illness are addressed by a team of caring and compassionate nurses, physicians, social workers, and chaplains. The patient and family are the focus of care. The palliative care team works together to enhance the quality of life and offers a support system to help patients live as actively as possible. The team affirms life by respecting individual choices, valuing beliefs, and honoring a person's cultural and spiritual beliefs.

Palliative care does not hasten or postpone death, although some studies have shown that patients with advanced disease actually live longer and/or have better quality of life if they have palliative care than they do without such care (Temel et al., 2010; Hearn, 1998). A major focus of palliative care is aggressive symptom management through customized care that provides comfort and enhances well-being. This attention to distressing symptoms assists the person and their family members to make the best of every day.

Who Can Benefit from Palliative Care?

Any patient who is coping with a serious, chronic, progressive, or life-threatening illness may benefit from palliative care consultation.

Seven domains of palliative care include

- Physical aspects of care

- Cultural aspects of care

- Psychological aspects of care

- Social aspects of care

- Spiritual, religious, existential aspects of care

- Ethical aspects of care

- Care of the imminently dying person

Whether you are newly diagnosed or have recurrent disease or advanced disease, you can benefit from palliative care. If you have advanced disease, you might especially want to explore the options for palliative care and hospice if those haven't already been discussed with you.

At the end of life, each person's journey is unique. Sometimes death comes suddenly; sometimes a person may linger, gradually failing over time. With palliative or hospice care, knowledgeable, compassionate, and respectful health care professionals will provide the comprehensive care needed to replace fear and suffering with hope, meaning, and support.

In her book *Fine Black Lines*, Lois Hjelmstad, a breast cancer survivor, states:

What is a happy ending? Is it having a face without wrinkles? Is it never being ill or disappointed? Is it never losing a loved one? I think not—because if a happy ending is those things, most of us are going to miss it.

For me, a happy ending is the knowledge that, even though my flame may flicker, my inner candle of joy burns brightly.

I have found an immense awareness, an incredible joy in treasuring each moment—a profound gratitude that greets each new dawn as if it were the First Morning.

"You matter because you are you. You matter to the last moment of your life, and we will do all we can, not only to help you die peacefully, but to live until you die."

Dame Cicely Saunders, Founder, St. Christopher's Hospice, London, England

The Lymphatic System and Lymphedema

Lauren Robins, OTD, OTR/L, CLT and Cathy Barnes RN, MSN

The primary function of the lymphatic system is to transport lymph, a clear, colorless fluid containing white blood cells that helps rid the body of toxins, waste, and other unwanted materials.

The lymphatic system, which is part of the circulatory system, has a number of functions including

- Removing the fluid that bathes and surrounds most cells in tissue and

- Acting as a highway to transport white blood cells to and from the lymph nodes into the bones and throughout the body to fight infections.

There are 600 to 700 lymph nodes in the human body that filter the lymph before it returns to the circulatory system.

There are two drainage areas that make up the lymphatic system. The right drainage area handles the right arm and chest. The left drainage area clears all of the other areas of the body, including the legs, the lower trunk, the upper left portion of the chest, and the left arm.

Cancer surgeries and/or treatments such as radiation can potentially remove or damage lymph nodes. This can decrease how well the lymphatic system can complete its jobs. If the lymph fluid can't flow through damaged nodes or if there are not enough lymph nodes left for the fluid to flow freely, fluid can collect.

Lymphedema is a swelling in the body that is caused by an accumulation of lymphatic fluid in the tissues. Breast cancer survivors, are at risk for lymphedema if they had lymph nodes removed under the arm or had radiation therapy. People who had lymph nodes in the leg, groin, or pelvis damaged or removed could also be at risk for lymphedema. The incidence of lymphedema in the arm seems to increase up to 2 years after

LYMPHATIC SYSTEM

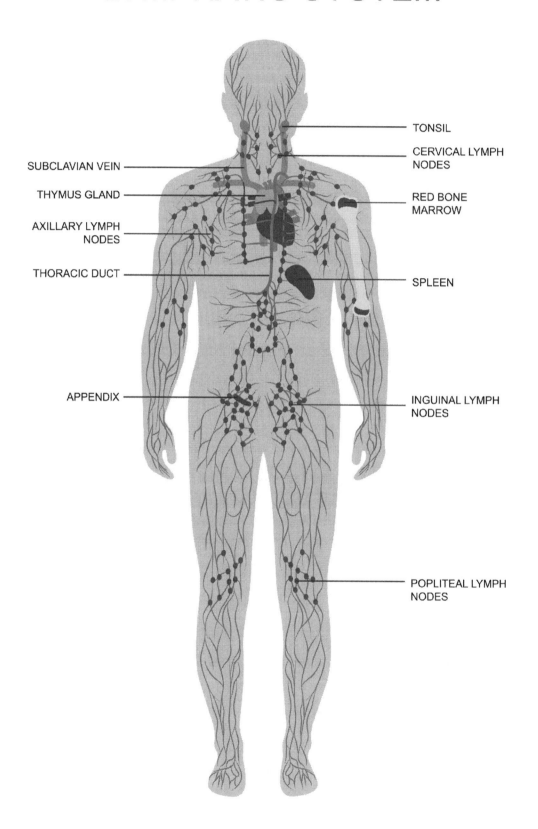

TONSIL

CERVICAL LYMPH
NODES

SUBCLAVIAN VEIN

THYMUS GLAND

RED BONE
MARROW

AXILLARY LYMPH
NODES

THORACIC DUCT

SPLEEN

APPENDIX

INGUINAL LYMPH
NODES

POPLITEAL LYMPH
NODES

surgery for breast cancer, but anyone who has had lymph nodes involved is at risk after the nodes were damaged or removed.

The strongest risk factors for lymphedema are extensive surgery, having a greater number of lymph nodes removed, infection, trauma, and being overweight or obese (Shahpar, 2013; Togawa, 2014). There is no real cure for lymphedema, so **survivors need to follow these guidelines for the rest of their lives:**

Self-care

- Tell your doctor about any swelling or pain in your arm, neck, face or legs.

- Wear loose-fitting clothing on your arm.

- Keep the skin clear and use lotion for moisture.

- Keep your affected limb free of cuts, burns, and insect bites.

- Allow no injections or blood pressure to be taken in the affected limb.

- Avoid extreme temperatures like extremely hot baths or showers. Hot tubs and saunas are not recommended.

- Protect your skin with sunscreen.

- Pace back to your previous activity levels. Use the involved body part as normally as possible; **however, if your limb feels heavy, tired, aches or fatigues, take a break and elevate the limb as much as possible.**

- Live a balanced life. Eat a well-balanced diet and stay physically active to maintain your recommended body weight. Added weight requires your lymphatic system to work harder.

- Wear a Medical Lymphedema Alert bracelet on your limb to alert medical personnel not to take a blood pressure or draw blood or give injections in that limb.

- Consult with a lymphedema specialist.

- Watch for signs of infection such as redness, heat, and pain.

IT IS VERY IMPORTANT TO AVOID INFECTION

- Be careful when you are shaving.
- Avoid manicures or pedicures.
- Any break in the skin could be an opening for an infection to get started.

Even many years after your cancer treatment, you are still at risk of lymphedema. Some medical personnel don't know this information, so you have to be your own best advocate. You should avoid having injections, having blood drawn, or having your blood pressure taken on the affected arm or leg. It is possible to take blood pressure readings or draw blood from your leg if both arms have been affected. Don't be embarrassed to stand up for yourself. You can order a bracelet from the National Lymphedema Network (www.lymphnet.org).

Be alert for signs of infection such as redness, heat, sudden swelling, or pain. If you see any of those, get medical attention IMMEDIATELY. If you can't be seen by your primary care doctor right away, call your oncologist or go to an emergency room and tell the staff you are a cancer survivor who has had lymph nodes removed on that side. Infection can move very quickly in a body part affected by lymphedema and can lead to sepsis. Sepsis is a dangerous systemic infection and requires antibiotic treatment. It won't go away by itself.

Please contact a lymphedema therapist if

- You notice visible swelling in your affected body part that is persistent.

- You experience feelings of fullness, tightness, fatigue or an ache associated with the affected body region.

- You notice jewelry or clothing is fitting tighter on the affected body region.

- You would like additional education regarding the lymphatic system or lymphedema.

Spontaneous Remissions and Miracles

Stephanie Koraleski, PhD

Most people who have cancer or have a loved one with cancer hope for a cure. Marketers for various products capitalize on that. You may have found yourself bombarded with pamphlets about the "cure doctors don't want you to know about" and the pill/herb/supplement that cures everything.

Most of these so-called cures have little or no research behind them that wasn't produced by the company that stands to profit. Beware of these. Dr. Edward T. Creagan, a cancer specialist at Mayo Clinic, and the medical advisor for *A Time to Heal*, says, "The cure for cancer is not on the Internet."

Nonetheless, there have been documented reports of miraculous healings, and he himself has patients whose remissions can't be explained any other way. Some have been vigorously investigated; for example, while 7,000 miracles have been reported at Lourdes, the Catholic Church officially recognizes only 69 of those (http://en.lourdes-france.org/deepen/cures-and-miracles/danila-castelli).

The Institute of Noetic Sciences (IONS) amasses data and research on verifiable reported miracles. While there is no way to know how many occur, they estimate that the number is far greater than that acknowledged in medical literature.

In 1993 Brendan O'Regan and Caryle Hirshberg of IONS surveyed medical literature and found 1,200 cases of unexpected, sudden complete healings. They called these "spontaneous remissions." Of those, 1,051 were remissions of cancer, and all of the patients fully recovered.

The Institute (www.noetic.org) reports that there are characteristics that are common among survivors who report remission and survival—all of which are addressed in *A Time to Heal*. Those miraculous survivors report:

- Changing from being dependent to being more autonomous and actively choosing activities that increase self-awareness, love, joy, and satisfaction.

- Facing the crisis of cancer and all of the feelings that go with that and discovering they have the power to find a new way of living a fulfilling and meaningful life.

- Taking control of their personal, professional, emotional, spiritual, and medical lives and living each day fully.

- Being willing to evaluate old beliefs, attitudes, and behaviors and to change those that are no longer helpful or adequate,

- Expressing all emotions and feelings and learning to say "no."

- Having at least one strong loving relationship.

- Partnering with doctors and participating in health care decisions.

- Finding meaning in the experience of cancer, finding reasons to live, accepting the diagnosis but not the prognosis (outcome).

- Actively reducing stress and renewing spiritual awareness.

Other experts talk about the fact that many people who have experienced a spontaneous remission made a dramatic psychological change just prior to the improved health. These people seemed to move from a place where they thought life was not worth living to a psychological place where they recreated a life that was satisfying and engaging.

A more recent study was conducted by Dr. Kelly Turner and published in the book *Radical Remission: Surviving Cancer Against All Odds* (2014). Dr. Turner reviewed 1,000 reports of people who, despite having stage 4 cancer that was said to be incurable, had their cancer go into total or partial stable remission. Dr. Turner found that these patients had done many different things they thought had helped, but the top nine strategies of these patients included the following:

1. Made a radical change in diet
2. Took control of their health
3. Followed their own intuition
4. Used herbs and supplements after careful study
5. Released suppressed emotions
6. Increased positive emotions
7. Embraced social support
8. Deepened a spiritual connection
9. Had a strong reason for living

These studies of unexpected cures and remissions show that healing is a holistic process. It involves the mind, the spirit, and the body, and it benefits from both medical help and taking personal responsibility for creating your own best life.

If there is anything that is sapping the joy from your life or making you feel that it would be easier to die than to face the problems, it could really help to get some assistance in dealing with the problems. In his book *Cancer as a Turning Point*, Dr. Lawrence Le Shan describes many cases of people who made minor to very dramatic changes to increase the zest and fulfillment in their own lives. While none of this guarantees a cancer cure, people who actively pursue this way of being in the world are likely to be happier and less stressed.

What will your first step be?

Talking to Children about Cancer

Lori Wingerter, MA, LIMHP, PLADC

Imagine this scenario: You're tucking your sweet 8-year-old daughter into bed for a peaceful night's sleep, and she becomes fidgety as she asks, "Do you have cancer? Are you going to die?"

Can there be a conversation more difficult for a mother or father than the one where you have to tell your children you have cancer? The one where you have to prepare them for the fact that you have an illness that frightens almost everyone and that has an uncertain outcome?

It's a scenario you most likely have thought about, over and over. One of the main concerns a parent often has when diagnosed with cancer is how the disease and its treatment will affect the children (Sutter, 2012). Most parents feel a little lost about how to best speak to their children about this difficult subject and worry about how their children will respond to this delicate and potentially frightening subject.

Here are a few thoughts that may help:

The first thought to understand is that *cancer affects the whole family* (Huang, 2013). Keeping your cancer a secret from your children is almost impossible. Kids have an uncanny knack for overhearing conversations. They also have a keen sensitivity to anxiety and depression of their parents and others. Even if you don't say anything directly to them or allow them to overhear conversations with others, they notice that you are acting differently, which leads them to think something is wrong. Remember, your children love and know you as well as you do them.

You may be concerned that talking to your children about your or your spouse's cancer diagnosis may increase your child's anxiety or fears. However, research suggests that the exact opposite often occurs: that being open, honest, and forthcoming may actually help reduce fears and anxiety

(Buchwald, 2011). The "not knowing" and the images a child creates in her mind are often much worse than reality.

Talking to your child about your cancer can help maintain and even reinforce your child's trust. It can alleviate his or her distress and facilitate safe expression of feelings and concerns. Research tells us that open, honest communication reassures your child that the family can get through this. Additionally, it sends the message that your child can trust you to take care of him on this journey.

It is important to know that families have different ways in which they communicate. Some families will immediately tell their children about the cancer diagnosis, while others will wait longer, perhaps waiting for more details, being concerned that the information will unnecessarily burden the children. *You* know your children best. There are many healthy ways to communicate this diagnosis with your children. What's critical is that you are telling them, you are including them, and you are setting the stage for the healthy communication that will unite and bond your family throughout this journey (Osborn, 2007) (Semple, 2013).

Communication Is Paramount

Prepare yourself. Talking to your children about your cancer may be one of the most difficult things you have ever done. Take some time to think about what you want to say. A good idea is to write down your main points, organize your thoughts, and then practice out loud! It will feel strange and uncomfortable, but doing so will make it much easier when the conversation starts. Knowing they can always talk to you in a serious and thoughtful way can provide great comfort and reassurance.

You may become emotional when telling your children the news. This is okay. In fact, this is healthy as it demonstrates that emotions and feelings, even crying, are good! When parents model feelings of sadness, anger, fear, and frustration, children then feel free to do so as well. It's healthy to show your vulnerable side, acknowledging that "this is all new to me too, but we will get through it together!"

Create the environment. Find a quiet time when you won't be disturbed and a time when both you and your child feel rested and calm. Perhaps sharing the news following a doctor visit or procedure will create a natural frame of reference and starting point. You may find it helpful to talk to each child individually so that the information can be tailored to each child's ability to understand. This may help your child feel more comfortable asking questions or showing emotion and may also help you tune into specific reactions and clues your child is exhibiting. Be sure to save some time for questions and discussion.

After speaking with each child individually, you may want to have a discussion with the entire family. Wrapping up this initial conversation with a family discussion conveys there are no secrets on this team and that no matter what, we will do this together!

Use real words. It is helpful to use real, accurate words and names such as "breast cancer" or "lymphoma." Telling a child that her mother is "sick" or has "bad cells" may make it difficult for a child to distinguish between the "boo boos" she sometimes has and the cancer. It is also advised to explain to your child that there are different types of cancer and that not all cancers have the same treatment and outcome. This will help your child distinguish between your cancer and the confusing information possibly encountered in conversations with others. Encouraging your children to share any information they may have heard or read can be helpful in clearing up any potential misconceptions or misunderstandings.

YOU share the news. It is much better for them to hear it directly from you rather than from someone else. Overhearing the information in someone else's conversation may cause your child to feel excluded or not important and to interpret the situation as a "secret" and not open for discussion. They may not know all the details, but they know something has changed. Maintaining trust and open communication will go a long way in supporting your child through this journey.

Honesty is important. Be honest with your child. They are smart little cookies. Children need to be able to trust that you are telling them the truth and that you will keep them informed. Their internal fears of what might be happening may be far worse than the real situation. They tend to cope best when they are well informed and up-to-date, and there are no surprises. Provide honest answers in a language they understand. If they know what to possibly expect, they cope better.

Difficult feelings are normal, and being open and honest about them will help your children cope (Gazendam-Donofrio, 2010). Helping your child label emotions—*scared, angry, neglected, lonely, embarrassed, guilty*— will validate them and will help foster continued open sharing. It's important to know that some days your child may feel fine and other days may be more challenging. There is no "right" way to respond to your mom or dad's cancer diagnosis. Making it okay for your child to feel any feelings at any time, and to honestly share them with you, will go a long way in promoting healthy coping and adjustment.

How to Address the Illness with Children of Different Ages

Age is an important factor in deciding what, how, and which details you should tell your child about your cancer. It can be helpful to know a little about the stage of life your child is in. Meeting your children where they are can facilitate effective communication and help to ensure your message is heard (Santrock, 2009).

To begin, children should know a few basic things: (1) The official name of the cancer, (2) The part of the body where the cancer is, (3) How it will be treated, and (4) How their lives may be affected. Here are some further guidelines for each age group:

Different Ages

Ages 0-2. Children of this age may be aware of their parent's absences and are very sensitive to changes in their routine as well as changes in the emotional climate in the home. You may notice things like separation difficulties, being fussier and less flexible and possible changes in sleeping and eating patterns.

Ages 3-6. Children of this age have the potential for understanding the illness but tend to engage in "magical thinking." This type of thinking may cause your child to believe your illness was caused by something he or she did or said, or that your disease is contagious. It is very important to reassure your child that she is not responsible for your illness and will not "catch" it by hugging or touching you.

Children of this age may react to a parent's inability to physically play, wrestle, or rough house. This may be interpreted as "rejection" when suddenly their favorite playmate doesn't want to play anymore. Questions and thoughts they may have tend to revolve around themselves and their needs. Talking to your children about the personal impact your illness and treatment will have on their daily lives will help calm some of these fears. This will help them better understand the reality of the situation and prevent them from taking it personally.

Changes you may notice in children of this age may include regression to earlier behaviors such as separation anxiety, bedwetting, thumb sucking, fear of the dark, or baby talk.

Ages 7-12. School-aged children have more of a worldly frame of reference and would most likely benefit from some general education about the specific cancer and its treatment. Even so, keeping your explanations simple may be helpful. This age group also needs to be reassured they did not cause or will not "catch" the disease. You may notice hesitation in mentioning their concerns or fears due to a fear of burdening you. As a result, they may go about their day, seemingly unaffected. Periodically checking with them regarding their feelings will keep the lines of communication open. Know that reactions may surface later, at any time or place.

Changes you may notice can include acting quiet or disconnected, anger, decreased interest in sports and school, declining grades, and others. Know that expression of feelings and emotions may come through behaviors rather than talking as it can be hard for children of this age to find the

336

words. If you're noticing a "strange or new behavior" there's a good chance it's a response to the cancer situation. Try to understand that naughty or unusual behavior may be their way of showing how upset they are.

Ages 13-18. Children in this group generally can understand most aspects of the cancer. As his or her individual personality is developing, your child may respond differently to your illness. Teens may become more distant or seem uninterested in your news. They may be worried about being "different" among their peers.

It can be helpful for them to know they are not alone and that other peers have parents who have cancer. They may be most concerned about how this news will impact their own plans, not because they don't care but because they are in the middle of this important developmental life stage and are trying to create independence, which is very normal. Just when they want to get away and be their own person, they feel they ought to be at home. This can create feelings of conflict and guilt. Other teens may try to be perfect and not "cause trouble." They want to protect their parents and not give them one more thing to worry about.

Changes you may notice for your older children include becoming withdrawn, angry, depressed, or anxious. There may be an increased reliance on friends and other nonparental adults. They may be overfocused on the future in terms of what will happen with their family, money, and other "what ifs."

Keeping other important adults (such as teachers, coaches, aunts, and uncles) in your child's life informed and encouraging them to connect with your teen can be a help. Sometimes the teen doesn't want to tell you how he or she is worrying about you; another safe, mature adult your child respects may provide that sounding board. This is a challenging phase of a child's development in any family. Adding a cancer diagnosis makes it even more challenging. If your child seems to be struggling, seek help through a high school counselor, mental health therapist, or a support group for teens whose parents have cancer.

All children need to be reassured that they will be taken care of. When something traumatic happens, children typically want to know two basics things: "Am I safe? Do you still love me?" Once this has been reassured, most children want to be part of the family and want to participate in your treatment plan in some way.

Other Thoughts about Communication

- How your child responds to the news of your cancer will vary from child to child. Some children become quite upset when learning about a new cancer diagnosis, while others act as if nothing is wrong. Whatever the response, the goal is to provide an honest, balanced viewpoint—"cancer is serious... but not hopeless."

- Remember, not all children are communicators. It will help if you can respect this while at the same time being tuned in to possible clues that your child wants to communicate. Once you have demonstrated to your child that you are open to hearing his or her thoughts and feelings, it may be best to wait for your child to initiate a conversation about cancer. Let him or her come to you when ready, rather than forcing conversations that can feel intrusive or nonsupportive. If your child continues to suppress or hide emotions, try inviting a trusted friend, family member, teacher, or professional counselor to assist.

- Children sometimes are more willing to talk if slightly distracted by something else such as sitting in the car while driving to practice, building legos, coloring, or after the end of a bedtime story. Take advantage of those moments that "feel right." And keep in mind that today's children may feel more comfortable initiating the discussion electronically (text or email).

- It's not likely your child will ask to sit down and have an in-depth conversation. One way to encourage a conversation that exceeds one-word answers like "Yes," "No," and "I dunno," is asking open-ended questions that require more than one-word answers. Questions such as, "What are two questions you have about my cancer?" "What made you think about that?" or "What is the one question you have been wanting to ask but were afraid to?" Try to make it safe to state, ask or express *anything*. This is a hard time for your child; the more she or he can express feelings, thoughts, and emotions, the better off he or she will be.

- But what if the question is *"Are you going to die?"* To be sure, this is a question that can rock even the strongest, most confident parent. A good place to start is take a step back, catch your breath, and start by exploring what led your child to ask this question. Referring back to your child's need to feel safe and loved, this question may be connected to a more personal question of, "Who is going to take care of me?"

- Another good place to start is to reassure your child that you and your treatment team are doing your best and that you intend on living as long as possible. Some possible responses may include, "Mommy has very good doctors and will have the best treatment available to make the cancer go away. Right now, the doctors say that I am doing fine and that the medicine is working. If there are any changes I will tell you." You can also acknowledge the difficulty in dealing with uncertainty and encourage your child to share specific concerns "What in particular makes you worry about that?"

Other Ways to Help Children Cope

As much as possible, stick to your child's normal routine.

- Maintain regular mealtimes, bedtime.

- Express interest in your child's activities.

- Use consistent, familiar caretakers.

- Use school as a haven where there is an opportunity for normalcy.

Protect family time.

- Limit family chats focused on cancer-related matters.

- Limit conversations with others about cancer during family time.

- Limit or eliminate phone calls and texts during meals.

- Choose one person (family member or close friend) to be the "go to" person for updates and information on your progress.

- Limit the number of unfamiliar people visiting while children are home—if meals are being delivered, have a neighbor intercept them for you.

Monitor hospital visits.

- Support any child who wants to visit a parent in the hospital or place of treatment.

- Investigate further about children who *do not* want to visit (use the communication guidelines).

- Prepare them in advance for what they might see.

- Provide structure to the visit.

- Bring an extra supportive adult if possible.

- Allow for and facilitate time afterward to process and de-brief.

Seek outside support.

- Enlist the assistance of trusted extended family and friends or peers of your child who may have been through a similar experience.

- Ask your medical team for information on local support groups.

- Utilize professional therapists and social workers who have training in this area.

Final Thoughts

Most children who have good support seem to cope pretty well over time. One research team looked at 52 studies of children of cancer survivors and found that while children were emotionally distressed by a parent's cancer, they generally did not have a lot of major social behavioral problems.

It seems that children react to the parents, and in families where the parents were psychologically doing well, the marriage was good, and there was good communication, the children were doing better (Visser, 2004). Remember that when children watch adults manage something difficult like cancer, they are learning "that people can carry on and do their best even in extremely challenging circumstances" (Bolletino, 2009). One of the best gifts we can give our children is to demonstrate that we can adapt when things are hard and do it while loving and supporting each other.

SPECIAL TOPICS

References

Session 1: Building Resilience—The Skills of Survivors

Borysenko, J. (2009). *It's Not the End of the World: Developing Resilience in Times of Change.* Hay House.

Borysenko, J. & Borysenko, M. (1994). *The Power of the Mind to Heal.* Hay House.

Botvin, G. (1990). *Life Skills Training: Promoting Health and Personal Development.* Cornell University Medical Center. Smithfield Press.

Greeff, Abraham P., & Colleen Thiel. (2012). Resilience in families of husbands with prostate cancer. *Educational Gerontology* 38 (3) 179-89.

Henderson, N. (2000). *Four Steps to Resiliency* (pamphlet). Resiliency in Action, Inc., San Diego.

Henderson, N., Sharp-Light, N. & Benard, B. (1999). (editors). *Resiliency in Action: Practical Ideas for Overcoming Risks and Building Strengths—in Youth, Families, and Communities.* Resiliency in Action, Inc. (All publications by Resiliency in Action can be ordered at (800) 440-5171 or www.resiliency.com.)

Henderson, N., Sharp-Light, N. & Benard, B. (2000). (editors). *Mentoring for Resiliency: Setting up Programs to Move Youth from "Stressed to Success."* Resiliency in Action, Inc.

Ishibashi, Akiko, et al. (2010). How to improve resilience in adolescents with cancer in Japan. *Journal of Pediatric Oncology Nursing* 27 (2) 73-93.

Jacelon, C. (1995). The trait and process of resilience. *Journal of Advanced Nursing* (25) 123-129.

Molina, Y., Jean, C., Martinez-Gutierrez, J., Reding, K., Yi-Frazier, J., & Rosenberg, A. (2014). Resilience among patients across the cancer continuum: Diverse perspectives. *Clin J. Oncol Nurs* 18 (1) 93-101.

Mueller, W. (1996). *How, Then, Shall We Live?* Bantam.

Northrup, C. (1998). *Women's Bodies, Women's Wisdom: Creating Physical and Emotional Health and Healing* (revised edition). Bantam.

O'Connell Higgins, G. (1994). *Resilient Adults: Overcoming a Cruel Past.* Jossey-Bass.

Remen, R. N. (1997). *Kitchen Table Wisdom: Stories that Heal.* Riverhead Books.

Saleebey, D. (1997). *The Strengths Perspective in Social Work Practice* (2nd ed.). Longman.

Staton, A., Ganz, P., Rowland, J., Meyerowitz, B., Krupnick, J. & Sears, S. (2005). Promoting adjustment after treatment for cancer. American Cancer Society.

Werner, E. & Smith, R. (1989). *Vulnerable but Invincible: A Longitudinal Study of Resilient Children and Youth.* Adams, Bannister, and Cox (publishers).

Werner, E. & Smith, R. (2001). *Journey from Childhood to Midlife: Risk, Resiliency & Recovery.* Cornell University Press.

Wolin, S. & Wolin, S. (1993). *The Resilient Self: How Survivors of Troubled Families Rise above Adversity.* Villard.

POWER TOOL: AFFIRMATIONS

Correll, J. Spencer, S. J. & Zanna, M. P. (2004). An affirmed self and an open mind: Self-affirmation and sensitivity to argument strength. *Journal of Experimental Social Psychology*, 40, 350-356.

Creswell, J. D., Dutcher, J. M., Klein, W.M.P., Harris, P., Levine, J. M. (2013). Self-affirmation improves problem-solving under stress. *PLoS One* 8(5): e62593.

Jaremka, L. M. (2011). Reducing defensive distancing: Self-affirmation and risk regulations in response to relationship threats. *Journal of Experimental Social Psychology*, (47), 264-268.

Sherman, D. K. & Cohen, G. L. (2006). The psychology of self-defense: Self-affirmation theory. In M. P. Zanna (Ed.) *Advances in Experimental Social Psychology* (38) 183-242, San Diego: Academic Press.

Williams, R. (2013). Do self-affirmations work? A revisit. Psychologytoday.com.

POWER TOOL: ENERGY PICK UP

Eden, D. (2008) *Energy Medicine*. Tarcher.

Session 2: The Power of the Mind

Albom, M. (1997). *Tuesdays with Morrie*. Broadway Books.

Bengston, W. (2010). *The Energy Cure: Unraveling the Mystery of Hands-on Healing*. Sounds True, Inc.

Borysenko, J. *Meditations for Inner Guidance and Self-Healing*. Audiotape set available through Nightingale Conant, (800) 323-5552.

Borysenko, J. (1994). *Pocketful of Miracles: Prayers, Meditations, and Affirmations to Nurture Your Spirit Every Day of the Year*. Warner Books.

Braun, S. M., Beurskens, A. J., Borm, P. J., Schack, T. & Wade, D. T. The effects of mental practice in stroke rehabilitation: A systematic review. *Archives of Physical Medicine and Rehabilitation* 87(6) 842-852.

Carlson, L. E., Doll, R., Stephen, J., Faris, P., Tamagawa, R., Drysdale, E., Speca., M. (2013). Randomized controlled trial of mindfulness-based cancer recovery versus supportive expressive group therapy for distressed survivors of breast cancer. *Journal of Clinical Oncology* (1) 3119-26.

Covey, S. (1994). *Daily Reflections for Highly Effective People*. Fireside.

Creswell, J. D., Dutcher J. M., Klein, W.M.P, Harris, P. R., Levine, J. M. (2013). Self-affirmation improves problem-solving under stress. *PLoS ONE* 8(5): e62593.

Cromie, W. J. (2002) Meditation changes temperatures: mind controls body in extreme experiments. *Harvard University Gazette*, April 18, 2002.

Donaldson, V. W. (2000) A clinical study of visualization on depressed white blood cellcount in medical patients. *Applied Psychophysiology and Biofeedback* 25(2) 117-128.

Dossey, L. (1995). *Healing Words: The Power of Prayer and the Practice of Medicine*. HarperOne.

Dyer, W. (2004). *The Power of Intention*. Hay House.

Elkins, G., Johnson, A., Fisher, W., Silwinski, J., Keith, T. (2013) A pilot investigation of guided self-hypnosis in the treatment of hot flashes among postmenopausal women. *International Journal of Clinical and Experimental Hypnosis* 61(3) 342-50.

Falk, E. B., O'Donnell, M. B., Cascio, C. N., Rinney, F., Kang, Y., Lieberman, M. D., Taylor, S. E., An, L., Resnicow, K. & Strecher, V. J. (2015) Self-affirmation alters the brain's response to health messages and subsequent behavior change. Proceedings of the National Academy of Sciences of the United States of America, 112(7) 1977-1982.

Frankl, V. *Man's Search for Meaning*. Various editions.

Gendler, R. (1988). *The Book of Qualities*. Harper Collins.

Granet, R. (2001). *Surviving Cancer Emotionally*. John Wiley.

Jackson, E., Kelley, M., McNeil, P., Meyer, E., Schlegel, L. & Eaton, M. (2008) Does therapeutic touch help reduce pain and anxiety in patients with cancer? *Clinical Journal of Oncology Nursing* 12(1), 113-20.

Kabat-Zinn, J. (1990). *Full Catastrophe Living: Using the Wisdom of Your Body and Mind to* Face Stress, Pain, and Illness. Delta Press.

Keith, K. (2001). *Anyway: The Paradoxical Commandments: Finding Meaning in a Crazy World.* Putnam.

Kushner, H. (2004). *When Bad Things Happen to Good People.* Anchor.

Kushner, H. (2006). *Overcoming Life's Disappointments.* Alfred A. Knopf.

Lavin, E. J. (1993). *Life Meditations: Thoughts & Quotations for All of Life's Moments.* Wings Books.

Lazar, S. (2000). Functional brain mapping of the relaxation response and meditation. *NeuroReport* 11, 1581-1585.

Legault, L. & Inzlicht, M. (2013). Self-determination, self-regulation, and the brain: Autonomy improves performance by enhancing neuroaffective responsiveness to self-regulation failure. *Journal of Personality and Social Psychology* 105, 123-138.

Leon-Pizarro, C., Gich, I., Barthe, E., Rovirosa, A., Rarrus, B., Casas, F., Vergr, E., Biete, A., Craven-Bartle, J., Sierra, J. & Arcusa, A. (2007) A randomized trial of the effects of training in relaxation and guided imagery techniques in improving psychological and quality of life indices for gynecologic and breast brachytherapy patients. *Psycho- Oncology* 16 (11) 971-979.

LeShan, L. (1980). *You Can Fight for Your Life.* M. Evans.

LeShan, L. (1989). *Cancer as a Turning Point.* Penguin Putnam.

Maltz, M. (2015) *Psycho-Cybernetics, Updated and Expanded.* Perigee Books.

McTaggart, L. M. (2007). *The Intention Experiment.* Free Press.

www.noetic.org. (2003). Effects of healing intention on cultured cells and truly random events.

www.noetic.org. (2008). Compassionate intention as a therapeutic intervention by partners of cancer patients.

Peck, S. (1978). *The Road Less Traveled.* Simon & Schuster.

Peters, R. M. (1999). The effectiveness of therapeutic touch; A meta-analytic review. *Nursing Science Quarterly,* 12 (1) 52-61.

Pitzele, S. (1998). *One More Day* (specifically for people with chronic illness). Hazeldon.

Ranganathan, I. et al. (2002). Level of mental effort determines training-induced strength increases. *Society of Neuroscience Abstracts* (32) 76.

Roffe, L., Schmidt, K. & Ernst, E. (2005).A systematic review of guided imagery as an adjuvant cancer therapy. *Psycho-Oncology* 14(8) 607-61.

Schaef, A. W. (2007). *Meditations for Women Who Do Too Much.* Harper and Row.

Schwartz, G. E. (2007) *The Energy Healing Experiments: Science Reveals Our Natural Power to Heal.* Atria Books.

Serra, D., Parris, C. R., Carper, E., Fleishman, S., Harrison, L. & Chadha, M. (2012). Outcomes of guided imagery in patients receiving radiation therapy for breast cancer. *Clinical Journal of Oncology Nursing* 16 (6) 617.

Sicher, F., Targ, E., Moore, D. & Smith, H. (1998) A randomized double-blind study of the effect of distant healing in a population with advanced AIDS; Report of a small scale study. *Western Journal of Medicine* 169 (5): 356-363.

Suinn, R. M. (1985). Imagery rehearsal applications to performance enhancement. *The Behavioral Therapist* (8) 155.

Turner, K. A. (2014). *Radical Remission: Surviving Cancer Against All Odds.* HarperOne.

Viorst, J. (1986). *Necessary Losses: The Loves, Illusions, Dependencies and Impossible: Expectations that All of Us Have to Give Up in Order to Grow.* Fawcett Gold Medal.

Zolkoski, S. M. & Bullock, L. M. (2012). Resilience in children and youth: A review. *Children and Youth Services Review* 34, 2295-2303.

Zuck, C. (1997). (editor). *Daily Word: Love, Inspiration & Guidance for Everyone,* Daybreak Press (also available in monthly magazines or online at www.dailyword.org).

POWER TOOL: BREATH COUNTING

Levinson, D. B., Stoll, E. L., Kindy, S. D., Merry, H. L. & Davidson, R. J. (2014). A mind you can count on: Validating breath counting as a behavioral measure of mindfulness. *Frontiers in Psychology* (5).

Session 3: Advocating for Me—Building My Survivorship Plan

American College of Surgeons. (2014). Accreditation committee clarifications for standard 2.2 survivorship care plan. Retrieved from http://www.facs.org/publications/newsletters/coc-source/special-source/standard.

American Society of Clinical Oncology. (2015). Long-term side effects of cancer treatment. Retrieved from http://www.cancer.net/survivorship/long-term-side-effects-cancer-treatment.

American Society of Clinical Oncology. (2015). Side effects. Retrieved from http://www.cancer.net/navigating-cancer-care/side-effects.

Broderick, J. M., et al. (2013). Feasibility and efficacy of a supervised exercise intervention in de-conditioned cancer survivors during the early survivorship phase: the PEACH trial. *Journal of Cancer Survivorship* 7 (4) 551-62.

Dana-Farber Cancer Institute, (2015). Cancer's "seasons of survivorship" [Supplemental material]. *Paths of Progress, Spring/Summer 2010.* Retrieved from http://www.dana-farber.org/Newsroom/Publications/Cancer-s-Seasons-of-Survivorship-.aspx.

DeSantis, C. E., Lin C. C., Mariotto, A. B., Siegel, R. L., Stein, K. D., Kramer, J. L., Alteri, R. (2014). Cancer treatment and survivorship statistics, 2014. *CA Cancer Journal for Clinicians* (64) 252-271.

Jackson, J. M., Scheid, K. & Rolnick, S. J. (2013). Development of the cancer survivorship care plan: What's next? Life after cancer treatment. *Clinical Journal of Oncology Nursing* (17) 280-284.

Journey Forward. (2015). Survivorship care planning tools. Retrieved from http://www.journeyforward.org/planning-tools/my-care-plan.

Journey Forward. (2015). Survivorship library. Retrieved from http://www.journeyforward.org/library.

LaTour, K. (2014). *The Nurse's Guide to Cancer Survivorship Care Plans.* Dallas, Texas: Cure Media Group.

Lee, C. & Decker, G. (2012). *Cancer and Complementary Medicine: Your Guide to Smart Choices in Symptom Management.* Oncology Nursing Society.

LIVESTRONG Foundation. (2015). LIVESTRONG survey: Searching for Information. Retrieved from http://www.livestrong.org/what-we-do/our-approach/livestrong-research-library/livestrong-surveys.

LIVESTRONG Foundation. (2015). Treatment Summaries and Survivorship Care Plans. Retrieved from http://www.livestrong.org/what-we-do/our-approach/livestrong-research-library/livestrong-surveys.

Mayer, D. K., Birken, S. A., Check, D. K. & Chen, R. C. (2014). Summing it up: An integrative review of studies of cancer survivorship care plans (2006-2013). *Cancer* (121) 978-996.

National Academy of Sciences, Committee on Cancer Survivorship: Improving Care and Quality of Life, National Cancer Policy Board. (2005). *From cancer patient to cancer survivor: Lost in transition.* Retrieved from http://www.iom.edu/Reports/2005/From-Cancer-Patient-to-Cancer-Survivor-Lost-in-Transition.aspx.

National Cancer Institute. (2009). Adjuvant and neoadjuvant therapy for breast cancer. Retrieved from http://www.cancer.gov/types/breast/adjuvant-fact-sheet#q5.

National Cancer Institute. (2010). Radiation Therapy for Cancer. Retrieved from http://www.cancer.gov/about-cancer/treatment/types/radiation-therapy/radiation-fact-sheet#q1.

National Cancer Institute. (2014). Targeted Therapies. Retrieved from http://www.cancer.gov/about-cancer/treatment/types/targeted-therapies/targeted-therapies-fact-sheet.

National Cancer Institute. (2015). Immunotherapy: Using the Immune System to Treat Cancer. Retrieved from http://www.cancer.gov/research/areas/treatment/immunotherapy-using-immune-system.

National Resources

American Society of Clinical Oncology (ASCO) Resource List http://www.cancer.net/survivorship/survivorship-resources

American Society of Clinical Oncology (ASCO): ASCOanswers Cancer Survivorship – for survivors

http://www.cancer.net/sites/cancer.net/files/cancer_survivorship.pdf?et_cid=34653101&et_rid=463566256&linkid=ASCO+Answers+Guide+to+Survivorship

The Center for Mind-Body Medicine for relaxation tips and health promotion (We recommend discussing all health practices with your health care team) http://cmbm.org/

Journey Forward Care Plan Builder for survivors and health care professionals, http://www.journeyforward.org/

LIVESTRONG Careplan, http://www.livestrongcareplan.org/

Online resource for survivorship (recommended by the Nebraska Oncology Society), http://www.cancer.net/

POWER TOOL: RELAXATION RESPONSE

Benson, Herbert. (2000). *The Relaxation Response.* Harper Collins.

Leon-Pizarro, C., Gich, I., Barthe, E., Rovirosa, A., Rarrus, B., Casas, F., Vergr, E., Biete, A., Craven-Bartle, J., Sierra, J. & Arcusa, A. (2007) A randomized trial of the effects of training in relaxation and guided imagery techniques in improving psychological and quality of life indices for gynecologic and breast brachytherapy patients. *Psycho- Oncology* (16) 11, 971-979.

Session 4: Comforting Myself

Armaiz-Pena, G. N., Allen, J. K., Cruz, A., et al. (2013). Src activation by beta-adrenoreceptors is a key switch for tumor metastasis. *Nat Commun* (4)1403, http://www.ncbi.nlm.nih.gov/pmc/articles/PMC3561638/.

Armaiz-Pena, G. N., Cole, S. W., Lutgendorf, S. K., et al. (2013). Neuroendocrine influences on cancer progression. *Brain Behavior and Immunity* (30) 519-525, http://www.positivehealth.com/research/armaiz-pena-and-colleagues.

Benson, H. (2000). *The Relaxation Response.* Harper Collins.

Bhasin, M. K., Dusek, J. A., Chang, B, Joseph, M.G., Denninger, J.W., Fricchione, G. L., Benson, H., Libermann, T.A. (2013) Relaxation response induces temporal transcriptome changes in energy metabolism, insulin secretion and inflammatory pathways. *PLoS ONE*, 2013; 8 (5): e62817.

Borysenko, J. (1987). *Minding the Body, Mending the Mind.* Bantam Books.

Borysenko, J. (2007). *Inner Peace for Busy People.* Hay House.

Cassileth, B. R., Vickers, A. J. (2008). Massage therapy for symptom control: outcome study at a major cancer centre. *Journal of Pain and Symptom Management* (3) 244-9.

Clegg, E. (2009). *Chemobrain: How Cancer Therapies Can Affect Your Mind.* Prometheus Books.

Cohen, Lorenzo, Sood, Anil K., Priusloo, Sarah & Chaoul, Alejandro. (2014). Stress and tumor biology: insights into managing stress to help improve cancer care, *The ASCO Post,* January 15, 5(1).

Davis, M., Eshelman, E. R. & McKay, M. (2000). *The Relaxation and Stress Reduction Workbook* (5th ed). New Harbinger.

Davis, P. (1999). *The Power of Touch.* Hay House.

Fellowes, D., Barnes, K., Wilkinson, S.S.M. (2008) Aromatherapy and massage for symptoms relief in patients with cancer. *Cochrane Database of Systematic Reviews* 4.

Greenlee. H., Balneaves, L. G., Carlson, L. E., Cohen, M., Deng, G., Hershman, D., Mumber, M., Perlmutter, J., Seely, D., Sen, A., Zick, S. M. & Tripathy, D.. (2014). Society for Integrative Oncology Guidelines Working Group, Clinical Practice Guidelines on the Use of Integrative Therapies as Supportive Care in Patients Treated for Breast Cancer, J Natl Cancer Inst Monogr (50):346-358.

Jackson, E., Kelley, M, McNeil, P., Meyer, E., Schlegel, L. & Eaton, M. (2008) Does therapeutic touch help reduce pain and anxiety in patients with cancer? *Clinical Journal of Oncology Nursing* 12(1) 113-20.

Jacobsen, P. B., Phillips, K. M., Jim, H. S., et al. (2013). Effects of self-directed stress management training and home-based exercise on quality in life in cancer patients receiving chemotherapy: a randomized controlled trial. *Psycho-Oncology* 22 (6):1229-35.

Jansen, C. E., Miaskowski, C., Dodd, M. & Dowling, G. (2005). Chemotherapy-induced cognitive impairment in women with breast cancer: A critique of the literature. *Oncology Nursing Forum* 32 (2), 329-42.

Katz, Lawrence C. & Rubin, M. (1999). *Keep Your Brain Alive: 83 Neurobic Exercises to Help Prevent Memory Loss and Increase Mental Fitness.* Workman Publishing.

Komda, V., Gita, S., Das, R. (2013). Molecular mechanisms of meditation. *Mol Neurobiol* 48:808–11, http://www.ncbi.nlm.nih.gov/pubmed/23737355.

Lazar, S. W., Bush, G., Gollub, R. L., Fricchione, G. L., Kailsa, G. & Benson, H. (2000). Functional brain mapping of the relaxation response and meditation. *NeuroReport* 11, 1581-85.

Lazar, Sara. (2011). How Meditation Can Reshape Our Brains. TedxCambridge. http://search.yahoo.com/yhs/search?p=ted+talks+sara+lazar&ei=UTF-8&hspart=mozilla&hsimp=yhs-001.

Leon-Pizarro, C., Gich, I., Barthe, E., Rovirosa, A., Rarrus, B., Casas, F., Vergr, E., Biete, A., Craven-Bartle, J., Sierra, J. & Arcusa, A. (2007) A randomized trial of the effects of training in relaxation and guided imagery techniques in improving psychological and quality of life indices for gynecologic and breast brachytherapy patients. *Psycho-Oncology* 16(11) 971-979.

Manoj, K., Bhasin, Jeffery A., et al. (2013). Relaxation response induces temporal transcriptome changes in energy metabolism, insulin secretion and inflammatory pathways. *PLoS ONE* 8 (5): e62817.

Moisse, K. (2010). Does stress feed cancer? *Scientific American*. April 13, 2010.

Nerem, R. M., Levesque, M. J. & Cornhill, J. F. (1980) Social environment as a factor in diet-induced atherosclerosis. *Science* 208 (4451) 1475-6.

Research Gate. www.researchgate.net/publication/270004614_Mindfulness_meditation_for_younger_breast_cancer_survivors_A_randomized_controlled_trial.

Stringer, J. (2008). Massage in patients undergoing intensive chemotherapy reduces serum cortisol and prolactin. *Psycho-Oncology* 17 (10) 1024-31.

Sapolsky, R. (2004). *Why Zebras Don't Get Ulcers.* Owl Books.

Wurtzem, H., Dalton, S. O., Elsass, P., et al. (2013). Mindfulness significantly reduces self-reported levels of anxiety and depression: results of randomized controlled trials among 336 Danish women treated for stage I-II breast cancer. Eur J Cancer 49 (6)1365-1373.

Session 5: Moving Forward in the Face of Fear

Butlow, P., Kelly, S., Thewes, B., Hruby, G., Sharpe, L. & Beith, J. (2015). Attentional bias and metacognitions in cancer survivors with high fear of cancer recurrence. *Psycho-Oncology* 24 (4), 426-423.

Dossey, L. (2006). *The Extra-Ordinary Healing Power of Ordinary Things.* Random House.

Everson, S. A., Goldberg, D. E., Kaplan, G. A., Cohen, R. D., Pukkala, E., Tuomilheto, J. & Salonen, J. T. (1996) Hopelessness and risk of mortality and incidence of myocardial infarction and cancer. *Psychosomatic Medicine* 58, 113-121.

Frankl, Viktor. *Man's Search for Meaning.* Various editions.

Hafen, B. (2006). *Mind/Body Health: The Effects of Attitudes, Emotions, and Relationships.* Allyn & Bacon.

Handy, C. (1999). *The Hungry Spirit*. Broadway Books.

Harris, S. R. & Niesen-Vertommen, S. (2000). Challenging the myth of exercise-induced lymphedema following breast cancer: A series of case reports. *Journal of Surgical Oncology* 74, 95-99.

Kabat-Zinn, J. (1990). *Full Catastrophe Living: Using the Wisdom of Your Body and Mind to Face Stress, Pain, and Illness*. Delta Press.

Keck, L. (2002). *Healing as a Sacred Path: A Story of Personal, Medical, and Spiritual Transformation*. Chrysalis Books.

Koch, L, Bertram, H., Eberle, A., Hollezek, B., Schmid-Hopfner, S., Waldmann, A., Zeissing, S., Brenner, H., & Arndt, V. (2013). Fear of recurrence in long-term breast cancer survivors—still an issue. Results on prevalence, determinants, and the association with QOL and depression from the Cancer Survivorship—a multi-regional population-based study. *Psycho-Oncology* 23 (5).

Koenig, H. G. (2012). Religion, spirituality, and health: The research and clinical implications. *ISRN Psychiatry*, Article ID 278730, 33 pps.

Kushner, H. (2004). *When Bad Things Happen to Good People*. Anchor.

Kushner, H. (2006). *Overcoming Life's Disappointments*. Knopf.

Kushner, H. (2009). *Conquering Fear: Living Boldly in an Uncertain World*. Knopf.

LeShan, L. (1989). *Cancer as a Turning Point*. Penguin Putnam.

Lebel, S., Maheu, C., Lefebvre, M., Secord, S., Courbasson, C., Singh, M., Jolicoeur, L., Benea, A., Harris, C., Fung, M.F.K., Rosberger, Z. & Catton, P. (2014). Addressing fear of cancer recurrence among women with cancer: a feasibility and preliminary outcome study. *Journal of Cancer Survivorship* 8, 485-496.

Lengacher, C. A., Shelton, M. M., Reich, R. R., Barta, M. K., Johnson-Mallard, V., Moscoso, M. S., Paterson, C., Ramesar, S., Budhrani, P., Carranza, I., Lucas, J., Jacobsen, P. B., Goodman, M. J. & Kip, K. E. (2014). Mindfulness based stress reduction (MBSRBC) in breast cancer: evaluating fear of recurrence (FOR) as a mediator of psychological and physical symptoms in a randomized control trial (RCT). *Journal of Behavioral Medicine* 37, 185-195.

Lucado, M. (2012). *Fearless*. Thomas Nelson.

Mueller, W. (1996). *How, Then, Shall We Live?* Bantam.

Musich, S., Adams, L. & Edington, D. (2000). Effectiveness of health promotion programs in moderating medical costs in the USA. *Health Promotion International* 15, 5-15.

Palmer, P. (2007). *The Courage to Teach: Exploring the Landscape of a Teacher's Life*. Wiley.

Peck, S. (1978). *The Road Less Traveled*. Simon & Schuster.

Pert, C. (1997). *Molecules of Emotion*. Touchstone Publications.

Quist, M., Adamsen, L., Rorth, M., Laursen, J., Christensen, K. B., Seppo, W. L. (2015). The impact of a multidimensional exercise intervention on physical and functional capacity, anxiety and depression in patients with advanced-stage lung cancer undergoing chemotherapy. *Integrative Cancer Therapy* 14 (4) 341-349.

Rankin, L. (2015). *The FEAR CURE: Cultivating courage as medicine for the body, mind, and soul*. Hay House.

Remen, R. N. (1997). *Kitchen Table Wisdom: Stories that Heal*. Riverhead Books.

Remen, R. N. (2001). *My Grandfather's Blessings*. Riverhead Books.

Ruiz, D. M. (1997). *The Four Agreements*. Amber-Allen.

Ruiz, D. M. (1997). *Beyond Fear*, Council Books.

Sarkar, S., Scherwath, A., Schirmer, L., Schulz-Kindermann, F., Neumann, K. Kruse, M. Dinkel, A., Kunze, S., Balck, F., Kroger, N., Koch, U. & Mehnert, A. (2014). Fear of recurrence and its impact on quality of life in patients with hematological cancers in the course of allogeneic hematopoietic SCT. *Bone Marrow Transplantation* 49, 1217-1222.

Schover, L. R. (2004). Myth busters: Telling the true story of breast cancer survivorship. *Journal of the National Cancer Institute* 96 (24) 1800-01.

Spudich, Tiffany. (2007). Cortisol and weight. www.project_aware.org/Resource/articlearchives/cortisol_weight.shtml.

Steiner, J. L., Wagner, C. D., Bigatti, S. M., Storniolo, A. M. (2014). Depressive rumination and cognitive processes associated with depression in breast cancer patients and their spouses. *Families, Systems & Health* 34(4) 378-88.

Tamm, J. & Luyet, R. (2004). *Radical Collaboration: Five Essential Skills to Overcome Defensiveness and Build Successful Relationships.* Collins.

Thewes, B., Breback, R., Dzidowska, M., Rhodes, P., Sharpe, L. & Butow, P. (2013). Current approaches to managing fear of recurrence: a descriptive survey of psychosocial and clinical health professionals. *Psycho-Oncology* 23 (4).

Tolle, E. (2004). *The Power of Now: A Guide to Spiritual Enlightenment.* New World Library,

Tsai, H F., Chen, Y., Chung, M. H., Liao, Y. M., Chi, M. J., Change, C. C., Chou, K. R. (2014). Effectiveness of music intervention in ameliorating cancer patients' anxiety, depression pain and fatigue: A meta-analysis. *Cancer Nursing* 37 (6).

Watson, T. & Mock V. (2004). Exercise as an intervention for cancer-related fatigue. *Physical Therapy* 84 (8) 736-42.

Wheatley, M. (2002). *Turning to One Another: Simple Conversations to Restore Hope to the Future.* Berrett-Koehler Publishers.

Wilson, M., Holman, P. & Hammock, A. (1996). A comprehensive review of the effects of worksite health promotion on health-related outcomes. *American Journal of Health Promotion* 10 (6) 429-35.

SPECIFIC RESOURCES FOR BREAST CANCER SUPPORT

BreastCancer.org, health information

Breast Cancer Network, www.breastcancer.net

Session 6: Refuel for Health and Energy

American Institute for Cancer Research. (1997).Food, Nutrition, and the Prevention of Cancer: A Global Perspective. AICR.

American Institute for Cancer Research. (2002).Dietary Options for Cancer Survivors: A Guide to Research on Foods, Food Substances, Herbals and Dietary Regimens that May Influence Cancer. AICR.

American Institute for Cancer Research. (2002). Nutrition After Cancer—The Role of Diet in Cancer Survivorship. AICR.

American Institute for Cancer Research. (2007). Food, Nutrition, Physical Activity, and the Prevention of Cancer: A Global Perspective.

Aune, D. (2011). Body mass index, abdominal fatness and pancreatic cancer risk: a systematic review and non-linear dose-response meta-analysis of prospective studies. *Annals of Oncol* 843-52.

Aune, D, Chan, D.S.M., Vieira, A. R., Navarro Rosenblatt, D. A., Vieira, R, Norat, T. & Greenwood, D. C. (2012). Fruits, vegetables and breast cancer risk: A systematic review and meta-analysis of prospective studies. *Breast Cancer Research and Treatment* 134 (2) 479.

Aune, D., Chan, D., Vieira, A., Navarro Rosenblatt, D., Vieira, R., Greenwood DC, Kampman, E., Norat, T. (2013) Red and processed meat intake and risk of colorectal adenomas: a systematic review and meta-analysis of epidemiological studies. *Cancer Causes Control* 611-27.

Chan, D. S. et al. (2014). Body mass index and survival in women with breast cancer: a systematic literature review and metal-analysis of 82 follow-up studies. *Annals of Oncology*, 25, 1901-1914.

Continuous Update Project, http://www.dietandcancerreport.org/cup/index.php.

Kuiper, J.G. et al. (2012). Recreational physical activity, body mass index, and survival in women with colorectal cancer. *Cancer Causes & Control* 21 (12) 1939-48.

Peek, P. (2001). *Fight Fat after Forty.* Penguin.

Tingting, L, Wei, S., Yun, S., Shuo, P. Qui, Q., Yin, J., Deng, Y., Chen, Q., Wei, S., Nie, S., Liu, L. (2015). The dose-response effect of physical activity on cancer mortality: findings from 71 prospective cohort studies. *British Journal of Sports Medicine*.

Session 7: May the Circle Be Unbroken

Belcher, A. J., Laurenceau, J. P., Graber, E. C., Cohen, L. H., Dasch, K. B. & Siegel, S. D. (2011). Daily support in couples coping with early stage breast cancer: Maintaining intimacy during adversity. *Health Psychology* 30, 665–73, 10.1037/a0024705.

Brandao, T., Schulz, M. S., Matos, P. M. (2014). Psychological intervention with couples coping with breast cancer: A systematic review. *Psychology & Health* 29 (5) 491-516.

Fergus, K.D. & Gray, R. E. (2009). Relationship vulnerabilities during breast cancer: Patient and partner expectations. *Psycho-Oncology* 18 (12) 1311-22.

Kahane, D. H. (1995). *No Less a Woman: Femininity, Sexuality and Breast Cancer*. Hunter House.

Kroenke, C. H., Kubzansky, L. D., Schernhammer, E. S., Holmes, M. D., and Kawachi, I. (2006). Social networks, social support and survival after breast cancer diagnosis. *Journal of Clinical Oncology*.

Manne, S. L., Siegel, S., Kashy, D., Heckan, C. J. (2014). Cancer-specific relationship awareness, relationship communication, and intimacy among couples with early stage breast cancer. *Journal of Social and Personal Relationships* 31(3) 314-34.

Otto, Amy K., Laurenceau, Jean-Philippe, Siegel, Scott D. & Belcher, Amber J. (2015). Capitalizing on everyday positive events uniquely predicts daily intimacy and well-being in couples coping with breast cancer. *Journal of Family Psychology* 29 (1) 69-79.

Pasipanodya, E. C., Parrish, B. P., Laurenceau, J., Cohen, L. H., Siegel, S.D., Graber, E. C. & Belcher, A. J. (2012). Social constraints on disclosure predict daily well-being in couples coping with early-stage breast cancer. *Journal of Family Psychology* 26 (4) 661-67.

Silver, M. (2004). *Breast Cancer Husband: How to Help Your Wife (and Yourself) through Diagnosis, Treatment, and Beyond*. Rodale.

Sprung, B. R., Janotha, B. L. & Steckel, A. J. (2011). The lived experience of breast cancer patients and couple distress. *Journal of the American Academy of Nurse Practitioners* 23 (11) 619-27.

Umberson, D. & Montez, J. K., (2010). Social relationships and health: A flashpoint for health policy. *Journal of Social Behaviors* 51(Suppl), S54-56.

Weiss, M. C. & Weiss, E. (1997). *Living Beyond Breast Cancer*. Times Books.

Yu, Y. & Sherman, K. A. (2015). Communication avoidance, coping and psychological distress of women with breast cancer. *Journal of Behavioral Medicine* 38 (3) 565-77.

Session 8: Renewing My Body, Regaining My Strength

American Heart Association. (2015). http://www.heart.org/HEARTORG/GettingHealthy/PhysicalActivity/FitnessBasics/Target-Heart-Rates_UCM_434341_Article.jsp.

Cole, R. P., Sciallal, S. J. & Bednarz, L. (2000). Functional recovery in cancer rehabilitation. *Archives of Physical Medicine & Rehabilitation* 81 (5) 623-27.

Deng, G. E., Frenkel, M., Cohen, L., Cassileth, B. R., Abrams, D. I., Capodice, J. L., Courneya, K. S., Dryden, T., Hanser, S., Kumar, N., Labriola, D., Wardell, D. W. & Sagar, S. (2009). Evidence-based clinical practice guidelines for integrative oncology: Complementary therapies and botanicals. *Journal of the Society for Integrative Oncology* 7 (3) 85–120.

Ehrman, J. (2010). Exercise as adjuvant therapy for cancer. *ACSM's Certified News* 20 (2) 7-8.

Engelking, C. & Cady, J. (2010). *Medical Surgical Nursing*.

Galvao, D. A. & Newton, R. U. (2005). Review of exercise intervention studies in cancer patients. *Journal of Clinical Oncology* 23 (4) 899-909.

Gerber, J. et al. (2011). Quantity of quality of exercise for developing and maintaining cardiorespiratory, musculoskeletal, and neuromotor fitness in apparently healthy adults: Guidance for prescribing exercise. *Medicine & Science in Sports & Exercise* 43 (7) 1334-59.

Harris, S. R. & Niesen-Vertommen, S. (2000). Challenging the myth of exercise-induced lymphedema following breast cancer: A series of case reports. *Journal of Surgical Oncology* 74, 95-99.

Haycock, D. (2013). Does exercise weaken the immune system? Livestrong.com: August.

Holmes, M. D., Chen, W. Y., Feskanixh, D., Kroenke, C. & Colditz, G. (2005). Physical activity and survival after breast cancer diagnosis. *JAMA* 293 (20) 2479-86.

Jeon, J., Sato, K., Niedzwiecki, D., Ye, X., Saltz, L. B., Mayer, et al. (2013). Impact of physical activity after cancer diagnosis on survival in patients with recurrent colon cancer: Findings from CALGB 89803/ Alliance. *Clin Colorectal Cancer* 12 (4) 233–38.

Kenfield, S. A., Stampfer, M. J., Giovannucci, E. & Chan, J. W. (2011). Physical activity and survival after prostate cancer diagnosis in the health professionals follow-up study. *Journal of Clinical Oncology* 29 (6) 726–32.

Kuiper, J., Phipps, A., Neuhouser, M., Chlebowski, R., Thomson, C., Irwin, M., Lane, D., Wactawski-Wende, J., Hou, L., Jackson, R., Kampman, E. & Newcomb, P. (2012). Recreational physical activity, body mass index, and survival in women with colorectal cancer. *Cancer Causes Control* 23, 1939-48.

Lee, I. M., Wolin, K., Freeman, S., Sattelmair, J. & Sesso, H. (2014). Physical activity and survival after cancer diagnosis in men. *Journal of Physical Activity and Health* 11 (1) 85–90.

Meyerhardt, J. A., Heseltine, D., Niedzwiecki, D., Hollis, D., Saltz, L. B., et al. (2006). Impact of physical activity on cancer recurrence and survival in patients with stage III colon cancer: Findings from CALGB 89803. *Journal of Clinical Oncology* 24 (22), 3535–41.

Patel, A. (2015). Leisure time sitting increases cancer risk in women. *Medscape Medical News*, July 14.

Ranganathan, I., et al. (2002). Level of mental effort determines training-induced strength increases. *Society of Neuroscience Abstracts* 32, 768.

Schmitz, K., Courneya, K., Matthews, C., Demark-Wahnefried, W., Galvao, D., Pinto, B., Irwin, M., Wolin, K., Segal, R., Lucia, A., Schneider, C., von Gruenigen, V., Schwartz, A. (2010). American College of Sports Medicine Roundtable on Exercise Guidelines for Cancer Survivors: Roundtable Consensus Statement. *Medicine and Sports Science*, 1409-26.

Suinn, R. M. (1985). Imagery rehearsal applications to performance enhancement. *The Behavioral Therapist* 8, 155-59.

Valenti, M., Porzio, G., Aielli, F., Verna, L., Cannita, K., Manno, R., Masedu, F., Marchetti, P., Ficorella, C. (2008). Physical exercise and quality of life in breast cancer survivors. *International Journal of Medical Sciences* 5 (1) 24-28.

Watson, T. & Mock V. (2004). Exercise as an intervention for cancer-related fatigue. *Physical Therapy* 84 (8) 736-42.

Wolin, K. Y., Schwartz, A. L., Matthews, C. E., et al. (2012). Implementing the exercise guidelines for cancer survivors. *J Support Oncol* 10:171–77 .

Session 9: Rebuilding My Core

Gendlin, E. T. (1982). *Focusing*. Bantam.

Hanh, T. N. (2009). *Present Moment, Wonderful Moment*. Parallax Press.

Hoffman, J. (1995) *Rhythmic Medicine, Music with a Purpose*, Jamillan Press.

Housden, R. (2003). (editor). *Ten Poems of Love and Revelation*. Harmony Books.

Johnson, E. (1992). *She Who Is: The Mystery of God in Feminist Theological Discourse*. Herder and Herder.

Kushner, H. (2004). *When Bad Things Happen to Good People*. Anchor.

Kushner, H. (2006). *Overcoming Life's Disappointments*. Knopf.

Link, M. (1996). *Psalms 2000, A School of Prayer (daily Bible meditation based on the psalms)*. Tabor Publishing.

Merrill, N. C. (1996). *Psalms for Living: An Invitation to Wholeness*. Continuum Press.

Metz, J. B. (1968). *Poverty of Spirit*. Paulist Press.

Moore, R. (2003). *Facing the Dragon: Confronting Personal and Spiritual Grandiosity*. Chiron Publications.

Nassal, J. (1997). *The Conspiracy of Compassion*. Forest of Peace.

Nemeth, M. (2007). *Mastering Life's Energies*. New World Library.

Oliver, M. (1992). *New and Selected Poems*. Beacon Press.

Remen, R. N. (1997). *Kitchen Table Wisdom: Stories that Heal*. Riverhead Books.

Remen, R. N. (2001). *My Grandfather's Blessings*. Riverhead Books.

Seligman, M. (2004). *Authentic Happiness: Using the New Positive Psychology to Realize Your Potential for Lasting Fulfillment*. Atria.

Shields, C. & Ferrell, C. (2001). *Spiritual Survival Guide: How to Find God When You're Sick*. Random House.

Spirituality & Health magazine, www.spiritualityhealth.com.

Von Franz, M. L. (1964). Part 3: The process of individuation. In *Carl Jung, Man and His Symbols*, 157-254, Dell.

Whyte, D. (2007). *River Flow, New and Selected Poems*. Many Rivers Press.

Session 10: Adventures and Misadventures in the Supplement Jungle

Asher, A. & Myers, J. S. (2015). The effect of cancer treatment on cognitive function. *Clinical Advances in Hematology & Oncology: H&O* 13 (7), 441-50.

Bauml, J., Langer, C. J., Evans, T., Garland, S. N., Desai, K. & Mao, J. J. (2014). Does perceived control predict Complementary and Alternative Medicine (CAM) use among patients with lung cancer? A cross-sectional survey. *Supportive Care in Cancer* 22 (9), 2465-72.

Bedell, S., Nachtigall, M. & Naftolin, F. (2014). The pros and cons of plant estrogens for menopause. *The Journal of Steroid Biochemistry and Molecular Biology*, 139, 225-36.

Benson, J. (2015). ALTERNATIVE MEDICINE CABINET: Bergamot. Alternative Medicine 21, 49.Chiru, A. Z., Popescu, C. R. & Gheorghe, D. C. (2014). *Melatonin and cancer. Journal of Medicine and Life* 7 (3), 373.

Cho, H. J. & Yoon, I. S. (2015). Pharmacokinetic interactions of herbs with cytochrome P450 and P-glycoprotein. *Evidence-Based Complementary and Alternative Medicine*.

Choi, S. Y., Kang, P., Lee, H. S. & Seol, G. H. (2014). Effects of inhalation of essential oil of citrus aurantium L. var. amara on menopausal symptoms, stress, and estrogen in postmenopausal women: A randomized controlled trial. *Evidence-Based Complementary and Alternative Medicine*.

Cutando, A., López-Valverde, A., De Vicente, J., Gimenez, J. L., Carcia, I. A., & de Diego, R. G. (2014). Action of melatonin on squamous cell carcinoma and other tumors of the oral cavity (Review). *Oncology Letters* 7 (4), 923-26.

Dauchy, R. T., Xiang, S., Mao, L., Brimer, S., Wren, M. A., Yuan, L. & Hill, S. M. (2014). Circadian and melatonin disruption by exposure to light at night drives intrinsic resistance to tamoxifen therapy in breast cancer. *Cancer Research* 74 (15), 4099-4110.

De Leo, V., Cappelli, V., Sabatino, A. D. & Morgante, G. (2014). Phyto-oestrogens and chaste tree berry: A new option in the treatment of menopausal disorders. *J Women's Health Care* 3, 182.

Depyperea, H. T. & Comhaire, F. H. (2014). Herbal preparations for the menopause: Beyond isoflavones and black cohosh. *Maturitas* 77, 191–94.

Drewe, J., Bucher, K. A. & Zahner, C. (2015). A systematic review of non-hormonal treatments of vasomotor symptoms in climacteric and cancer patients. *SpringerPlu*, 4, 65.

Erkkola, R., Vervarcke, S., Vansteelandt, S., Rompotti, P., De Keukeleire, D. & Heyerick, A. (2010). A randomized, double-blind, placebo-controlled, cross-over pilot study on the use of a standardized hop extract to alleviate menopausal discomforts. *Phytomedicine* 17 (6), 389-96.

Ferrini, K., Ghelfi, F., Mannucci, R. & Titta, L. (2015). Lifestyle, nutrition and breast cancer: facts and presumptions for consideration. ecancermedicalscience 9.

Ghaderi, R., Sehatbakhsh, S., Bakhshaee, M., & Sharifzadeh, G. R. (2014). Urinary melatonin levels and skin malignancy. *Iranian Journal of Medical Sciences* 39 (1), 64.

Greenlee, H., Balneaves, L. G., Carlson, L. E., Cohen, M., Deng, G. & Hershman, D. (2014). Clinical practice guidelines on the use of integrative therapies as supportive care in patients treated for breast cancer. *J Natl Cancer Inst* Monogr 50, 346-58.

Hachul, H., Brandao, L. C., D'Almeida, V., Bittencourt, L.R.A., Baracat, E. C. & Tufik, S. (2011). Isoflavones decrease insomnia in postmenopause. *Menopause* 18 (2), 178-84.

Haefeli, Walter Emil, and Alexandra Carls. (2014). Drug interactions with phytotherapeutics in oncology. *Expert Opinion on Drug Metabolism & Toxicology* 10.3, 359-77.

Hamidpour, M., Hamidpour, R., Hamidpour, S. & Shahlari M. (2014). Chemistry, pharmacology, and medicinal property of sage (salvia) to prevent and cure illnesses such as obesity, diabetes, depression, dementia, lupus, autism, heart disease, and cancer. *J Tradit Complement Med* 4 (2) 82–88.

Hamidpour, R., Hamidpour, S., Hamidpour, M. & Shahlari, M. (2014). Sage: The functional novel natural medicine for preventing and curing chronic illnesses. *International Journal of Case Reports and Images* (IJCRI) 4 (12) 671-77.

Kaur, G., Mukundan, S., Wani, V. & Kumar, M. S. (2015). Nutraceuticals in the management and prevention of metabolic syndrome. *Austin J Pharm Therapeut* 3, 1063.

Kazemifar, A. M., Hajaghamohammadi, A. A., Samimi, R., Alavi, Z., Abbasi, E. & Asl, M. N. (2012). Hepatoprotective property of oral silymarin is comparable to n-acetyl cysteine in acetaminophen poisoning. *Gastroenterology Research* 5 (5) 190-94.

Kelly, J. L., Salles, G., Goldman, B., Fisher, R. I., Brice, P., Press, O. & Friedberg, J. W. (2015). Low serum vitamin D levels are associated with inferior survival in follicular lymphoma: a prospective evaluation in SWOG and Lysa Studies. *Journal of Clinical Oncology*, JCO-2014.

Kim, M. Y., Choi, S. D. & Ryu, A. (2015). Is complementary and alternative therapy effective for women in the climacteric period? *Journal of Menopausal Medicine* 21 (1) 28-35.

Kodiyan, J. & Amber, K. T. (2015). A review of the use of topical calendula in the prevention and treatment of radiotherapy-induced skin reactions. Antioxidants 4 (2) 293-303.

Kohama, T. & Negami, M. (2013). Effect of low-dose French maritime pine bark extract on climacteric syndrome in 170 perimenopausal women. *J Reprod Med* 58, 39-46.

Lin, P. H., Aronson, W. & Freedland, S. J. (2015). Nutrition, dietary interventions and prostate cancer: the latest evidence. *BMC Medicine* 13 (1) 3.

Lv, Z. D., Liu, X. P., Zhao, W. J., Dong, Q., Li, F. N., Wang, H. B. & Kong, B. (2014). Curcumin induces apoptosis in breast cancer cells and inhibits tumor growth in vitro and in vivo. *International Journal of Clinical and Experimental Pathology* 7 (6) 2818.

Ma, H., Sullivan-Halley, J., Smith, A. W., Neuhouser, M. L., Alfano, C. M., Meeske, K. & Bernstein, L. (2011). Estrogenic botanical supplements, health-related quality of life, fatigue, and hormone-related symptoms in breast cancer survivors: a HEAL study report. *BMC Complementary and Alternative Medicine* 11 (1) 109.

Malagi, K. J. & Madhusudhana, K. (2015). Significance of herb-drug interactions in clinical practice: A narrative review. *Manipal Journal of Nursing and Health Sciences* 1 (1) 63-68.

Münstedt, K., Voss, B., Kullmer, U., Schneider, U. & Hübner, J. (2015). Bee pollen and honey for the alleviation of hot flushes and other menopausal symptoms in breast cancer patients. *Molecular and Clinical Oncology* 3 (4), 869-74.

Perry, E. & Howes, M.J.R. (2011). Medicinal plants and dementia therapy: herbal hopes for brain aging? *CNS Neuroscience & Therapeutics* 17 (6) 683-98.

Ranzato, E., Martinotti, S., Calabrese, C. M. & Calabrese, G. (2014). Role of nutraceuticals in cancer therapy. *Journal of Food Research* 3 (4) 18.

Rausch Osian, S., Leal, A. D., Allmer, C., Maurer, M. J., Nowakowski, G., Inwards, D. J. & Thompson, C. A. (2015). Widespread use of complementary and alternative medicine among non-Hodgkin lymphoma survivors. *Leukemia & Lymphoma* 56 (2) 434-39.

Reiter, R. J., Tan, D. X., & Galano, A. (2014). Melatonin: exceeding expectations. *Physiology* 29 (5), 325-33.

Richard, T. S., Kamdje, A. H. N., & Mukhtar, F. (2015). Medicinal plants in breast cancer therapy. *Journal of Diseases and Medicinal Plants* 1 (1) 19-23.

Sierpina, V., Levine, L., McKee, J., Campbell, C., Lian, S. & Frenkel, M. (2015, February). Nutrition, metabolism, and integrative approaches in cancer survivors. In *Seminars in Oncology Nursing* (Vol. 31, No. 1, pp. 42-52). WB Saunders.

Smith, P. J., Clavarino, A., Long, J. & Steadman, K. J. (2014). Why do some cancer patients receiving chemotherapy choose to take complementary and alternative medicines and what are the risks? Asia-Pacific *Journal of Clinical Oncology* 10 (1) 1-10.

Vandecasteele, K., Ost, P., Oosterlinck W., Fonteyne, V., De Neve, W. & De Meerleer, G. (2012). Evaluation of the efficacy and safety of Salvia officinalis in controlling hot flashes in prostate cancer patients treated with androgen deprivation. *Phytother Res* 26, 208–13.

Varinska, L., Gal, P., Mojzisova, G., Mirossay, L. & Mojzis, J. (2015). Soy and breast cancer: Focus on angiogenesis. *International Journal of Molecular Sciences* 16 (5), 11728-49.

Wang, C. Z., Cai, Y., Anderson, S. & Yuan, C. S. (2015). Ginseng metabolites on cancer chemoprevention: An angiogenesis link? *Diseases* 3 (3), 193-204.

Yang, L., Yang, L., Tian, W., Li, J., Liu, J., Zhu, M. & Qi, Z. (2014). Resveratrol plays dual roles in pancreatic cancer cells. Journal of Cancer Research and Clinical Oncology 140 (5) 749-55.

Z Tal, J., A Suh, S., L Dowdle, C. & Nowakowski, S. (2015). Treatment of insomnia, insomnia symptoms, and obstructive sleep apnea during and after menopause: Therapeutic approaches. *Current Psychiatry Reviews* 11 (1) 63-83.

Zhang, L., Wang, S., Che, X. & Li, X. (2015). Vitamin D and lung cancer risk: A comprehensive review and meta-analysis. *Cellular Physiology and Biochemistry* 36 (1) 299-305.

Zuo, Z., Huang, M., Kanfer, I., Chow, M. S. & Cho, W. C. (2015). Herb-drug interactions: Systematic review, mechanisms, and therapies. *Evidence-based Complementary and Alternative Medicine: eCAM.*

Session 11: Where Am I Going Now?

Antoni, M. H., Lutgendorf, S. K., Cole, S. W. (2006). The influence of bio-behavioural factors on tumour biology: Pathways and mechanisms. *Nature Reviews Cancer* 6 (3) 240-48.

Bleiker, M. A., Hendriks, J., Otten, J., Berbeek, A. & van der Ploeg, H. (2008). Personality factors and breast cancer risk: a 13-year follow up. *Journal of the National Cancer Institute* 100 (3) 213-18.

Dalton, S. O., Boesen, E. H., Ross, L., Schapiroo, I. R. & Johansen, C. (2002). Mind and cancer: Do psychological factors cause cancer? *European Journal of Cancer* 38 (10)1313-30.

Everson, S. A., Goldberg, D. E., Kaplan, G. A., Cohen, R. D., Pukkala, E., Tuomilheto, J. & Salonen, J. T. (1996). Hopelessness and risk of mortality and incidence of myocardial infarction and cancer. *Psychosomatic Medicine* 58, 113-21.

Garssen, B. (2004). Psychological factors and cancer development: Evidence after 30 years of research. *Clinical Psychology Review* 24 (3) 315-38.

Helgesson, O., Cabrera, C., Lapidus, L., Bengtsson, C. & Lissner, L. (2003).Self-reported stress levels predict subsequent breast cancer in a cohort of Swedish women. *European Journal of Cancer Prevention* 12 (5) 377-81.

LeShan, L. (1966). An emotional life history pattern associated with neoplastic disease. *Annals of NY Academy of Science* 125, 780-93.

LeShan, L. (1980). *You Can Fight for Your Life*. M. Evans.

LeShan, L. (1989). *Cancer as a Turning Point*. Penguin Putnam.

Moisse, K. (2010). Does stress feed cancer? *Scientific American*, April 13.

Moreno-Smith, M., Lutgendorf, S. K. & Sood, A. K. (2010). Impact of stress on cancer metastasis. Future Oncology 6(12) 1863-81.

Nakaya, N. (2014). Effect of psychosocial factors on cancer risk and survival. *Journal of Epidemiology* 24 (1) 1-6.

Pert, C. B. (1985). Neuropeptides, receptors and emotion. *Cybernetics* 1, 33-34.

Pert, C. (1999). *Molecules of Emotion*. Simon and Schuster.

Pert, C. B., Ruff, M. R., Weber, R. J. & Herkenham, M. (1985). Neuropeptides and their receptors: a psychosomatic network. *Journal of Immunology* 135, 820-25.

Price, M. A., Tennant, C. C., Smith, R. C., Butow, P. N., et al. (2001). The role of psychosocial factors in the development of breast carcinoma: Part 1 and Part 2. *Cancer* 15:91 (4) 679-97.

Rosch, P. (1996). Stress and cancer: Disorders of communication, control, and civilization. In *Handbook of Stress, Medicine, and Health*. CRC Press.

Sood, A. K. & Lutgendorf, S. K. (2011). Stress influences on anoikis. *Cancer Prevention Research* 4, 481.

Temoshok, L., Heller, B. W., Sagebiel, R. W., Blois, M. S., Sweet, D. M., DiClementey, R. G., Gold, M. L. (1985). The relationship of psychosocial factors to prognostic indicators in cutaneous malignant melanoma. Journal of Psychosomatic Res 23, 139-54.

Temshok, L. (1987). Personality, coping style, emotion and cancer: towards an integrative model. *Cancer Survival* 6 (3) 545-67.

Wu, M., Pator-Pareja, J. C. & Xu, T. (2010). Interaction between Ras (v12) and scribble clones induces tumour growth and invasion. *Nature*, 462 (7280) 545-48.

Session 12: Happiness Is...

Allen, R. & Kraft, C. (1980). *Beat the System! A Way to Create More Human Environments*. McGraw-Hill.

Baker, D. & Stauth, C. (2003). *What Happy People Know: How the New Science of Happiness Can Change Your Life for the Better*. Rodale.

Blair, J. (2000). *Who Gets Sick: How Beliefs, Moods, and Thoughts Affect Your Health* (2nd ed). Peak Press.

Blanchard, K. & Bowles, S. (1997). *Gung ho!* Morrow.

Bolletino, R. (2009). *How to Talk with Family Caregivers about Cancer*. Norton.

Bolman, L. & Deal, T. (1995). *Leading with Soul*. Jossey-Bass.

Buckingham, M. & Coffman, C. (1999). *First, Break All the Rules: What the World's Greatest Managers Do Differently*. Simon & Schuster.

Costantino, C. & Merchant, C. (1996). *Designing Conflict Management Systems*. Jossey-Bass.

Costanzo, C. (2004). *The Twelve Gifts for Healing*. HarperCollins.

Crawford, R. (1998). *How High Can You Bounce?* Bantam Books.

The Dalai Lama & Cutler, H. (2003). *The Art of Happiness at Work*. Riverhead.

Diener, E., Tay, L. & Myers, D. (2012). Easterlin was wrong—and right: Income change and happiness. Manuscript submitted for publication, *American Psychologist*, November, 2012.

Dossey, L. (2006). *The Extra-Ordinary Healing Power of Ordinary Things*. Random House.

Foster, R. & Hicks, G. (1999). *How We Choose to Be Happy: The 9 Choices of Extremely Happy People, Their Secrets, Their Stories*. Berkley.

Frederickson, B. (2009). *Positivity*. Crown.

Gilber, D. (2007). *Stumbling on Happiness*. Vintage.

Glencavage, L. & Norcross, J. (1990). Where are the commonalities among the therapeutic common factors? *Professional Psychology: Research and Practice* 21, 372-78.

Goleman, D. (1998). *Working with Emotional Intelligence*. Bantam Books.

Hafen, B. (2006). *Mind/Body Health: The Effects of Attitudes, Emotions, and Relationships*. Allyn & Bacon.

Handy, C. (1999). *The Hungry Spirit*. Broadway Books.

Hanson, R. (2013). *Hardwiring Happiness: The New Brain Science of Contentment, Calm, and Confidence*. New York: Harmony.

Johnson, S. (2000). *Who Moved My Cheese?* Putnam.

Keck, L. (2002). *Healing as a Sacred Path: A Story of Personal, Medical, and Spiritual Transformation*. Swedenborg Foundation Publishers.

Kuchler, B. (2003). *One Heart: Wisdom from the World's Scriptures*. HCI.

LeShan, L. (1989). *Cancer as a Turning Point*. Penguin Putnam.

Levering, R. & Moskowitz, M. (1994). *The 100 Best Companies to Work for in America*. Penguin.

Musich, S., Adams, L. & Edington, D. (2000). Effectiveness of health promotion programs in moderating medical costs in the USA. *Health Promotion International* 15 (1) 5-15.

Myers, D. G. (1993). *The Pursuit of Happiness*. William Morrow.

Myss, C. (1996). *Anatomy of the Spirit*. Three Rivers Press.

Myss, C. (2001). *Sacred Contracts: Awakening Your Divine Potential*. Harmony Books.

Nanus, B. & Dobbs, S. (1999). *Leaders Who Make a Difference*.

Neff, K. & Germer, C. (2013) A pilot study and randomized controlled trial of the mindful self-compassion program. *Journal of Clinical Psychology*, Wiley Online Library.

Ornish, Dean. (1998). *Love & Survival: The Scientific Basis for the Healing Power of Intimacy*. HarperCollins.

Pert, C. (1997). *Molecules of Emotion*. Touchstone Publications.

Quindlen, A. (2000). *A Short Guide to a Happy Life*. Random House.

Rosen, R. & Brown, P. (1996). *Leading People*. Viking.

Rubin, G. (2009). *The Happiness Project*. Harper Collins.

Ruiz, D. M. (1997). *The Four Agreements*. Amber-Allen.

Sauvage, L. (1996). *The Open Heart*. HCI.

Seligman, M. (2002). *Authentic Happiness: Using the New Positive Psychology to Realize Your Potential for Lasting Fulfillment*. Free Press.

Senge, P. (2006). *The Fifth Discipline*. Doubleday.

Vaillant, G. (2015). *Triumphs of Experience: The Men of the Harvard Grant Study*. Belknap Press.

Wheatley, M. (1992). *Leadership and the New Science*. Berrett-Koehler.

Wheatley, M. (2002). *Turning to One Another: Simple Conversations to Restore Hope to the Future*. Berrett-Koehler.

Wilson, M., Holman, P. & Hammock, A. (1996). A comprehensive review of the effects of worksite health promotion on health-related outcomes. *American Journal of Health Promotion* 10 (6) 429-35.

Special Topics

BODY IMAGE

Fingeret, M. C., Nipomnick, S., Guindani, M., Baumann, D., Hanasono, M. & Crosby, M. (2014). Body imge screening for cancer patients undergoing reconstructive surgery. *Psycho-Oncology* 23 (8) 898-905.

Fong, D., Ho, J. W., Hui, B., Lee, A., Macfarlane, D., Leung, S., Cerin, E., Chan, W., Leung, I., Lam, S., Taylor, A. & Cheng, K. (2011). Physical activity for cancer survivors: meta-analysis of randomized controlled trials. *BMJ* 344:e70.

Kahane, D. H. (1995). *No Less a Woman: Femininity, Sexuality and Breast Cancer*. Hunter House.

Penttinen, H. M., Saarto, T. & Kellokumpu-Lehtinen, P. (2011). Quality of life and physical performance and activity of breast cancer patients after adjuvant treatments. *Psycho-Oncology* 20 (11) 1211-20.

Preston, Margaret M. (2010). An exploration of appearance-related issues of breast cancer treatment on sense of self, self-esteem, and social functioning in women with breast cancer. Dissertations. Paper 10. http://repository.upenn.edu/edissertations_sp2/10.

Silver, M. (2004). B*reast Cancer Husband: How to Help Your Wife (and Yourself) through Diagnosis, Treatment, and Beyond*. Rodale.

Weiss, M. C. & Weiss, E. (1997). *Living Beyond Breast Cancer*. Times Books.

CANCER AND SEXUALITY

Baumgart, J., Nilsson, K., Evers, A. S., Kallak, T. K. & Poromaa, I. S. (2013). Sexual dysfunction in women on adjuvant endocrine therapy after breast cancer. *Menopause* 20 (2) 162–68.

Binkhorst, L., Mathijssen, R. H., van Herk-Sukel, M. P., Bannink, M., Jager, A., Wiemer, E. A., & van Gelder, T. (2013). Unjustified prescribing of CYP2D6 inhibiting SSRIs in women treated with tamoxifen. *Breast Cancer Research and Treatment* 139 (3) 923–29.

Carter, J., Stabile, C., Seidel, B., Baser, R. E., Gunn, A. R., Chi, S. & Goldfrank, D. J. (2015). Baseline characteristics and concerns of female cancer patients/survivors seeking treatment at a female sexual medicine program. *Supportive Care in Cancer: Official Journal of the Multinational Association of Supportive Care in Cancer*.

Chang, K. L., Fillingim, R., Hurley, R. W. & Schmidt, S. (2015). Chronic pain management: Nonpharmacological therapies for chronic pain. *FP Essentials* 432, 21-26.

Dahir, M. & Travers-Gustafson, D. (2014). Breast cancer, aromatase inhibitor therapy, and sexual functioning: A pilot study of the effects of vaginal testosterone therapy. *Sexual Medicine* 2 (1) 8–15.

Feldhaus-Dahir, M. (2009). Female sexual dysfunction: Barriers to treatment. *Urologic Nursing* 29 (2) 81–5; quiz 86.

Ford, J. V., Barnes, R., Rompalo, A. & Hook, E. W. (2013). Sexual health training and education in the U.S. *Public Health Reports* 128 (Suppl 1) 96–101.

Glaser, R.L. (2010). Subcutaneous testosterone-anastrozole therapy in breast cancer survivors. In American Society of Clinical Oncology Breast Cancer Symposium, Washington, DC.

Glaser, R., York, A. E. & Dimitrakakis, C. (2011). Beneficial effects of testosterone therapy in women measured by the validated menopause rating scale (MRS). *Maturitas* 68 (4) 355–61.

Goetsch, M. F., Lim, J. Y. & Caughey, A. B. (2015). A practical solution for dyspareunia in breast cancer survivors: A randomized controlled trial. *Journal of Clinical Oncology*.

Goncalves, P. & Groninger, H. (2015). Sexual dysfunction in cancer patients and survivors #293. *Journal of Palliative Medicine* 18 (8), 714–15.

Lester, J., Pahouja, G., Andersen, B. & Lustberg, M. (2015). Atrophic vaginitis in breast cancer survivors: A difficult survivorship issue. *Journal of Personalized Medicine* 5 (2) 50–66.

Schover, L. R., Baum, G. P., Fuson, L. A., Brewster, A. & Melhem-Bertrandt, A. (2014). Sexual problems during the first 2 years of adjuvant treatment with aromatase inhibitors. *The Journal of Sexual Medicine* 11(12) 3102–11.

Shiri, R., Koskimaki, J., Hakama, M., Hakkinen, J., Tammela, T. L., Huhtala, H. & Auvinen, A. (2003). Prevalence and severity of erectile dysfunction in 50- to 75-year-old Finnish men. *The Journal of Urology* 170 (6 Pt 1) 2342–44.

Ussher, J. M., Perz, J., Gilbert, E. & Australian Cancer and Sexuality Study Team. (2015). Perceived causes and consequences of sexual changes after cancer for women and men: A mixed method study. *BMC Cancer* 15, 268.

Witherby, S., Johnson, J., Demers, L., Mount, S., Littenberg, B., Maclean, C. D., Muss, H. (2011). Topical testosterone for breast cancer patients with vaginal atrophy related to aromatase inhibitors: A phase I/II study. *The Oncologist* 16 (4) 424–31.

World Health Organization. (2002). Defining sexual health: Report of a technical consultation on sexual health, January 28–31, 2002. Geneva: WHO Press, March 13, 2006.

CHEMOBRAIN

Biegler, K. A., Chaoul, M. A. & Cohen, L. (2009). Cancer, cognitive impairment, and meditation. *Acta Oncologica*, 48 (1) 18-26.

Brezden, C. B., Phillips, K., Abdolell, M., Bunston,T. & Tannock, I. F. (2000). Cognitive function in breast cancer patients receiving adjuvant chemotherapy. *Journal of Clinical Oncology* 18 (14) 2695-2701.

Clegg, E. (2009). *Chemobrain: How Cancer Therapies Can Affect Your Mind.* Prometheus.

Conroy, S. K., McDonald, B. C., Smith, D. J., Moser, L. R., West, J. D., Kamendulis, L. M., et al. (2013). Alterations in brain structure and function in breast cancer survivors; effects of post-chemotherapy interval and relation to DNA damage. *Breast Cancer Res, Treat* 137, 493-502.

Deprez, S., Vandenbulcke, M., Peeters, R., Emsell, L., Smeets, A., Christiaens, M., Amant, F. & Sunaert, S. (2014). Longitudinal assessment of chemotherapy-induced alterations in brain activation during multitasking and its relations with cognitive complaints. *Journal of Clinical Oncology*, May 27.

Gordon, D. (2014). Chemo brain: cognitive problems after cancer treatment are not imaginary. *Neurology Now* 10 (2) 20-27.

Janelsins, M. C., Kohli, S., Mohile, S. G., Usuki, K., Ahles, T. A. & Morrow, G. R. (2011). An update on cancer and chemotherapy related cognitive dysfunction: current status. *Seminars in Oncology* 38 (3) 431–38.

Jansen, C. E., Miaskowski, C., Dodd, M. & Dowling, G. (2005). Chemotherapy-induced cognitive impairment in women with breast cancer: A critique of the literature. *Oncology Nursing Forum* 32 (2) 329-42.

Kaiser J., Bledowski C. & Deitrich J. (2014). Neural correlates of chemotherapy-related cognitive impairment, *Cortex* 54, 33-50.

Katz, L. C. & Rubin, M. (1999). *Keep Your Brain Alive: 83 Neurobic Exercises to Help Prevent Memory Loss and Increase Mental Fitness.* Workman Publishing.

Kesler, S., Janelsins, M., Koovakkattu, D., Palesh, O., Mustain, K., Morrow, G., et al. (2013). Reduced hippocampal volume and verbal memory performance associated with interleukin-6 and tumor necrosis factor-alpha levels in chemotherapy-treated breast cancer survivors. *Brain Behav Immun* 30 (Suppl), S109-116.

Lopez Zunini, R. A., Scherling, C., Wallis, N., Collin,s B., MacKenzie, J., Bielajew, C., et al. (2013). Differences in verbal memory retrieval in breast cancer chemotherapy patients compared to healthy controls, a prospective fMRI study. *Brain Imaging Behav* 7, 460-477.

McDonald, B. C., Conroy, S. K., Smith, D. J., West, J. D., Saykin, A. J. (2013). Frontal gray matter reduction after breast cancer chemotherapy and association with executive symptoms: A replication and extension study. *Brain Behav Immun* 30 (Suppl), S117-125.

McDonald, B. C., Saykin, A. J. (2013). Alterations in brain structure related to breast cancer and its treatment: chemotherapy and other considerations. Brain Imaging Behav 7, 374-387.

Morean, D. F., O'Dwyer, L. & Cherney, L. R. (2015). Therapies for cognitive deficits associated with chemotherapy for breast cancer: A systematic review of objective outcomes. *Arch Phys Med Rehabil* May 27.

Nelson, W. L., Suis, J. & Padgett, A. (2014), Understanding chemobrain: A challenge and invitation for psychological scientists. *Observer* (Association for Psychological Science 27 (2).

O'Farrell, E., MacKenzie, J. & Collins, B. (2013). Clearing the air: a review of our current understanding of "chemo fog." *Curr Oncol Rep* 15, 360-369.

Pomykala, K. L., de Ruiter M. B., Deprez, S., McDonald, B. C. & Silverman, D. H. (2013). Integrating imaging findings in evaluating the postchemotherapy brain. *Brain Imaging Behav* 7, 436-452.

Scherline, Carole S., & Smith, Andra. (2013). Opening up the window into "chemobrain": A neuroimaging review. Sensors (Basell) March.

Silverman, D., Dy, C., Castellon, S., Lai, J., Pio, B., Abraham, L., Waddell, K., Petersen, L., Phelps, M. & Ganz, P. (2007). Altered frontocortical, cerebellar, and basal ganglia activity in adjuvant-treated breast cancer survivors 5-10 years after chemotherapy. *Breast Cancer Research and Treatment* 103 (3)303-11.

Simo M., Rifa-Ros X., Rodriguez-Fornells, A. & Bruna J. (2013). Chemobrain: a systematic review of structural and functional neuroimaging studies. *Neurosci Biobehav* Rev 37, 1311-21.

Syrjala, K. (2011). *Chemobrain*, www.fredhutch.org/en/treatment/survivorship/survival-strategies/chemobrain.html.

CURE, HEALING, AND PALLIATIVE CARE

Center to Advance Palliative Care. (2015). America's Care of Serious Illness: 2015 state-by-state report card on access to palliative care in our nation's hospitals.

Hearn, J., Higginson, I. J. (1998). Do specialist palliative care teams improve outcomes for cancer patients? A systematic literature review. *Palliat Med* 12, 317–32.

Hjelmstad. L. (2003). *Fine Black Lines: Reflections on Facing Cancer, Fear, and Loneliness.* Mulberry Hill Press.

Myss, C. (1996). *Anatomy of the Spirit.* Three Rivers Press.

Temel, J., Greer, J., Muzikansky, A., Gallagher, E., Admane, S., Jackson, V., Dahlin, C., Blinderman, C., Jacobsen, J., Pirl, W., Billings, J. & Lynch, T., (2010). Early palliative care for patients with metastatic non-small-cell lung cancer. *New England Journal of Medicine* 363, 733-43.

THE LYMPHATIC SYSTEM AND LYMPHEDEMA

Bernstein, L. (2014). Risk factors for self-reported arm lymphedema among female breast cancer survivors: a prospective cohort study. *Breast Cancer Research* 16, 414.

Burt, J. & White, G. (1999). *Lymphedema, A Breast Cancer Patient's Guide to Prevention and Healing.* Hunter House.

Clark, B., Sitzia, J. & Harlow, W. (2005). Incidence and risk of arm edema following treatment for breast cancer: a three-year follow-up study. *QJM* 4 (4) 481-85.

Haghighat Shahpar, Akbari Atieh, Ansari Maryam, et al., (2013). Risk factors of lymphedema in breast cancer patients. *International Journal of Breast Cancer.*

Harris, S. R. & Niesen-Vertommen, S. (2000). Challenging the myth of exercise-induced lymphedema following breast cancer: A series of case reports. *Journal of Surgical Oncology* 74, 95-99.

Stadt, Amy Halver & Leonard, Andrea. (2000). *Essential Exercises for Breast Cancer Survivors.* The Harvard Common Press.

Swirsky, Joan & Nannery, Diane Sackett. (1998). *Coping with Lymphedema.* Avery.

Togawa, K., Ma.,H., Sullilvan-Halley, J., Neuhouser, M. et. al (2013). Risk factors for self-reported arm lymphedema among female breast cancer survivors: a prospective cohort study. *Breast Cancer Research* 16 (4).

SPONTANEOUS REMISSIONS AND MIRACLES

Hirschberg, C. & O'Regan, B. (1993). *Spontaneous remissions. An annotated bibliography.* Institute of Noetic Sciences.

Institute of Noetic Science, www.noetic.org.

Lipton, B. H. (2008). *The Biology of Belief.* Hay House.

Turner, K. (2014). *Radical Remission: Surviving Cancer Against All Odds.* HarperOne.

Weil, Andrew. (1995). *Spontaneous Healing.* Fawcett Columbine.

TALKING TO CHILDREN ABOUT CANCER

American Cancer Society. www.cancer.org.

Bolletino, R. C. (2009). *How to Talk with Family Caregivers about Cancer.* Norton.

Buchwald, D., Delmar, C. & Schantz-Laursen, B. (2012). How children handle life when their mother or father is seriously ill and dying. *Scandinavian Journal of Caring Sciences* 26 (2), 228-35.

Chen, Y. (2014). Exploration of the short-term and long-term effects of parental illness on children's educational and behavioral functioning using a large Taiwanese sample. *Western Journal of Nursing Research* 36 (5), 664-84.

Cox, R. P. & Farr, K. (2003). Family development, caregiving, and functioning over the life span. In R. P. Cox (ed). *Health-related Counseling with Families of Diverse Cultures: Family, Health, and Cultural Competencies,* pp. 17-72, Greenwood Press/Greenwood Publishing Group.

Gazendam-Donofrio, S., Hoekstra, H. J. et al. (2011). Adolescents' emotional reactions to parental cancer: Effect on emotional and behavioral problems. *Journal of Pediatric Psychology* 36 (3), 346-59.

Huang, X., O'Connor, M. & Lee, S. (2014). School-aged and adolescent children's experience when a parent has non-terminal cancer: A systematic review and meta-synthesis of qualitative studies. *Psycho-Oncology* 23 (5), 493-506.

Huizinga, G. A., Visser, A., Van, d. G., Hoekstra, H. J., Stewart, R. E. & Hoekstra-Weebers, J. (2011). Family-oriented multilevel study on the psychological functioning of adolescent children having a mother with cancer. *Psycho-Oncology* 20 (7), 730-37.

John, K., Becker, K. & Mattejat, F. (2013). Impact of family-oriented rehabilitation and prevention: An inpatient program for mothers with breast cancer and their children. *Psycho-Oncology* 22 (12), 2684-92.

Krattenmacher, T., Kühne, F., Halverscheid, S., Wiegand-Grefe, S., Bergelt, C., Romer, G., et al. (2014). A comparison of the emotional and behavioral problems of children of patients with cancer or a mental disorder and their association with parental quality of life. *Journal of Psychosomatic Research* 76 (3), 213-20.

Kühne, F., Krattenmacher, T., Beierlein, V., Grimm, J. C., Bergelt, C., Romer, G., et al. (2012). Minor children of palliative patients: A systematic review of psychosocial family interventions. *Journal of Palliative Medicine* 15 (8), 931-45.

Kühne, F., Krattenmacher, T., Bergelt, C., Beierlein, V., Herzog, W., v. Klitzing, K., et al. (2013). "There is still so much ahead of us"—Family functioning in families of palliative cancer patients. *Families, Systems & Health* 31 (2), 181-93.

Maynard, A., Patterson, P., McDonald, F. E. J. & Stevens, G. (2013). What is helpful to adolescents who have a parent diagnosed with cancer? *Journal of Psychosocial Oncology* 31 (6), 675-97.

McCarthy, B. (2011). Family members of patients with cancer: What they know, how they know and what they want to know. *European Journal of Oncology Nursing* 15 (5), 428-41.

Moore, R. P. (2010). Addressing the needs of children when a parent has cancer. *Psycho-Oncology* 527-31.

Munro, HeatherScott et al. (2015). Patterns and predictors of disclosure of a diagnosis of cancer. *Psycho-Oncology* 24 (5), 508-14.

National Cancer Institute. www.nci.gov.

Osborn, T. (2007). The psychosocial impact of parental cancer on children and adolescents: A systematic review. *Psycho-Oncology* 16 (2), 101-26.

Pennebaker, J. W. (1990). *Opening Up: The Healing Power of Expressing Emotions.* Guilford Press.

Quindlen, A. (2000). *A Short Guide to a Happy Life.* Random House.

Rackner, Vicki. (2009). *Caregiving without Regrets: 3 Steps to Avoid Burnout and Manage Disappointment, Guilt, and Anger.* Medical Bridges.

Rainville, F., Dumont, S., Simard, S. & Savard, M. (2012). Psychological distress among adolescents living with a parent with advanced cancer. *Journal of Psychosocial Oncology* 30 (5), 519-34.

Santrock, J. (2009). *Life-Span Development* (12th ed.). McGraw Hill.

Semple, C. J. & McCaughan, E. (2013). Family life when a parent is diagnosed with cancer: Impact of a psychosocial intervention for young children. *European Journal of Cancer Care* 22 (2), 219-31.

Sutter, C. & Reid, T. (2012). How do we talk to the children? Child life consultation to support the children of seriously ill adult inpatients. *Journal of Palliative Medicine* 15 (12), 1362-68.

Visser, A., Huizinga, G. A., Windette, T. A., van der Graaf, W.T.A., Hoekstra, H. J., Hoestra-Weebers, J. (2004). The impact of parental cancer on children and the family: a review of the literature. *Cancer Treatment Reviews* 30 (8) 683-94.

Whitlow, Puja et al. (2015). Strategies to improve success of pediatric cancer cooperative group quality of life studies: A report from the children's oncology group. *Quality of Life Research* 24 (6), 1297-1301.

www.parentingwithcancer.com (a website and blog for people who are parenting with cancer; sections for parents, spouses, caregivers, kids, and friends/family)

When Your Parent Has Cancer: A Guide for Teens (available from the National Cancer Institute at www.cancer.gov)

**[With special thanks to the medical librarians at the
University of Nebraska Medical Center, McGoogan Library of Medicine,
for their contributions to this list.]**

Websites and National Resources for Cancer Information and Support

This list is a place to start your Internet search instead of simply searching for terms on a search engine. As of this printing, the links are correct, but of course there can always be issues with link quality. We recommend discussing all health practices with your health care team.

ALL CANCERS

American Cancer Society, www.cancer.org

American Society of Clinical Oncology, www.cancer.net

Association of Cancer Online Resources, www.acor.org/

Block Center for Integrative Cancer Care, www.blockmd.com/

Cancer Care—online counseling, support groups, education, and financial assistance, www.cancercare.org/

CancerGuide by Steve Dunn—a cancer survivor's personal story and guide to survivorship, cancerguide.org/

Cancer Hope Network, www.cancerhopenetwork.org/

Cancer Legal Line—assistance for cancer related legal issues such as insurance, employment and Advance Directives, cancerlegalline.org/

Cancer Legal Resource Center, www.disabilityrightslegalcenter.org/

Cancer Support Community—support resources for cancer survivors and their families, www.cancersupportcommunity.org/

Cancer Survivors Network—toll-free service of the American Cancer Society, answers to and information on cancer related topics addressed by cancer survivors and their families 1-877-333-HOPE (4673)

Lance Armstrong Foundation, www.livestrong.org

Livestrong—Fertile Hope—education on fertility risks and issues, www.livestrong.org/we-can-help/fertility-services/

MedlinePlus: Cancers—access to medical literature with links to other sites, www.nlm.nih.gov/medlineplus/cancer.html

Memorial Sloan-Kettering Cancer Center, www.mskcc.org/

National Cancer Institute—subpages for various cancer types, www.cancer.gov

National Cancer Institute, Office of Cancer Survivorship—information for survivors, caregivers, health care providers and the research community, survivorship.cancer.gov

National Cancer Institute in Spanish, www.cancer.gov/espanol

National Coalition for Cancer Survivorship, www.canceradvocacy.org/

National Comprehensive Cancer Network—patient and caregiver resources, www.nccn.org

National Lymphedema Network, www.lymphnet.org/

OncoLink—information on treatments, diagnoses survivorship, and risk, www.oncolink.org/

BREAST CANCER

ABCD After Breast Cancer Diagnosis—find a mentor and get breast cancer information, www.abcdbreastcancersupport.org/, www.breastcancer.org www.breastcancer.net

BreastCancer.org, health information

Breast Cancer Network, www.breastcancer.net

Breast Cancer Wellness magazine—free to cancer survivors, www.breastcancerwellness.org/

Dr. Susan Love Research Foundation, www.dslrf.org/breastcancer/index.asp?

Living Beyond Breast Cancer—conferences and teleconferences, survivor's hotline (1-888-753-5222), special resources for African Americans and Spanish language resources, www.lbbc.org/

Men Against Breast Cancer, www.menagainstbreastcancer.org

National Breast Cancer Coalition, www.breastcancerdeadline2020.org/homepage.html

Sisters Network, Inc.—increases local and national attention about the impact of breast cancer in the African American community, www.sistersnetworkinc.org/

Susan G. Komen for the Cure-provides breast health and breast cancer educational materials, hold events around the country to advocate for breast cancer, www.komen.org

Young Survival Coalition—dedicated to concerns and issues affecting women 40 and under with breast cancer, www.youngsurvival.org/

OTHER SPECIFIC CANCERS

Bladder Cancer:

bladdercancersupport.org/, www.urologyhealth.org/urologic-conditions/bladder-cancer

Colon Cancer:

www.coloncancerfoundation.org/

Colon Cancer Alliance, www.ccalliance.org/, fightcolorectalcancer.org/

Chris4Life Colon Cancer Foundation, www.chris4life.org/

Global Colon Cancer Association, www.globalcca.org/

Kidney Cancer:

www.kidneycancer.org/

National Kidney Foundation, www.kidney.org/atoz/content/kidneycancer

International Kidney Cancer Coalition, ikcc.org/

Action to Cure Kidney Cancer, www.ackc.org/

Urology Care Foundation, www.urologyhealth.org/urologic-conditions/kidney-cancer

Leukemia:

Leukemia and lymphoma Society, www.lls.org/

Leukemia Research Foundation, www.allbloodcancers.org/

Lung Cancer:

www.lungcancer.org/

www.lungcanceralliance.org/

Free to Breathe—Lung Cancer Survivorship, www.freetobreathe.org/

Lung Cancer Foundation of America, www.lcfamerica.org/

Uniting Against Lung Cancer, www.unitingagainstlungcancer.org/

Melanoma:

Melanoma Research Foundation, www.melanoma.org/

American Melanoma Foundation, www.melanomafoundation.org/

Melanoma Research Alliance, www.curemelanoma.org/

Skin Cancer Foundation, www.skincancer.org/

Lymphoma:

Lymphoma Research Foundation, www.lymphoma.org/

Leukemia and Lymphoma Society, www.lls.org/

Pancreatic Cancer:

Pancreatic Cancer Action Network, www.pancan.org/

National Pancreatic Cancer Foundation, www.npcf.us/

Pancreatic Cancer Research, www.pancreatic.org/

Pancreatic Cancer Alliance, www.pancreaticalliance.org/

Prostate Cancer:

Prostate Cancer Foundation, www.pcf.org/

Thyroid Cancer:

Thyroid Cancer Survivors Association, www.thyca.org/

Light of Life Foundation, www.lightoflifefoundation.org/

American Thyroid Association, www.thyroid.org/

INSURANCE and FINANCIAL ASSISTANCE

Good Days—Chronic Disease Fund Assistance Program—financial assistance for medication co-pays, www.gooddaysfromcdf.org/

Health Insurance Information—information on getting and keeping health insurance, healthinsuranceinfo.net/

Healthwell Foundation—financial assistance for specific cancers including co-pays, deductibles, insurance premiums, healthwellfoundation.org/

Patient Advocate Foundation—advocacy and assistance for problems with insurance, financial issues and job discrimination, www.patientadvocate.org/

Susan G. Komen Financial Resources—listing of resources for financial assistance, www.komen.org/BreastCancer/FinancialResources.html

BASIC HEALTH, EXERCISE, and NUTRITION

American Institute for Cancer Research, www.AICR.org

American College of Sports Medicine, www.acsm.org/public-information/search-by-topic/search-by-topic

Dr. Jeanne Wallace's nutritional consultation, www.nutritional-solutions.net/

Food and Drug Administration—current resource on US food and drug news, www.fda.gov/

GoodSleep.com—program to help individuals get a better night's sleep with guided relaxation and behavior modification, www.circadian.com/solutions-services/corporate-sleep-programs/goodsleep.html

US Department of Health and Human Services—free and reliable health care information, www.healthcarefinder.gov

ALTERNATIVE MEDICINE

American Botanical Council—information on herbal medicine, abc.herbalgram.org/

Institute of Noetic Sciences—information about consciousness and healing, distance healing, effects of prayer, meditation, and the mind-body connection, www.noetic.org/

National Center for Complementary and Alternative Medicine, nccam.nih.gov

The Center for Mind-Body Medicine – for relaxation tips and health promotion, cmbm.org/

PHARMACY RESOURCES

Consumer Lab—information and warnings on health and nutritional products, www.consumerlabs.com

Pharmaceutical Information Network—articles and blogs, www.pharmainfo.net/

U.S. Pharmacopeia Convention, www.usp.org/

MENTAL HEALTH and Emotional Needs of Cancer Patients and Families

American Oncology Social Work, www.aosw.org/

American Psychosocial Oncology Society, www.apos-society.org

American Psychological Association—has books and articles about living with cancer and the emotional aspects of coping with cancer, www.apa.org

American Psychosocial Oncology Society—information and referrals to psycho-oncologists, psychiatrists and mental health counselors trained to understand the emotional needs of people affected by cancer, www.apos-society.org/

The Center for Mind-Body Medicine – for relaxation tips and health promotion, cmbm.org/

SPECFICALLY FOR CAREGIVERS

American Cancer Society—Coping as a Caregiver, www.cancer.org/treatment/caregivers/copingasacaregiver/

Cancer Support Community—Tips for Caregivers, www.cancersupportcommunity.org/MainMenu/Family-Friends/Caregiving/Tips-for-Caregivers.html

The Caregiver Club, www.caregivingclub.com/

Center for Disease Control—Caregiver Resources, www.cdc.gov/cancer/survivorship/caregivers/resources.htm

Help for Cancer Caregivers, www.helpforcancercaregivers.org/

Medicare—Caregiving, www.medicare.gov/campaigns/caregiver/caregiver.html

MedlinePlus—For Caregivers, www.nlm.nih.gov/medlineplus/caregivers.html

National Family Caregiver Association, caregiveraction.org/

Strength for Caring, www.strengthforcaring.com/

RESEARCH RESOURCES

American Institute for Cancer Research, www.AICR.org

Herb Research Foundation—information on herbs as preventative medicine www.herbs.org/

National Institutes of Health, Clinical Trials—regularly updated information about federally and privately supported clinical research, clinicaltrials.gov/

SURVIVORSHIP RESOURCES AND SURVIVORSHIP PLANS

American Society of Clinical Oncology (ASCO) Resource List, www.cancer.net/survivorship/survivorship-resources

American Society of Clinical Oncology (ASCO): ASCOanswers Cancer Survivorship – for survivors, www.cancer.net/sites/cancer.net/files/cancer_survivorship.pdf?et_cid=34653101&et_rid=463566256&link id=ASCO+Answers+Guide+to+Survivorship

Journey Forward Careplan Builder – for survivors and healthcare professionals, www.journeyforward.org/

LiveSTRONG careplan, www.livestrongcareplan.org/

About the Contributors

Cathy Barnes, RN, MSN

Cathy Barnes is an Associate Professor of Nursing at Nebraska Methodist College in Omaha where she teaches oncology care to nursing students. She has a clinical specialty in Oncology nursing from Vanderbilt University. Her career has included many years of caring for people with cancer. Ms. Barnes has additional clinical expertise in palliative and hospice care that includes loss, grief and dying. She is also certified in death education. An outstanding teacher, she has been named to *Who's Who in American Nursing,* in *American Education*, and *Among American Teachers* numerous times. She has twice received the Positive Image of Nursing Award from her nursing colleagues at Nebraska Methodist College. She has been awarded the Master Teacher by students four times. She has been honored by students for three consecutive years as Faculty Member of the Year as well.

Shanda Berg, PT, CLT-LANA

Shanda Berg has been a Physical Therapist for thirty-plus years and has specialized in lymphedema. She is certified in the treatment of lymphedema from the Lymphology Association of North America. She is also a Certified Cancer Exercise Specialist. Ms. Berg has written grants and received funding from the Susan G. Komen for the Cure Foundation, Nebraska Affiliate, to develop and implement exercise programs for women diagnosed with breast cancer. She has taught aerobics, weight training, and Pilates for all cancer survivors.

Deborah Vonderharr Carlson, PhD

Deborah Vonderharr Carlson is Executive Vice President at Nebraska Methodist College in Omaha. She is a former college professor, researcher, and grant writer. Dr. Carlson previously taught educational psychology courses and worked for the Center for Instructional Innovation at the University of Nebraska–Lincoln. She taught for ten years at Wayne State College in Wayne, Neb., where she received her MSE. Her PhD is in Cognition, Learning and Development. Dr. Carlson's research interest is resilience and hope, which was the focus of her doctoral dissertation. She developed a resilience scale that is being widely used in colleges across the country. She studied in California with Nan Henderson, the founder of Resiliency in Action. Her current focus for research and speaking engagements focuses on resilience in cancer survivors.

Edward T. Creagan, MD, FAAHPM

An advisor to *A Time to Heal*, Dr. Edward T. Creagan is the John and Roma Rouse Professor of Humanism in Medicine at the Mayo Clinic Medical School, where he is a Professor of Medical Oncology. He directs the Palliative Care Program and is among only a few doctors to be certified in the specialties of both oncology and hospice and palliative medicine. He has published more than 400 scientific papers and made more than 1,000 presentations throughout the world. He was named the Mayo Clinic Distinguished Clinician not only for his clinical mastery but for his compassionate care. Dr. Creagan is the associate medical editor of MayoClinic.com, Mayo Clinic's online website for consumer health information. His triple industry award-winning, best-selling book—*How NOT to Be My Patient*—provides an additional forum for him to deliver his message of health and prevention and patient empowerment. View more about his book at www.HowNotToBeMyPatient.com.

Melissa Dahir, DNP, IF

Melissa Dahir is a board certified family practice nurse practitioner with a clinical doctorate from Creighton University. She has specialty training in women's sexual health and has been the Midwest's leading expert on the subject since 2006. Her clinical specialties include evidence-based treatments for vulvodynia; issues with sexual functioning such as low libido and pain with intercourse; vulvar skin conditions such as lichen sclerosis; recurrent vaginal infections; and women transitioning through menopause. She also offers testosterone replacement therapy for men and women.

Dr. Dahir is dedicated to advancing the field of sexual medicine. She lectures at the local and national levels and has authored numerous articles and chapters on sexual health. She is a Fellow with the International Society for the Study of Women's Sexual Health (ISSWSH) and has received several awards for her research study titled *Breast Cancer, Aromatase Inhibitors, and Sexual Function: A Pilot Study on the Effects of Vaginal Testosterone Therapy*.

Natalie Dowty, PT, MPT, EdD

Natalie Dowty is the president and founder of Integrative Wellness, Inc., Physical Therapy and Consulting in Omaha, where she provides physical therapy services based on a mind-body model and a wellness approach to rehabilitation. She provides presentations, individual and small group consultation, and coaching in content areas related to stress management, mind-body wellness, health promotion, fitness, rehabilitation, personal empowerment, and professional enrichment. Dr. Dowty serves as an Associate Professor in the Physical Therapist Assistant Program at Clarkson College.

Kalyn Flierl, BSW

Kalyn Flierl will graduate from Creighton University with a bachelor's degree in Social Work in May 2016. During her senior year, she completed her 440-hour social work practicum with *A Time to Heal*. In the next few years, she plans to pursue a dual master's degree in Social Work and Public Health in hopes of doing health promotion and community health education.

368

Teri L. Gabel, PharmD, BCPP, MH

Teri L. Gabel is cofounder of Drug Therapy Consultants, PC (in Omaha). Through her company, Dr. Gabel provides private consultation and educational programming. She speaks throughout the region and nationally on herbal medications, neutraceuticals, and psychiatric medications, and other topics. Dr. Gabel is the author of several professional chapters and articles on substance abuse, psychiatric medications, herbal medications, and neutraceuticals. Board certified in psychiatric pharmacy practice, Dr. Gabel is the Clinical Pharmacy Specialist in Psychiatry at the Veterans' Affairs Nebraska–Western Iowa Health Care System—Omaha Division and is a Volunteer Assistant Professor in the Department of Psychiatry in the College of Medicine at the University of Nebraska Medical Center. She has also earned the Master Herbalist diploma.

Jeannie Hannan, PhD, ACSM-HFD, CEF, GEL

Jeannie Hannan is a wellness professional, cancer survivor, trained wellness coach, and member of the Medical Fitness Association. She is the Wellness Manager for the EngAge Wellness program at the University of Nebraska Medical Center and former Assistant Professor at a private college. She facilitates a variety of evidence-based programs and has presented regionally and nationally on multiple topics related to whole-person wellness, exercise, the healing power of pets, and cancer survivorship. Dr. Hannan has her doctorate in Human Sciences with emphasis in Gerontology and Distance Education, a master's degree in Health Promotion with an emphasis in Human Resources Management, and a bachelor's degree in Management of Human Resources. In addition, she has three levels of American College of Sports Medicine (ACSM) certifications (Health Fitness Director, Certified Physiologist, and Group Exercise Leader).

Mary Hogan, OSM, MA

Mary Hogan is a Servant of Mary who originally hailed from Detroit. Omaha is home now having spent most of her life there. She has a Master of Arts degree in Theology and another master's degree in Spirituality as well as certifications as a Healing Touch Practitioner and Spiritual Director. As an educator Sister Mary taught grades three through college as well as adult education programs. She has been involved in administration both in her Religious Community and in the Catholic Archdiocese of Omaha. For three years she served in the missions in Kingston, Jamaica, West Indies. Her past experience includes seeing clients for spiritual direction and healing touch sessions at the Servite Center of Compassion.

Chandy Lockman Hoke, MS, RD, CSO, LMNT

Chandy Lockman Hoke is a registered dietitian with the American Dietetics Association and a member of the Specialized Dietetic Practice Group "Oncology Nutrition" and "Research." She is board certified as a Specialist in Oncology Nutrition, licensed with the State of Nebraska as a Medical Nutrition Therapist, and certified in Adult Weight Management. Ms. Hoke graduated from the University of Nebraska–Lincoln with a bachelor of science in Human Resources and Family Consumer Science with a major in Dietetics. She completed a dietetic internship at

California State University, Fresno, where she also earned her RD credentials and a master of science in Food and Nutritional Science. She holds a certificate in Adult Weight Management through the Academy of Nutrition and Dietetics, is licensed in Nebraska as a Medical Nutrition therapist, is one of only three RDs in Nebraska who is a board certified specialist in Oncology Nutrition (CSO) and is Clinical Dietitian for the Methodist Estabrook Cancer Center.

Stephanie Koraleski, PhD

Stephanie Koraleski, PhD, is co-creator and CEO of *A Time to Heal* Foundation. She is a licensed psychologist specializing in psycho-oncology (work with people affected by cancer). She is a diplomate with the American Board for Clinically Certified Hypnotherapists, a Reiki master, and holds a certificate in interspiritual mentoring. In her work, she concentrates on individual patients and families, facilitating support groups, and training and consulting with medical staff about the psychological and emotional impact of disease. She served as an adjunct faculty member at the University of Nebraska at Omaha teaching classes in the graduate counseling program and supervising internships for masters and doctoral students in counseling and psychology. She has presented at professional conferences locally, nationally, and internationally about issues of psychology, cancer, and cancer survivorship.

Dr. Koraleski has served as the president of the Nebraska chapter of the American Liver Foundation, on the community boards of the American Cancer Society, the National Ovarian Cancer Coalition, Nebraska Chapter, and on the professional advisory council for the Multiple Sclerosis Society Midlands Chapter. She is a current member of NC2 (the Nebraska Cancer Coalition) and the Nebraska Breast Cancer Control Plan Advisory Board. Dr. Koraleski is a passionate advocate for whole person care for everyone, but especially for those with serious illnesses.

Lisa Merrifield, PhD

Lisa Merrifield, PhD, received a BA with a major in biology from Agnes Scott College; MA and PhD degrees in psychology from the University of Southern Mississippi. She works as a Licensed Psychologist in Omaha, Nebraska, where she maintains an independent, general practice integrating psychotherapy and neurofeedback to help clients with a wide variety of concerns. Dr. Merrifield is a member of the Biofeedback Society of Nebraska, the International Society for Neurofeedback and Research, and Omaha's Coalition for the Advancement of Children's Mental Health.

Vicki Rackner, MD, FACS

Dr. Vicki Rackner, an advisor to *A Time to Heal*, is a board-certified surgeon and nationally noted expert in the doctor-patient relationship. She has treated tens of thousands of patients, taught medical students to think like doctors, and served as an expert witness who reviewed scores of malpractice cases. She served as a faculty member at the University of Washington School of Medicine. She is the founder of The Caregiver Club (www.thecaregiverclub. com), has been on all sides of the dire diagnosis: as the patient facing a life-threatening medical condition, as the doctor delivering the dreaded diagnosis, and as a family caregiver advocating for sick loved ones. She is passionate about offering caregivers the message they are not alone, the reminder they have choices, and the light of hope even on dark days.

Dr. Rackner, or "Dr. Vicki," based in Seattle, is a regular source on CNN.com, has been quoted in *The Wall Street Journal, USA Today, The Washington Post, Reader's Digest, Bottom Line Health, Woman's Day, Real Simple* and many others. She has been interviewed on over 100 radio shows, including NPR, Martha Stewart Living and Health Talk. Her book *Caregiving without Regrets* joins her other books, including *The Personal Health Journal*, and *The Biggest Skeleton in Your Doctor's Closet*. Dr. Rackner co-authored *Chicken Soup for the Soul Healthy Living Series: Heart Disease* and contributed a compelling story to *Chicken Soup for the Soul Healthy Living Series: Breast Cancer*.

James Reilly, MD

Dr. James Reilly received his medical degree from the University of Nebraska Medical Center in Omaha. He also completed his residency at the University of Nebraska Medical Center and a fellowship at MD Anderson Cancer Center in Houston. Dr. Reilly is board certified in general surgery and surgical oncology and is the Clinical Medical Director for the Breast Care Center at Methodist Estabrook Cancer Center.

Lauren Robins, OTD, OTR/L, CLT

Lauren Robins is a Certified Lymphedema Therapist and Occupational Therapist who specializes in lymphedema and oncology at the Nebraska Methodist Hospital in Omaha. She is trained in Healthy Steps (Lebed Method) as well as Tai Chi and healing touch. She received her doctorate in Occupational Therapy from Creighton University in Omaha and became certified in lymphedema through the Norton School of Lymphatic Therapy. She is a member of the Nebraska Cancer Coalition and regularly presents on the topics of exercise, wellness, and lymphedema education for health care professionals as well as cancer survivors across the region. Dr. Robins enjoys the outdoors, spending time with her family, and is an avid runner.

Kay Ryan, PhD, RN

Kay Ryan, PhD, RN, co-created and serves as President of *A Time to Heal*. Dr. Ryan is the Coordinator for Nursing Professional Development at Children's Hospital and Medical Center in Omaha and a consultant for cancer survivorship and creating healthy cultures. She is a former college professor and administrator. She is certified as a *Radical Collaboration* Facilitator, a Health Fitness Specialist by the American College of Sports Medicine, and a Certified Health Education Specialist by the National Center for Health Education Credentialing. Dr. Ryan is a member of the Oncology Nursing Society. She has published multiple scientific research articles and won numerous national awards and honors in the fields of nursing, education, and wellness including Master Teacher and Distinguished Professorships for holistic health education. She was recognized as a Distinguished Alum of the University of Nebraska at Omaha and was awarded the 2009 Gillian Anne Piannett Survivor Award by the Susan G. Komen for the Cure Foundation,

Nebraska Affiliate. Dr. Ryan was a visiting fellow at the National University of Ireland in Galway. She has served on the Board of Trustees for the National Wellness Institute.

A regular presenter at wellness conferences, Dr. Ryan presents keynotes and research findings internationally on the topics of happiness, holistic health, and collaboration. She is a breast cancer survivor who believes in the healing power of kindness.

Joyce Swanson, MS, LMPH, NCBTMB

Joyce Swanson, a licensed professional counselor and nationally certified therapeutic massage/bodyworker, is a consultant in private practice in Omaha. She is an adjunct faculty member at Doane University. Ms. Swanson teaches graduate classes on subjects including positive discipline, active learning, emotional intelligence, and stress reduction. She presents workshops to schools, businesses, and medical centers throughout the Midwest and has spoken at national conferences. She uses her background in massage and other bodywork modalities to help clients deal with chronic and phantom pain, the effects of chemotherapy and radiation, and autoimmune diseases as well as a variety of other health issues. She is a Reiki Teaching Master and has trained in the areas of cranio-sacral work, acupressure, healing touch and infant massage.

Marilyn Wadum, RD, LMNT

Marilyn Wadum is a registered dietitian and a member of the Academy of Nutrition and Dietetics. She is licensed with the state of Nebraska as a Medical Nutrition Therapist. Ms. Wadum holds a Certificate in Chronic Illness Health Management and a Certificate in Adult Weight Management. She is a member of the National Specialized Dietetic Practice Groups of Nutrition Education for the Public, Nutrition in Complementary Care, and Weight Management and Bariatrics.

She graduated from the University of Nebraska–Lincoln with a bachelor of science degree in Food and Nutrition. She has worked in health care throughout her career and has experience working in hospitals, medical clinics, chronic disease management, health promotion and marketing, coordinating weight management programs and currently works with people with obesity.

In her position as Bariatric Nutrition Therapist with Saint Elizabeth Hospital in Lincoln, Nebraska, she facilitates patient support groups, provides nutrition education, and teaches the pre-op surgery class for patients pursuing weight loss surgery.

Lori Wingerter, MA, LIMHP, PLADC

Lori Wingerter is a Licensed Independent Mental Health Practitioner. She is 14-year Stage III colon cancer survivor. Diagnosed at age 38, with three small children, she felt there was a large unmet psychological need of cancer patients and set forth to relieve that need. She currently has a full-time practice providing psycho-oncology therapy support to patients, caregivers, and families. She believes emotional support is an integral part of the cancer treatment and recovery process—treating the mind/body/spirit—from the first day of diagnosis. She also volunteers much of her efforts to many oncology-related organizations and is a member of professional organizations including American Psychosocial Oncology Society, Society for Integrative Oncology, and

American Counseling Association. Ms. Wingerter believes *life after cancer is all about living*…and to that end she runs marathons, hikes tall mountains, kayaks peaceful rivers, cycles endless miles on long, rolling roads, and travels around the world uncovering new adventures.

Rhonda Wise, RN, MSN, OCN

Rhonda Wise is a A Time to Heal facilitator in both the 12-week program and the Metastatic Cancer Support Group. She attended nursing school at College of Saint Mary and received her BS in Nursing in 2005. In 2014 she earned her MSN in nursing education at College of Saint Mary. Ms. Wise has been an Oncology Certified Nurse since 2007. As a nurse, Ms. Wise has worked in oncology her entire career; starting as a floor nurse on a surgical oncology unit at Methodist Hospital in Omaha. She later worked in oncology research at Methodist Estabrook Cancer Center as a clinical trial nurse. Ms. Wise has worked as an adjunct clinical instructor at Nebraska Methodist College where she taught oncology content to nursing students. She is passionate about the needs of cancer survivors and is an active member of Oncology Nursing Society, Metro Omaha Chapter of Oncology Nursing Society, and Nebraska Oncology Society.

Made in the USA
Columbia, SC
12 August 2021